Surveying
Fiberglass Power Boats

by

David H. Pascoe

D. H. Pascoe & Company, Inc.

Surveying Fiberglass Power Boats

Published by D. H. Pascoe & Company, Inc.
www.yachtsurvey.com

First Printing 2001
Second Printing 2003

Printed in the United States of America by Rose Printing, Tallahassee, Florida

ISBN   0-9656496-0-1

To order copies, visit our web site
www.yachtsurvey.com

Preface

The writing of this book was first started in 1995 based on my perception that the surveying profession was sorely in need of a basic text on the subject of pre-purchase surveys. Up to that point, only one book on this subject had been published, and that on wooden boats over twenty years ago. My question as to why this was so, was answered several years later when my completed manuscript was sent to various marine publishers whom I found to have little or no interest in producing a book that they felt had a far too limited market.

One publisher did express an interest, but it came with a caveat. He would consider a book if I rewrote it in such a way as to broaden popular appeal; this publisher wanted a book written for boat buyers to perform their own self surveys. Naturally, as a professional, I had little interest in writing a book that would have as its theme, a subject matter designed to put surveyors out of business. Moreover, after an enormous amount of work, the publishers offered pitifully small royalty percentages.

For these reasons, I opted for self-publishing, something that I undertook with great trepidation, and which is only made possible by the Internet. The greatest obstacle to the success of any self-published book is the inability to access the major distribution channels that are locked up by large national wholesalers and chain stores. To sell this book through normal retail channels would have meant that, in addition to becoming a self publisher, I would also have to become a salesman and one man marketing department.

Fortunately, my web site, **www.yachtsurvey.com** with its high volume of traffic, makes it possible to sell this book direct.

As with all self-published works, it suffers somewhat from a lack of a professional staff of editors, graphic and layout artists. We have had to learn and do all this ourselves, discovering the hard way that producing a professional quality book is anything but easy. After years of work, the book has finally become a reality. Whatever faults and shortcomings it has stem from our own lack of expertise at writing and production. Even so, I felt that it was more important to get even a flawed book published and into print, than for there to continue to be no serious texts available. I can only apologize for whatever shortcomings it may have.

Over the six year period in which this book was produced, I learned just how rapidly the pleasure boating industry has changed and is changing. The original manuscript written in 1995-96 was, by 1999 becoming obsolete. Thus began a period of revising and updating that took another two years. Even so, as the manuscript was about to go off to the printer in the summer of 2001, it became clear to me that it simply is not possible for books to keep up with the latest developments. That's the job of magazines and seminars that do not have the tremendous production lead times that books do.

Ultimately, I trust you will find that we have done a creditable job in producing a thorough text that can be used by novices and old salts alike as a standard reference on how to perform a thorough survey, as well as illuminating some of the finer points on getting the job done quickly and efficiently. We all need, from time to time, to review our procedures to help ensure that we don't fall into bad habits through endless repetition. I know that I would certainly benefit by having a text to review from time to time.

Moreover, as time goes on, I hope to keep the book up to date with revised editions as the industry continues to go through rapid changes. Anyone with comments or suggestions for future revisions can drop me an e-mail through my web site at **www.yachtsurvey.com**. It is unlikely that I will be able to respond to questions, but I will be keeping a file on suggestions for revision.

Introduction

How to Use This Book

During the course of his weekly work, a marine surveyor is faced with a dizzying array of different sizes and types of craft. Though it would certainly be desirable, it is not possible to produce a step-by-step guide as to how to perform a survey since the survey will vary so much from boat to boat. By necessity, this book is intended to be read cover-to-cover.

Each chapter starts with a discussion of the basic principles involved, then gives an overview of the kinds of problems the surveyor routinely faces. In many ways, it begins to resemble a compendium on proper marine engineering and standards. From this, the surveyor is expected to be able to extrapolate the faults he discovers in his work.

No one book could possibly begin to cover the virtually infinite variations that surveyors encounter in boats. In the end, the surveyor is required to sufficiently develop his knowledge to the point where he is capable of rendering his own judgement on any given issue. The purpose of this book is to help you learn to do that.

* * * * *

The production of this book was undertaken as a self-published work in order to help fill the void created by a near total lack of good texts on the subject of pre-purchase surveying pleasure craft. It is the most extensive and thorough book of it's kind ever produced, if only because there are so few of them.

Although this book deals mainly with motor yachts, including styles such as express and convertibles, I have included chapter nine *Cockpits*, which covers many of the problems to be found with outboard boats, particularly the high end center console boats that have become so popular. Surveyors tend to get very enthusiastic about surveying bigger and bigger boats; we should not forget that there's a good business to be done with smaller boats that might well be more profitable than their larger cousins.

While the theme is primarily directed at the novice surveyor and the aspiring surveyor, the subject is the actual business of marine surveying. However, the business of marine surveying is not about boats alone, for every survey starts with a client for whom the service is being rendered. Therefore, as a primary theme you will find that the relationship between surveyor and client is close at hand, for they are inseparable. Always at the back of his mind is a customer who wants to know about the nature of the used boat he is about to purchase. No, this profession is not just about boats; it's about *people* and boats.

Underlying every situation is the question of what exactly is the surveyor's responsibility to the client? What kind of information does the client need to be informed of? Are there differences between legal and moral responsibilities? These are questions that surveyors face every day, and for which I'll provide some answers and the reasons why.

It is not the purpose of this book to educate the reader on the subject of pleasure craft generally. By necessity I have assumed that the reader is possessed of certain prerequisites, including a solid knowledge of technical basics. I am frequently asked by people whose backgrounds and education are in other fields, how they can become marine surveyors. They seem to think it's an easy thing to change careers because this profession seems to them to be glamorous, and requires no college diplomas or licenses. There is also the siren song of self employment, which is a tougher taskmaster than any boss one has ever had.

My answer to them is that if they do not have a background in boat building or repair, or similar allied field, then they should not even consider trying to become a marine surveyor. Lacking such expertise, they are inherently unqualified. There are no schools that can provide that education, only the college of long experience in allied fields. Neither will this book provide those qualifications, as one book cannot make a professional expert. And expertise is what our clients hire us for. If a surveyor lacks it, he is nothing more than a quack, something this profession already has too many of.

Due to a perceived lack of literature on the subject of modern boat construction, chapter five deals extensively with hull construction, devoting some 45 pages and over two dozen photos and drawings to help the surveyor in identifying structural deficiencies. Because stress cracks are so common to boats, an entire chapter is devoted to this sometimes mystifying subject. Chapter eight then deals with decks and superstructures.

Many newcomers enter the profession every year, but few survive for very long. While I can't know all the reasons why, I have to believe it's because most were unaware that marine surveying is not a casual activity that just anyone with a whim could enter and expect to succeed. Many seem to think that being a marine surveyor is somehow glamorous, as if surveyors do little but ride around on yachts sipping pina coladas and enjoying the scenery. Others seem to think that they can attend a few classes or seminars and get everything they need to know to be successful in a matter of weeks.

Nothing could be further from the truth. If you have any ideas about this being a glamorous profession, let me disabuse you of that notion right now. Marine surveying is a work of hard, physical labor, that is usually dirty, noisy and puts him in an adversarial position with sellers and brokers. Surveys are almost always conducted in difficult circumstances, and almost never under ideal working conditions. The surveyor is routinely exposed to extremes of weather, poor working conditions, dirt, grime, foul odors, harsh chemicals, extremely loud noise and the constant threat of physical injury from unexpected sources. You'll end up working in engine rooms with temperatures as high as 130°F.

You'll spend a good part of your time lifting and laying carpet, moving mattresses and furniture, taking things apart and putting them back together. You'll empty lazarettes, closets and lockers and then put everything back again. At times you'll feel like you work for a moving company. You'll handle lines, fenders, anchors and chains, remove and replace seat cushions and enclosures thousands of times.

And you'll quickly come to understand why successful surveyors are never overweight. How could they be when they exercise ten hours a day, every day. If you haven't the stamina for continuous hard labor, then don't even consider becoming a surveyor.

This book begins by taking a hard look at some of the basic principles involved in surveying, including the surveyor's legal responsibilities, the scope of the service provided, and the definition of terms such as seaworthiness and soundness. Next, it moves into issues of client relations, including topics such as how to avoid getting tangled up in situations that should be avoided, and generally how to stay out of trouble. The novice should be aware that every job that comes his way is not necessarily a job that he can profit from. More than a few jobs turn out to be tar babies that were best avoided.

Chapters five through sixteen cover the practical work of conducting the survey. These twelve chapters are illustrated with nearly two hundred photos and drawings of the actual conditions the surveyor will find in the field. These are photos I've collected for over twenty years and will prove invaluable toward helping the novice understand what he's dealing with. No one book could begin to cover everything that ought to be addressed. However, by the time anyone is done studying these chapters, he can expect to be well grounded in the principles of what constitutes a thorough survey, and how to best serve his client.

Last, but not least, chapter seventeen covers how to make appraisals and chapter eighteen deal with how to write reports. This chapter was included because it is my perception that the reports of much of the profession leave a lot to be desired. Unless one has a business or legal education, writing is not something most people put much effort into learning. For the marine surveyor, writing a professional report is a critical skill. What many seem to fail to realize is that the report is the surveyor's *work product,* the primary thing by which his work will be judged by others, and the only thing which others will see. If the report is poorly written, the end result is like painting a boat with a mop.

Ultimately, marine surveying is not about the business of boats; eventually one comes to discover that it's about people who buy and own boats; that boats don't lie at the heart of the business, but what people think about them that does. As they say, "One man's trash is another man's treasure." In the end, it's not about how much you know about boats, but how much you know about people and what *they* want to know. Satisfy that demand and you'll have a lot of happy clients. In this business, people skills are paramount, technical skills are secondary but equal importance.

If you don't know something, you can always find someone who does know. Although the surveyor is the one who's supposed to know everything about boats, most of my clients would be surprised to hear me say that it seems like I've spent a good part of my career calling other people and asking questions. We don't know everything there is to know about boats and never will. Our objective should be to become reasonably competent and, above all, learn to develop the sources through which we can get fast answers to our endless questions. A well-stocked Rolodex can be worth more than a library full of books, most of which are outdated.

This book will help the novice make a good beginning, and help the experienced surveyor brush up on his skills and knowledge.

David H. Pascoe
Fort Lauderdale
June, 2001

Contents

Chapter 1

What is a Pre-Purchase Survey?

At first glance, the answer to the question that is the title of this chapter may seem obvious. Yet, when we consider the question in depth, with all of the responsibilities and difficulties involved, further reflection will reveal that the answer is not so easy as we may have first assumed. For inherent in whatever definition we may arrive at, the fact is that the marine surveyor does not operate in a vacuum, but an environment that makes many demands on him and greatly influences the nature of the service he provides. Foremost among these influences are the legal obligations imposed by the society in which we function. This is closely followed by the personal desires and demands of the client, along with the demands of other persons or businesses which also make use of the service, even though they are not our direct clients.

Before we attempt to arrive at a precise definition of a pre-purchase survey, it will be helpful to take a look at some of these many influences so that we may better understand how they mold and shape the work of the professional surveyor. Let's first start by looking at who and what a surveyor is.

What is a Marine Surveyor

Marine surveyors are indeed expected to be professionals, and professionalism begins and ends with knowledge. As defined by the dictionary, a professional is: *A person engaged in one of the learned professions or an occupation requiring a high level of training and proficiency.* This clear, concise definition of professionalism establishes a tall order for anyone who would style his or herself a professional. It is a much abused term these days that is often extended to trades or mere jobs, as opposed to a specialty that requires an extraordinary level of knowledge and training.

Attaining the true definition of professional can pose considerable difficulties, for a high level of training and proficiency cannot be had by obtaining a college degree because there are no such programs in marine surveying. Altogether, there are probably no more than 1,500 practicing, full-time marine surveyors in the U.S. and many of these are commercial, not yacht surveyors. True, there are several schools that offer six week courses on the subject, but six weeks of training do not make a professional.

So how does a surveyor attain his knowledge and experience? Traditionally, surveyors have attained their experience through either apprenticeship with a practicing surveyor or attaining years of experience in related fields such as boat building and repair. Most of the real professionals have come to the profession in this way, and it remains the primary training grounds for surveyors.

Marine surveyors provide a very diverse range of services to an equally diverse clientele. The most prominent of these is the yacht surveyor whose primary business is the service of providing pre-purchase or buyer's surveys. But the largest number of surveyors are those who provide other services such as marine insurance claims, consulting work for new construction and repairs, refits, new yacht commissioning, insurance surveys and general problem solving. While the subject of this book is the survey of fiberglass motor yachts and vessels, our discussion here will not be limited solely to pre-purchase surveys, but will provide useful information and advice on these other areas as well. Whether you're performing a failure analysis for an owner or insurance company, or a pre-purchase survey, the fundamentals are covered in this book.

Therefore, our definition of a professional yacht surveyor must include all of these various areas of expertise. A true professional marine surveyor is a person who has attained a high level of training, knowledge, expertise and proficiency in whatever specialized field of marine surveying he has chosen to practice. Notice that I've added two additional words to the dictionary definition of professional: knowledge and expertise. Knowledge, because the accumulation of information, more than just training, provides the foundation for the surveyor's work. Expertise, because it is the skillful application of knowledge and training that distinguishes the real professional from the dabblers.

The basic fundamentals for surveying professionalism goes far beyond mere knowledge of boats and all things marine. A surveyor is, first and foremost, a businessman who conducts his trade or business based upon his knowledge of vessels and training in the conduct of the survey process. But that's not all, for in addition to this are his skills in negotiation, report writing and communication with a diversity of clientele and the marine community in general. This includes insurance, banking, boat yards, marine manufacturing, and government and law at all levels. Last, but definitely not least, the busy marine surveyor is frequently involved with lawyers and the justice system.

The surveyor's involvement and interaction with law and lawyers is a subject on which volumes could be written. Neophyte surveyors rarely envision the extent to which surveyors are involved with the law and the role that law will play in their daily work. They are likely at first to believe that their work will be little more than a relationship between client and surveyor, and perhaps yacht brokers and banks. But the fact is that legal considerations figure into every aspect of the surveyor's daily work and woe to the surveyor who ignores this reality. For that reason, woven into every chapter of this book is the consideration of the surveyor's legal responsibilities. This is all part of the vast body of knowledge and expertise which distinguishes the true professional.

Being a professional surveyor means being well grounded in the fundamentals of yacht design, machinery, systems and electronics. No one can evaluate the integrity of hull construction without first having some knowledge of what constitutes good hull design and why. And in this era of space age materials and high tech wizardry, just staying current with the vast array of basic materials such as resins, reinforcements, plastics, metals, components, systems, electronics and machinery becomes increasingly difficult year by year. Fortunately, the number of seminars dealing with these topics is growing at a similar pace so that the practicing surveyor is afforded numerous opportunities to keep up to date.

Some professions, like the medical profession, have inherently clear definitions of the functions of their members. The Hippocratic Oath makes it very clear what a physician's responsibilities are. Other professions, such as marine surveying, are not so straightforward. In attempting to define the role of the marine surveyor in the business of performing pre-purchase surveys for boat buyers, it will be of great help to first consider some of the legal responsibilities placed on the surveyor by the society he serves.

Legal Responsibility

Whether we are aware of it or not, our society and its legal system places a very heavy burden on the marine surveyor. In defining what a survey is, we cannot escape from what the law of the land has to say about the service he offers. It is inherently bound up in the statutes of the states in which we operate. All throughout this book the reader will find that, underlying every decision the surveyor has to make, is a legal consideration, i.e., what is our responsibility under the law. This is not, of course, a legal treatise, nor are we required to be lawyers. Knowing your legal responsibilities is, for the most part, a matter of common sense and ethics. If you behave sensibly, responsibly and ethically, you're not likely to get in trouble so long as you have a basic understanding of professional responsibility.

A Written Record of Performance

The one thing that distinguishes a surveyor's work product from many other types of service is that he issues his findings in writing. What he does and what he says becomes memorialized in a written record. Herein lies the heaviest burden, one that poses serious liability hazards to the surveyor. The report provides an obvious illustration of the surveyor's expertise as well as his performance for all to see. If a surveyor is not truly qualified to practice the profession, it is impossible for him to conceal his shortcomings in the written report, much as he might think he can bluff his way through. As Ralph Waldo Emerson put it, "What you are speaks so loudly I cannot hear what you say." Remember that a surveyor is responsible for all that he writes and lack of knowledge or training cannot be concealed in a report.

Pass-On Surveys

Moreover, that report, although initially given to the client, may be given to others such as insurance companies, finance companies, or other prospective buyers who are not the surveyor's client, and who have not paid him a fee. Or, if your client doesn't buy the boat, he may even sell your report to another buyer. There have been several cases of which I am aware where surveyors have been held liable for errors in "pass on" surveys. These are surveys that the client has given to others who have held the surveyor liable for the survey's contents, even though the service was not provided for that individual. How could this be? Well, by reason of the fact that the survey was construed to be a document of fact provided by an expert in his field, for which it mattered not who was relying on the information contained therein. It was deemed irrelevant for whom the service was provided since the document ended up in the hands of another, to whom it caused harm. I've avoided using legal jargon here, but that is essentially what some courts have ruled. Whether we think it's fair or not, our actions should be guided by that reality, a reality of which we should be constantly aware. If we hold ourselves out as professionals, we can and will be held to a much higher standard than others. It is therefore wise to remember that the client is rarely the only person who relies on our work.

Having said that, it also needs to be said that the marine surveyor does not have to be heavily versed in law to know what his responsibilities are. The surveyor's legal responsibility is easily defined as: *liability for the accuracy and thoroughness of the advice for which he was hired to provide, regardless of who ultimately makes use of it.* It is only when we get into the scope of the service provided that we run into more than a little difficulty in trying to determine what it is we are supposed to do.

Defining A Pre-Purchase Survey

This discussion of the definition of a surveyor begins laying the groundwork for defining what a survey is. That's because we first have to understand the qualifications of a professional surveyor before we can know what kind of service he is capable of offering. After all, one doesn't go to a podiatrist for brain surgery.

Having testified in over a hundred cases in court in which the scope of a marine survey was at issue, it is more than clear to me that there is not a universally understood definition, not even amongst surveyors, as to just exactly what a buyer's survey is or should be. It's rather like trying to define what is a lawyer or what is an engineer. At fist glance, the subject seems too broad to be able to sum it up succinctly. It's unfortunate that neither the profession nor its several professional societies have never promulgated a concise, standard definition or general outline of what constitutes a proper survey. Yet, if we give it a little thought, it's not really all that difficult once we've explored some of the legal ramifications. Once we know what society expects of us, it's a lot easier to perform.

Primary Objective

For nearly thirty years I've heard yacht brokers complain that the surveyor's job is to determine the condition of the yacht, not to comment on design or construction problems. On the other hand, I've never seen a broker assume that responsibility and co-sign a survey report. This disingenuous argument suggests that if a vessel has a design problem that poses a serious hazard, the surveyor should ignore it. One can anticipate that, in the event of a dispute, this would be a difficult argument to sell to a judge or jury.

First and foremost, the primary objective of the pre-purchase survey should be safety. This is dictated for both moral and legal reasons. The client is relying upon the surveyor's expertise as to the safety of a vessel, regardless of whether the client has asked any questions about safety, or whether the surveyor does, or does not, make any overt representations as to the safety of a vessel. Secondly, when a survey is carried out, it is legally implied that safety is the overriding purview of the service being provided. Safety is inherent in the meaning of the survey itself. The client doesn't have to ask about it, nor does the report have to mention it. From a legal standpoint, a surveyor must assume that any court would agree that the primary concern of the surveyor must be the safety of the vessel and its occupants.

The surveyor can be held liable for errors and omissions, regardless of how fancy his disclaimers may be. Many surveyor's reports contain disclaimers that are utterly worthless in face of the law. The novice surveyor should not be fooled into thinking that he is protected by such nonsense. He cannot disclaim his legal responsibilities.

The second factor involved in conducting a survey is purely economic. The surveyor's job is to determine the condition of the vessel, and since condition is tied directly to maintenance costs, part of the survey function is to assist the client in avoiding economic loss by providing accurate assessment of condition. To fail to discover a condition that requires costly repair is a failure of assessing condition, a failure for which a surveyor can be held liable.

With these points in mind, it is readily apparent that the performance of a marine survey is a serious responsibility that should not be undertaken by amateurs as a means of supplementing one's income on a part-time basis. The prospective surveyor would be wise to remember that, upon completion of a survey, he has to write a report and sign his name to it. His conclusions and findings become memorialized in a written record that imposes serious legal responsibilities on him ranging far beyond just the client/surveyor relationship.

For the person who intends to make a career of surveying yachts and small craft, one of the best ways to answer the question "what is a survey?" is from the legal standpoint. Every time a surveyor is contracted by a purchaser to perform a pre-purchase survey, he should be aware of his legal responsibility. The fact that the client is relying on the surveyor for information on which he intends to base his purchase decision should give every surveyor pause for frequent consideration. Having a precise definition that defines the scope of his service will help.

A marine survey is a service intended to provide a prospective buyer with sufficient information as to the condition, safety and performance of a vessel, its equipment and machinery to enable the buyer to make an informed purchase decision. The survey includes a signed, written report that will be provided as verification of the surveyor's findings and therefore relied upon by other persons or businesses as a basis for making financial decisions.

Seaworthiness

Note that the three key words here are condition, safety and performance. You'll probably also note that conspicuously absent from that definition is the word seaworthiness, and for good reason. As defined by hundreds upon hundreds, perhaps thousands, of Admiralty court decisions, seaworthiness is a relative term. It means that a vessel is suitably designed, constructed, equipped, maintained and manned in order to carry out a particular voyage safely. The neophyte surveyor should pay particular attention to these distinctions.

Seaworthiness is actually a legal doctrine that includes the experience and skill of the vessel operator and crew to safely operate the vessel. It also means that a vessel is suitably designed for the particular voyage it is undertaking. For example, a canoe may be seaworthy to cross a small inland lake, but not to cross a large lake many miles wide. A small cabin cruiser might be considered seaworthy for Sunday sailing on the ocean within a few miles offshore; that same cruiser is probably not seaworthy for an open water passage of several hundred miles. Similarly, a vessel that does not meet legislated safety requirements is equally unseaworthy.

The point here is that seaworthiness is a relative term. In performing a pre-purchase survey, in most instances a surveyor would have no way of knowing whether the vessel is truly seaworthy simply because he does not, at that point, have sufficient information to make that determination; he does not know how it will be used or by whom.

Conversely, can a surveyor safely declare a vessel unseaworthy? Most definitely. It may seem ironic that the surveyor can, in many situations, safely declare a vessel unseaworthy while not being able to declare the opposite. This is because there are situations in which a vessel is not safe under any conditions. Or, at best, it may become apparent that the vessel cannot safely perform its obviously intended function. A fiberglass cruiser with a crack in the hull would not be seaworthy to sit at the dock, yet alone go to sea.

We can conclude from these examples that the function of a pre-purchase survey is not to make a general assessment of a yacht's seaworthiness. We can assess its condition, the performance of its equipment and machinery, and even the overall performance characteristics of the vessel itself. But how it will be used, and who will be operating and crewing it, that we do not know. Therefore, the word "seaworthiness" is best left out of our vocabulary unless we intend to use it strictly in the negative. This issue will be discussed in greater detail in Chapter Three.

Among the prerequisites required for a solid surveying background is a good knowledge in basic engineering and design. That does not mean that a surveyor should have a degree in engineering, but that he should be conversant with general design and the structural strength of materials and their proper use. It is not unusual that yacht designers who have no formal training at all are capable of engineering a truly fine design. They obtained their training through experience, just as most surveyors do. In fact, like boat builders, most surveyors do not have formal engineering training. Therefore, we will be devoting considerable time on the subject of structural and systems design because design is the foundation on which all else rests.

What Does the Client Want?

The expectations of a client often exceed the ability of the surveyor to deliver. This is largely due to the client's ignorance and so it becomes incumbent upon the surveyor to educate him. This subject is dealt with further on in this, and the next chapter under the subject of Qualifying the Client.

Client expectations always have to be tempered against the very real physical and financial limitations of even the most thorough survey. As indicated above, a fair definition of the purpose of the survey is to enable the client to make an informed purchase decision, but one tempered by the physical and economic limitations. Obviously, destructive testing is a costly and risky option that is seldom done. And while it's possible to spend days or weeks conducting investigations and evaluations, is the client willing to pay the cost? In the vast majority of instances the answer is no; the client is willing only to pay the going rate and require what we might term the "average" survey.

Unless the surveyor can meet the client's demands, or reconcile his desires against economic reality, the surveyor is headed for trouble. For that reason alone, it is imperative that the surveyor makes sure that the client fully understands the scope of the service he offers.

Scope of the Survey

Having defined the objective of a survey, we can now discuss the actual survey process, meaning what, exactly, should the surveyor do. Further on in this chapter is a list of all the various categories of structures, machinery, systems and equipment that may be found on a yacht. It covers 147 items in over 20 categories sufficient to make any survey a daunting task. Take a few minutes and study this list. It will give you a greater appreciation of just how difficult a survey can be. To conduct a thorough examination of all aspects of every item of every category would clearly result in a survey that would take days or even weeks to perform, and at a very high cost.

This leads us to the question of just how thorough should a survey really be? We answer that question by taking a look at the usual and customary practice by surveyors that is commonly accepted by clients. For it is common practice[2], combined with what the law defines as our legal responsibility, that should guide our efforts.

Limitations of Scope

When a surveyor undertakes to conduct a pre-purchase evaluation of a vessel for a client, that surveyor's obligation to that client can be either as all-inclusive or as narrow as he can legally make it. It is up to the surveyor to determine the scope of the service he provides. On the other hand, the surveyor does have an obligation to make sure that the client fully understands any and all limitations of that service. In other words, lacking the benefit of some agreement between client and surveyor as to the scope of the surveyor's service, it would not be unreasonable to assume that the surveyor's responsibilities are open-ended. Unless, that is, the surveyor takes steps to define the limitations of the service provided to the client.

There are limitations on this, of course, as when a surveyor provides a partial service but charges a prevailing fee for a full service. Or, as when he only does a partial survey but gives the impression that the partial survey is providing the basic necessities of a full service when, in fact, it does not. A surveyor who purports to be providing a pre-purchase evaluation of a vessel, but seriously limits the scope of the survey to less than the common practice, is setting himself up for trouble.

It goes without saying that a surveyor doesn't have x-ray vision and doesn't have the ability to tear a boat apart, examine every detail, and then put it back together again. But it would be foolish to assume that a client fully understands those limitations. For that reason alone we need to take steps to ensure that the client is made aware of the scope of the service and its limitations. However, there is a general rule of common law that says that a product or service provider cannot contract out of law. In other words, he can't make agreements that abrogate, say, existing consumer laws currently on the books or, for that matter, existing legal precedents. Attaching disclaimers at the end of survey reports stating that the surveyor is not responsible for his mistakes has no legal standing whatsoever. Nor can he obtain a waiver from the client absolving him from negligence and expect to be protected by that waiver when the law mandates responsible behavior. That's what is meant by the term "contracting out of law."

Further, with respect to the subject of engineering, a surveyor cannot claim ignorance of structural engineering as a defense when he has contracted to conduct a survey and then something goes wrong. He cannot claim ignorance about a subject which his profession as a marine surveyor should reasonably require him to be knowledgeable of, and expect any reasonable person to be sympathetic to his defense. Nor can he claim that consideration of the safety of the vessel was not a part of his service.

In a very real sense, surveyors are like medical general practitioners; we know a little about everything but we are not experts on all things marine. Our job is to be knowledgeable enough about vessels, machinery, systems and equipment to be able to competently evaluate the general condition. As with a G.P., when we spot trouble, we often have to refer the client to a specialist who has the expertise we lack. And when we do run across situations which exceed our knowledge, it is in our own best interest, as well as that of the client, to inform him of our limitations. The true professional surveyor, like the family doctor, is continually aware of this necessity. In the course of his work, he frequently advises his clients of his limitations, and then follows up by providing advice on how and where to seek qualified experts.

The apprentice or novice surveyor shouldn't be fooled by claims to the contrary that we needn't be well versed in basic engineering principles and not be ready to convey that knowledge to our clients. When we come across inadequately designed structures or systems, as we often will, we need to be prepared to give a detailed description of the problem, including an assessment of what could happen if it is not corrected. More than likely, we'll be asked for advice on how to fix it. But that's not all. We have to be sufficiently confident of our analysis and be prepared to defend our assessment against those who will surely challenge it. And, when it comes to criticizing the property and products of others, not only is it embarrassing to be proven wrong, it can also be very costly if the surveyor gets sued by an owner, seller or manufacturer who claims a large loss is the result of the surveyor's incompetence or negligence.

Think Like a Lawyer

It cannot be over stressed to both the neophyte and the seasoned surveyor the importance of considering everything he does with a view toward whether he can defend his work in court. It's a sad commentary on the state of affairs in this nation that it has to be this way, but the constant fear of being sued goes a long way toward ensuring that the surveyor does his job properly. If he doesn't, the likelihood of his remaining in business for more than a few years is slim.

Let's use an example to illustrate. Lets' say that you were surveying a fast cruiser that has a cockpit deck that has a very low gunwale and no railing around it. The gunwale height comes only up to your knee. As the vessel got underway, you noticed a pronounced tendency for anyone standing in the cockpit to be thrown backwards with the likelihood that they could easily lose balance and fall overboard. Spicing up the situation a bit, let's also say that you were aware that your client had two small children. The question is, would you report this situation in your survey report? An even better question is whether you would be willing to risk the consequences of not reporting it.

The answer to the question is painfully obvious. But it is equally obvious to anyone who has reviewed hundreds of survey reports that there are thousands of boats with problems like this that never, ever, get written up on survey. Why not? The answer lies, I believe, in the belief by many practicing surveyors that it's not within their purview to comment upon design safety. Yet there are plenty of court decisions handed down that disprove this notion. A recent example is a case which involves a charter yacht that had a mooring cleat installed on a deck in an unprotected location in a high traffic area. A woman walking on that deck hooked her foot under the cleat, fell and was seriously injured. Survey reports going back over ten years failed to mention the hazard. Needless to say, in the blizzard of suit papers filed, the last surveyor was implicated. The defendant, the owner of the vessel, alleged that the surveyor was negligent in failing to point this out and enjoined the surveyor. The court agreed with his argument.

This illustrates that surveyors can be, and occasionally are, held liable for failure to detect and report hazardous or faulty design. This, for the reason that courts have held that a surveyor should be sufficiently knowledgeable on a subject on which he holds himself out as an expert. That holds true whether we're talking basic structural integrity or minimum necessary railing height.

Another factor that bears on the surveyor liability question stems from the fact that the boating public is becoming increasingly ignorant of the vessels they own and operate, as well as the limited body of rules under which they are operated. The situation is not unlike a recent judgment and multi-million dollar award against MacDonalds. In this case a woman put a cup of hot coffee purchased from the restaurant between her legs while she was driving her car. Naturally, the coffee spilled and the woman was burned on a rather sensitive portion of her body. The jury reasoned, not that the woman was foolish to place the cup of hot coffee where she did, but that MacDonalds was at fault because their coffee was too hot!

Specious reasoning? Of course, but it does point out that surveyors need to be constantly on guard against opening themselves to such claims. Where the obvious possibility of damage, injury or loss exists, the law of the land insists that we, the experts, have a duty to advise our clients of such hazards.

From the surveyor's standpoint, he needs to be prepared to comment upon any condition or situation that has a reasonable likelihood of causing damage, injury or loss to the vessel, its owner and passengers. This includes economic as well as physical injury. In any instance where he fails to do that, he is exposing himself to a liability challenge. I've intentionally tried to scare the hell out of you about lawsuits because you should be scared, or at least highly vigilant about protecting yourself. If you protect yourself, it follows that you are doing an equally good job of protecting your client. Ultimately, that's what our business is all about. Much like a defense attorney, we protect ourselves by offering our clients vigorous advice and protection.

Survey Parameters

Getting Started

When a client makes his first call to a surveyor, the most commonly asked question is "what do you do on a survey?" That's not an easy question to answer unless you're prepared to spend the next thirty minutes giving a run-down on all the things you do. This question points out how important it is that, when you consent to perform a survey, you are able to convey to the client a general idea of the service you offer. Even more important than being able to describe what you can do is the ability to describe your limitations, despite the many pressures not to do this.

Every surveyor has to deal with the fact that he is not omniscient and that he cannot dismantle a vessel in order to evaluate the thing completely. A survey is a process of discovery and is necessarily limited. It is based on what it is possible to discover without dismantling the vessel or otherwise causing damage. Further, we have to consider whether we're prepared to examine eight bags of sails, climb to the top of the mast, evaluate sophisticated electronics systems, testing washing machines and ice makers, perform engine and machinery surveys and so on. When we stop to consider that a typical 45 foot yacht can be an extraordinarily complex vessel, we come to the realization of just how "general" the typical survey really is.

Fortunately, in North America the methods of performing a pre-purchase survey are fairly well standardized and accepted. By and large, clients don't expect surveyors to omniscient, and they don't expect that a survey is a comprehensive engineering analysis of the vessel. However, from time to time we do run into clients who expect just exactly that and we need to be prepared for them. Only by being aware that some of our clients may be ignorant or have unreasonable expectations can we then be prepared to deal with them effectively.

Qualifying the Client

The best method for preparing yourself, and therefore the client, is to use a process I call "qualifying the client." The best way to find out what your client needs or wants is to ask him. There's a big difference between someone buying his first boat and someone purchasing his sixth. Either way, once you've discovered something about his experience and what he expects from you, you're in a much better position to satisfy his needs and his expectations. If a client has unrealistic expectations, the time to find out is before the survey is completed, not after. In my own experience, I end up turning down about one out of every five inquiries simply because I perceive that the client has unrealistic expectations that are likely to lead both of us into trouble. If the client expects more than I can deliver, I do myself a favor and send him on his way.

The qualification period is the time to reach an agreement with the client on what the extent of your services will be. Not only do I want to know about the customer, but I want to get from him a fairly detailed description of the vessel; age, general condition, refits, overhauls, how extensively it is equipped, whether it is modified or customized, has unusual characteristics or problems; these are all things that help to paint a general picture of what the surveyor will be faced with. The more I can learn in advance, the better opportunity I have to avoid those problems. This is discussed in greater detail in the next chapter.

Lawyers often recommend, and many surveyors have tried, to obtain a signed survey agreements. On paper, that sounds like a good idea but in reality it is difficult. In a perfect world we would all operate this way but a busy surveyor, more often than not, is arranging his next survey while on the job of the present survey. For such a relatively low cost service, there is rarely time to enter into formal contracts. Nor is it really necessary if we know how to qualify the client properly.

I'm also of the opinion that if I introduce legalities into the process right at the outset, I'm creating a state of mind in the client that is more likely to hold me to my legal responsibilities. Over a long career, surveyors make a lot of mistakes. My experience has been that if they're honest mistakes and I own up to them, 99% are forgiven. But how will the client react if you shove a legal document under his nose at the start of the survey? My personal belief is that establishing good communications with the client is far more important than legal documents. However, if you feel more comfortable with getting signed orders, by all means do so.

Once I've got the job sized up, then I'm ready to discuss the extent of the survey the client desires and my price. If we're talking about a 53' Hatteras, then we know that we're faced with a fairly routine job. On the other hand, if it's a 53' custom boat built of exotic materials by some obscure builder, chances are we'll be looking more closely and spending a lot more time on the job. Not only am I then better able to price the job properly, but also have the opportunity to fully brief the client. The importance of qualifying the client is that it allows you to size up the job, reveals potential problems, and permits you the opportunity to educate the client on the limitations of the survey.

Finally, there is probably no greater incentive for a surveyor to perform less than a thorough survey (intentionally or accidentally) than to grossly underquote a survey fee. This is a problem that constantly plagues surveyors when dealing with older or custom vessels. The problem, of course, is that if the job takes twice as long as expected, the tendency is to spend less than the full amount of time required. The hazards involved in this should be obvious. The best way to avoid the problem is to take the time to size up each and every job at the outset during the qualifying process.

The Order of Progression

The preferred order of conducting the survey is as follows, for reasons that will be clarified in the following chapters:

1. Static, in-water survey

2. Haul out

3. Sea Trial

Hull Survey

The hull survey is entirely within the domain of the surveyor and he alone is responsible for evaluating its condition. A hull survey is not complete unless a haul out and a sea trial have been conducted. Two full chapters are devoted to surveying the hull, along with further discussion on evaluating the hull in the SEA TRIAL chapter.

Main Engines

Every survey job should be evaluated based upon the client's experience and requirements. It is poor practice to fall into a routine and apply that routine to every job. After qualifying the client, the next step is to reach an agreement with the client as how extensive the survey will be and, of course, the cost.

The most important consideration with respect to engines is whether the surveyor will survey the engines himself or leave that part to others. When it comes to powerboats with expensive diesel engines, most surveyors leave that to trained diesel engine specialists. On boats with gasoline engines and sailboats with single engine auxiliaries, more often than not the surveyor will survey the engine(s) himself.

Often times clients attempt to get the surveyor to evaluate diesel engines and save the cost of an engine survey. He should do this only on the conditions that the engines are fairly new, and on the understanding that both his abilities, equipment and qualifications, are limited. Further, he should spell out the parameters of his service and back it up in his written report. I would suggest that it's very unwise for the new surveyor to attempt to do this because he is going to have his hands full just dealing with the hull survey.

Gas engines are simple enough, and are found in boats small enough that the surveyor can reasonably manage to do both hull and machinery surveys. However, on larger yachts, it is simply not possible for one man to cover this much ground within the normal time allotted to complete a survey. In major yachting centers, professional diesel engine surveyors can be found; in less populous regions, either the engine surveyor will have to be brought in from elsewhere, or a man brought in from the nearest engine company dealer. We should be also be aware that there may be a conflict of interest with engine people who do surveys *and* repairs. Independent engine surveyors should be used whenever possible.

Very often, the surveyor is requested by the client to locate a specialist to survey the engines, and it is here that the surveyor should be extra careful in making such arrangements. The most obvious reason is that if the surveyor is making the selection and hiring of the engine surveyor, he could technically be held liable for any errors or omissions, or possibly even damage, caused by what might essentially be a subcontractor relationship to the hull surveyor. Under the laws of many states, a primary contractor can be held liable for the actions of a subcontractor. I've seen it happen. For that reason, it is exceedingly important that these arrangements be approached with caution.

It is wise to make it a rule to never personally engage an engine specialist on behalf of the client. If the surveyor contracts with the engine man, he could also be held liable for the engine surveyor's fee in the event that the client doesn't pay. I will make a recommendation, if asked, and give out phone numbers, but I insist that it be handled either one of two ways. First, I advise the client that he should call the engine man himself and discuss directly with him (a) his pricing and, (b) the extent of the service that he will perform. Diagnostics can be time consuming and costly, so it's important to make sure that the parameters of the engine survey are fully understood.

Sometimes this doesn't always work out and the surveyor finds himself in the position of having to make the arrangements. If that's the case, it's necessary to explain to the client that you'll be happy to do this, however, it must be made clear that this is being done on his behalf and that you accept no responsibility for the engine surveyor's actions, work product, or fee. You are doing this strictly as a courtesy. Then cover yourself by sending the client a fax, confirming his request, outlining the service to be performed, and the price quoted by the engine man.

Electrical Systems

Of all systems on board vessels, this is the one that surveyors are least able to inspect and evaluate. Marine electrical systems are complex, often mostly hidden, and amenable mainly to test operating and not technical evaluation as to whether it meets any kind of code or standard. It is not normal that surveyors perform electrical system surveys, by which it is meant a complete metering out and/or analysis of system design and installation. By definition, that would be an analysis, not a survey.

Visual inspection and test operation of electrical equipment, systems and circuits are the primary objective of the survey. Should a system appear to warrant recommendation of a technical analysis, the engagement of a qualified expert or specialist should be recommended.

Electronics

It's mind boggling the rate at which new electronic systems are introduced and become obsolete. It seems like yesterday's latest and greatest is tomorrow's old hat. Even so, it is within the purview of the hull surveyor to be proficient enough in his expertise to be able to test operate and prove most of this equipment at least functional. This does not mean that all equipment and the broad range of their functions are to be tested and proved. For unless one wishes to devote full-time to learning the operation of the myriad varieties of electronics found on yachts, it is simply not possible to be proficient at every piece of computerized wizardry for which there is a 60 page operating manual. The objective of the surveyor should be to sufficiently prove the basic operation of any given system.

However, having said that, every surveyor would do well to specifically advise the client as to every piece of major equipment which he was unable to fully test.

Plumbing

This category constitutes another major component of the survey that falls completely within the surveyor's responsibility, and one which should be fully inspected and test operated. This is covered in detail in Chapter Fifteen,

Performance

It is not the industry standard to evaluate the operation, handling and performance of a vessel although in my opinion it should be. I do it and most of the better surveyors do as well. If one agrees with my definition of the purpose of the survey, then to fail to do so is to render an incomplete survey.

We will be dealing with the specific issues of thoroughness under each category of survey in later chapters. Generally speaking, we need to have it clear in our own mind just how far we need to go to assure that we have done a good job. If we always approach this question from the legal standpoint of determining that we have taken all "reasonable and necessary" steps to evaluate every given category, we're not likely to go wrong.

No matter whether you're a neophyte or have been surveying for twenty years, it's always a good idea to review your procedures, what you do and why you do it. It's all too easy to fall into a routine of doing something the same way over and over again, until the process becomes mechanical.

Geographic Considerations

Geography and climate can make for major differences in the way surveys are conducted. For a period of about five years I performed surveys on the Great Lakes so that I was acutely aware of the problems associated with a client who wants a survey of a boat that is laid up in the dead of winter. Under these circumstances, the surveyor needs to be extremely careful. These are circumstances under which it is advisable to utilize a signed survey agreement in advance. All of the limiting conditions of the survey should be spelled out and the client should sign it as acknowledgment of these limiting conditions.

Ideally, a survey should never be done in the dead of winter. However, there's nothing wrong with a client paying you for what you are reasonably capable of doing. The point here is that the client should be presented in writing as to what you can and cannot do. The objective here is to head off any unrealistic expectations the client might have about your service under these extremely limiting conditions. So long as you can prove that the client was made aware of these facts, you have covered yourself.

Moreover, the client should be made aware that by requesting a survey in dead of winter, he's going to be paying more for less. The surveyor should not be expected to endure these hardships for a lower fee because a boat is laid up and covered up. The client should be made to realize that you are performing this service under duress, and that these factors seriously interfere with your performance.

Pass or Fail?

It's not unusual for clients to expect the surveyor give a pass or failing mark to a vessel. I don't know any surveyors who "grade" the boats they survey so I can't imagine where they get this idea. However, I have seen an occasional report that assigns numbers or letter grades. It is advisable not to do this, for grading in this manner is purely a subjective exercise. Unless you provide a summary of what each grade means, the readers are left to guess whether the surveyor's "10" or "A+" is the same as theirs. This is discussed further in the chapter on REPORTS.

Nor is it wise to advise a client to not to purchase a vessel, no matter how unwise you may think his decision may be. When a surveyor does this, he is attempting to make the decision for the client; that's consulting, not surveying. If the surveyor does this, he'd better be prepared to accept responsibility for his advice. There's nothing wrong to help him come to his own conclusions, whether by asking questions or educating the client, but it's best to try to be scrupulously neutral.

How far a surveyor should go in giving this advice is a matter of individual preference, but it's probably best to wait until you're asked, rather than offering advice that may be unwanted. Some people want to buy a wreck; others don't know a wreck when they're looking at it. You run the risk of insulting the client unless you're sure that he wants to hear what you have to say.

List of Survey Categories and Items

This list could probably be expanded indefinitely, but is representative of the extent of what's encountered in a typical survey. It's a good reminder that on any survey there is always more there than first meets the eye.

Hull, interior and exterior

    Bulkheads, stringers, frames

    Deck joint

    Decks, superstructure

    Windows, ports, doors, hatches

    Engine beds

    Bilge water communication

    Fittings, attachments & hardware

    Paint, gelcoat finish

Propulsion

    Main engines

        Mounts

        Starters, solenoids, cables

        Ventilation/aspiration

        Controls

        Wiring

        Cooling systems

        Instrumentation warning systems

        Shafting

        Stuffing box

    Specialty Diagnostics

        Oil analysis

Compression Test

Borescope

Exhaust back pressure test

Exhaust system

Turbochargers & cooling

Risers & back surge protection

Mufflers, piping, & connections

Exhaust ports, location & height

Carbon monoxide hazards

Fire hazards

High temperature alarms

Performance Evaluation

Load/no load RPM's

Back down test

Single engine load test

Control cable function

Vibration/noise levels

Performance/Handling

Basic stability

Stability at speed

Handling characteristics, steering

Backing, docking, at speed

Trim tab operation

Engine Room

Accessibility

Lighting

Ventilation

Fire control

Used oil systems & tanks

Fuel Systems

Tankage

Fuel fills & deck plates

Supply & return systems

Fuel transfer systems & pumps

Fuel filtration

Ventilation for gasoline systems

Generator/electric plant

Basic condition

Exhaust system

Cooling system

Belts, hoses, wiring

Primary circuit protection

Specific condition/diagnostics

Vibration/ noise levels

Warning systems

Hi-lo, oil pressure shut downs

Full load test

Voltage output

Drive Train

Shafts, couplings

Propellers

Struts, mount bolts, bearings

Stuffing box

Transmissions

Electrical Systems

DC Systems

Batteries, condition & performance

Primary circuit protection

Secondary circuit protection

Wiring

System layout & standards

Engine alternators & battery chargers

AC Electrical systems

Primary & branch circuits & panels

Primary circuit protection

Secondary circuit protection

System layout and standards

Wiring

Polarity check

Voltage load tests

Check shore receptacles

Power plant system operation

Plumbing Systems

Sea water systems

Engine cooling systems

Air conditioning cooling

Sea cocks, hoses, clamps & bonding

Thru-hull discharge fittings

Heads, holding tanks & associated pumps

Gray & brown water discharge systems

Wash down systems

Bait wells & systems

Fresh water systems

Potable water systems

Water tanks

Pumps & plumbing

Shower sumps, sink drains

Water makers

Dockside plumbing

Heating & cooling

Air conditioning systems

Heating

Bilge Pumping

Pumps, number & capacity

Pump operation test

Bilge alarms

Hoses & discharge fittings

Wiring & switching

Appliances

Refrigerators & freezers

Icemakers

Stoves, electric, gas & microwave

Dishwashers, compactors, disposers

Bar refrigerators & equipment

Engine driven refrigeration equipment

Clothes washers & dryers

Central vacuum systems

Electronics

Televisions, stereos, VCR's, CD players, etc.

Radios, communication equipment

VHF, HF, cell & sat phones

Radar

Loran, GPS

Computerized plotters, chart systems

Sonar, speed & depth meters

Wind instruments

Stabilizers

Fax machines & weather fax

Shipboard computers

Autopilots & navigation interfaces

Synchronizers

Fishing Gear

Outriggers

Downriggers

Fighting chairs

Bait & tackle centers, freezers, bait wells & pumps

Tuna & Marlin Towers

Safety

Life rafts

EPIRBS, signalling devices

Fire control

Automatic systems

Portable fire extinguisher

Chapter 2

Business Practices and Client Relations

This chapter discusses the very important relationship between the surveyor, his client and the service being offered. Extensive travel is a fact of life for the professional surveyor, one which frequently complicates his work and causes serious financial difficulties. Further, the surveyor will occasionally, if not frequently, find himself dealing with an international clientele. This usually presents problems of logistics, language, finances and local customs that must be confronted and successfully overcome. For that reason I have devoted considerable discussion to outlining some of the pitfalls and how to avoid them.

One of the most important skills that a surveyor can develop is the ability to establish a good client repoire. The surveyor's ability to communicate with the client is every bit as important as his knowledge and surveying skills. It's not enough that the surveyor does a good job surveying the vessel; unless he develops the ability to effectively communicate with the client, his efforts and good intentions may be for naught if, for whatever reason, the client is not satisfied with the surveyor's efforts. Complaints and disputes most often result from a lack of, or poor communications. So let's take a look at some of the dynamics involved.

Qualifying the Client

Taking a little time to assess a clients motives vis-a-vis the service you are providing can go a long way toward heading off trouble. If we can learn what the clients expectations are, we at least have a chance to satisfy those expectations or to explain why we might not be able to fulfill them. As with a physician, merely providing the service is not enough. The client is looking to us to provide professional advice, but this advice usually goes well beyond merely performing a survey. Like a doctor, we have to develop a bedside manner.

Occasionally surveyors encounter clients who want them to catalogue virtually everything that they can find wrong with a boat, every nick, scratch and burned out light bulb. In all likelihood, such clients intend to beat up the seller with a long list of defects and is angling for a large adjustment in the price. Yet, the surveyor's objective is not to present as negative view of the vessel as possible, nor do we want to be put in the position of doing so.

The opposite extreme is a client who is so in love with a particular yacht, that he's willing to blind himself to any bad news. This is the most dangerous type of client because he is unwilling to hear what the surveyor has to say. This is the type of buyer that is prone to getting himself in financial trouble by overlooking or glossing over some of the real costs of ownership. Then, when he does get in trouble, he starts searching for a way out, a scapegoat, and the surveyor is likely to be "it".

The later type is quite common. He's usually a first time buyer and is likely to have some very unrealistic concepts of boat ownership. A similar type of client is the one whose ambitions are bigger than his checking account and is attempting to buy too much boat for too little money. And while our first reaction might be, *"That's not MY problem,"* a little careful thought about that reaction will show that it very well could end up YOUR problem, i.e., when the client decides that you didn't do enough to properly advise him of some little problem that is now a very big problem.

We want to avoid falling into this trap and the best way to do that is through a process of qualifying the client. It is a process in which the surveyor interviews the client in order that he can become sufficiently familiar with him or her that he can gain a better understanding of both his expectations and his actual needs. In actual practice, there are some clients whom we may never speak to, and communicate only through intermediaries. This is a situation every surveyor should try to avoid simply because having no direct communication with the client puts the surveyor in a tough spot. It's the lack of communication that usually causes the most trouble.

Only the novice surveyor might be surprised to hear that there are a lot of clients who become so in love with a boat that they don't want to hear what the surveyor has to say. In fact, there are a lot of people like this, people who are primarily looking for the surveyor to confirm their beliefs, not critique the object of their infatuation. The client who doesn't want to hear what you have to say, or the one who is getting in over his head, requires special handling. Therefore, to avoid being made a scapegoat for the client's foolishness, we need to size up the situation and make sure that he both *hears* and *understands* what we are saying.

A typical example of how such a problem can develop occurs when we encounter a client who is buying an older yacht and has big plans for fixing it up and sailing around the world, or at least as far as Aruba or Tahiti. Experienced surveyors hear a lot of such wishful thinking. Of course he knows very well that if the man could afford the cost of fixing up that old clunker, he wouldn't be buying a clunker in the first place, but a much better one. Almost without exception, people who buy run down boats can't even afford the cost of restoring them, let alone routine maintenance. If the surveyor hasn't bothered to take the time to find out more about the client, his desires as well as his bank account, then the surveyor is operating just as blindly as the client. If he takes the time to ask questions and find out what the client's expectations are, then he'll be in a much better position to either head him in the right direction or, at least protect himself against the client's foolishness with a well-written report.

Initial Contact

The initial phone call from the client usually starts out something like this: "I need a survey. Tell me what you do? What do you charge?" At this point it's a mistake to launch into a dissertation of how you conduct a survey. Rather than answering his questions, this is the time to be asking questions.

Now is the time to find out all about who he is, what he's buying, and what he expects from you. At this point you can't give him a satisfactory answer because you don't know what he wants. Chances are, he doesn't either. At this point, you're going to help him decide what it is that he wants. If he's buying his tenth boat, well and fine; you'll know that he's an experienced owner and won't need as much attention from you. If it's his first, you now know he needs a lot of help from you.

The first thing to try to pin him down on is whether he is getting in over his head with his proposed purchase. Is the boat too big or too old for his budget? If the boat is older, does he expect it to be "turnkey," requiring no repairs to get it in the kind of condition it needs to be in? While you may think that you're about to talk your way out of a job, you need to balance this against whether upon completion of the survey the deal is likely to crash. In any case, you may only loose the survey on this particular boat, while steering the client toward something more suitable and your work for the client is merely delayed by a few weeks while he locates something else.

Of course, questioning the client about his budget can be a touchy subject, but there are appropriate ways to ease into this. Such as asking indirect questions about his estimate of the cost of ownership. Or asking how much he's budgeted for initial repairs. Once the conversation is well under way, there's usually no problem with asking straight out what his overall budget is. Once you have this, you immediately know whether he is being realistic or not. At the same time you get a sense of how strongly he's committed to this particular purchase, and whether he's open to your advice at all. If so, great! But if not, you need to drop the subject before he drops you. If he's insisting on getting in over his head, you will at least know that you will need to prepare yourself like a lawyer and take every means to protect yourself against a client who's about to take a long walk off a short dock.

Once the client is sized up, now comes the time to settle such issues as to whether he wants a specialized engine survey, where the haul out takes place, what to do if the bottom is dirty and who pays. He's probably seen the boat and you now want to get as much information about it as possible; you want to size up the job and find out just what you're getting into. At this point, he's the person who knows more about the boat than the surveyor does.

The qualification period is the time to reach an agreement with the client on what the extent of your services will be. Not only do I want to know about the customer, but I want to get from him a fairly detailed description of the vessel: age, general condition, refits, overhauls, how extensively it is equipped, whether it's been modified or customized, or whether he knows about any particular problems. These are all things that will paint a general picture of what the surveyor will be faced with. The more I can learn in advance, the more problems I'm likely to avoid. Equally important, it gives me a better idea on how to set my pricing. I don't want to charge for one day's work when the job will end up taking two days.

A Good Sales Technique

One of the first questions that the client asks is, "How much will it cost?" So why not just quote him your usual price? There are several reasons why a surveyor should never immediately quote a price. First, if it's an old clunker, you're going to work a lot harder and longer than if it is a very late model boat. Are you going to charge the same price for a clunker as you would a newer boat? Second, and even more importantly, if you immediately quote a price, he's very likely to say, "Thanks, I'll get back to you." And, of course, he never will; he's gone onto the next guy looking for a lower price. By taking the time to qualify the client, you will have fully engaged him; he will have invested time in you, and you him. Under these circumstances, you're a lot more likely to sign him up right then and there. He's much less likely to go off shopping price. And even if he does, he's more likely to come back to you because the other guy will probably shoot him a price first and not engage him. The other guy will likely give an answer that doesn't satisfy him as well as you did.

If a potential client is just shopping price, that's something else you want to know. The guy who's looking for the cheapest price is a fool. He's a fool because he he's not interested in quality, only the price. And if you do business with a fool, you'll probably pay a price yourself. Many clients can be quickly educated out of their foolishness, not by telling them about the mistakes they are making. No, you can't ever do that because he'll just think it's a sales pitch. The proper technique here is to lead them to their own process of discovery by asking questions designed to help them understand that they get what they pay for. Questions like, "I suppose you just want the survey to satisfy the bank." Or, "I don't suppose the quality of a survey has anything to do with its price." "Is price your only consideration?" If price is not their only interest, then you can lead them to other areas of concern. Get them to express those concerns, and when they do, it will start to dawn on them that a cut-rate survey is similar to a cut-rate brain surgery. Ask them straight out what it is they expect from the survey. If they don't know, lead them. "Does it make a difference to you how much you'll have to spend repairing things?" If price is their only concern, then this is the kind of client that I stay away from. I don't want their business. My work then is no longer a business transaction but a fleecing — of me.

Getting Paid

This goes hand in hand with commanding a fair price, for both involve the discussion of money. Many surveyors, long into their careers, still have trouble getting paid. I had that problem, and with the help of a professional sales training program, it was solved completely and permanently. Getting a fair price and collecting it are two of the beginning surveyor's biggest problems. He's the new kid on the block and often ends up with the rejects that the established surveyors don't want. The one advantage that the young surveyor does have is that this kind of client has probably been rejected himself and has been softened up a bit. Probably the best piece of advice I can give the novice is to hone up his sales skills and learn how to command a fair price. Unless the surveyor takes command of the client, the client will take command of him.

For the first ten years of my career I had bad debt lists as long as my arm. I was young and not all that self-confidant about my abilities. Because of that, I was less demanding about the payment of my fee until one day I woke up and realized that I was beginning to look like a maritime charity. Changing my attitude and my procedures, the next year I cut my bad debts from thousands to $400.00, and the following year to zero. And for the next 20 years they've stayed near zero. The rule is this: If you have to argue about money, do it up front. The difference between loosing a client up front and not getting paid can be about 16 hours of free labor. To add insult to injury, there are even instances of surveyors getting sued by clients who didn't pay the surveyor for the service over which he's being sued. The money issue has to be settled before the surveyor ever leaves his office, and in no uncertain terms.

What do I mean by that? Well, what I learned from a sales training pro is that most people are reluctant to discuss the issue of money, and this is what leads to their downfall. The issue of how and when you get paid must be settled decisively. If you are reluctant to discuss this for fear of loosing the client, then I can guarantee you you'll have big problems with bad debts. The surveyor must get the client's agreement that he'll be paid at a specific time. If the surveyor is wishy-washy or vague about it, the client may sense that and take advantage. Remember that these clients didn't become well off by being saints.

First I had to get over my concern for whether I lost a job over a fee quote. Doctors, dentists and lawyers don't negotiate their fees, I reasoned, so why should I? I had to learn to set a price, despite brutal competition, and get it. Up front the client was told that he was expected to bring a check for me. And that he would present it to me the moment when the physical survey was completed. When I arrived at the boat in the morning, I would immediately ask him if he brought his check book. On more than one occasion the client said, "Gee whiz, I forgot my checkbook!" And I would reply, "Golly, I just realized that I have another appointment. Have a nice day." And started to leave. It was amazing how quickly forgotten checkbooks could suddenly appear. When the client comes on with something like, "Shouldn't I at least get the written survey first?" I would reply with a flat "No." No explanations about my "policy," no chance to argue. "Remember, you agreed that . . . ." When a client wants to argue about your fee, that means he doesn't want to pay it. Don't do it. Stand firm, look him in the eye. Ninety five percent of the time he'll promptly back down.

It's an amazing thing, though, that after learning these techniques, I no longer even have to ask most of my clients to pay me. They'll pull out their check book and ask me, "How much do I owe you?" They do this because (1) I've taken the time to find out their needs, (2) they're comfortable that I've fulfilled those needs , and (3) we have an up front understanding of when I will get paid.

There will be instances when special arrangements are required. The first of these is when the client will not be attending the survey. In this case, it is essential to get paid in advance. Another occasion that necessitates advance payment is when a foreign or out of state customer will be arriving on the day of the survey and seeing the boat for the first time. It is truly amazing how many people will sign a sales agreement sight unseen, but subject to survey.

What is likely to happen to you is that client arrives on the appointed day, shows up at the boat, takes one look at it and says, "I don't want this hunk of junk — survey cancelled." And there you are standing with your hands in your pockets feeling pretty darn dumb. Oh, no, we don't work like that, do we? No, because what we're going to get the client to agree to in advance is that if this happens, he's going to pay you something for this day on which you potentially don't make a dime. A no pay day.

Surveyors policies vary on how they handle this. Some ask for 50% of the quoted fee while others ask for the whole thing. My view is that it's hard to get someone to write you a check for their perception of you not doing anything. Or to have to go through the effort of explaining that you could be doing a paying job today, but for them. I resolved this issue by getting a credit card merchant account and asking the client for an advance payment.

Funny thing about credit cards, it's a lot easier getting paid by this method than asking for the client to write and possibly mail a check. Beware, however, managing a merchant account can be a hassle. If you have to do it by yourself, without help, it's probably not worth the extra effort. On the other hand, skillful salesmanship and use of the account can greatly increase your income if you are willing to work at it.

Setting and Quoting Fees

As stated earlier, it's not a good idea to quote a fee until you've fully engaged the client and have all necessary information at hand. Most surveyors

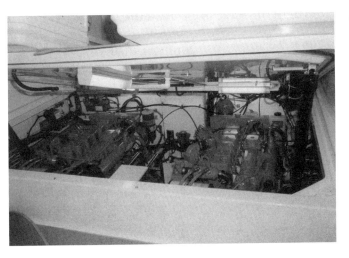

The unexpected strikes again. This large cockpit hatch with built in seating attached, only opens up this far. Not only is it extremely difficult to survey this engine room, but the boat cannot be operated with the hatch open. Just one of many things that can make an easy job very difficult.

base their fees based on a per foot rate with qualifiers. These include such things as age, production versus custom boats, or other unusual characteristics. Quoting a per foot rate is usually predicated on the hope that the job can be completed within a certain period of time. But it doesn't always work out that way, which is why all the parameters of the survey circumstances, such as difficult logistics, need to be known before quoting.

It is advisable not to use the per foot rate for jobs involving any kind of travel, unless you can control your time closely. The vagaries of traffic and travel make for too much uncertainty and a lot of long days for the same pay. Therefore, for all travel jobs, it's a good idea to quote the job based on an hourly or day rate calculation. You need not to inform the client the basis for your quote, just the flat rate amount. Some surveyors quote a mileage rate, but unless it is a very high rate, it can never make up for many lost hours in travel.

Let's take a close look at this. Say you have surveyed a particular boat in your hometown and know how long it took you, about eight hours. Now you're faced with the same job one hundred miles away. This time you're faced with traffic jams that add two hours more travel time than expected, and for reasons uncontrollable by you, the survey took two hours longer than expected. The result is that the job now took 50% longer than anticipated. If you'd calculated your flat rate to earn you $60 per hour, on this job you're only bringing in $30. That's a whopping 50% percent pay cut. On the other hand, had you set your fee based on a day rate, you'd get the full days pay. Assuming the day rate is considerably more than the per foot rate comes to, you're well ahead.

When setting fees, bear in mind that your rate must make up for a good deal of no pay days, those days when you have no job, or when jobs run over time, or you unavoidably get caught up in payless tasks. The beginning surveyor who attempts to start out by undercutting everyone else's price is ensuring that he has to run twice as fast to stay in the same place. And that's not a good way to start.

Cancellations

When a job is quoted and contracted for, that means that the client is contracting for that period of time that takes to do the job. Therefore, most surveyors do not give the client the right to terminate the survey at any time and pay a lower fee. The client has reserved the surveyor's time and he deserves to be paid for it. Consider other professionals: There was one occasion where I had scheduled elective surgery with a surgeon for in-office surgery. A rush job came up and I called him from the Bahamas to tell him that I couldn't make it. He sent me a bill for his time anyway. Did he have a right to do that? Of course he did; I'd reserved his time and didn't give him adequate notice to change his scheduling. The surveyor should think the same way. The client is reserving his time and he should pay for it.

Merchant Account and Credit Cards

To accept credit card payments, first you need to get a merchant account.

If you're willing to go to all the trouble to get a merchant account, and can qualify for one, I can guarantee you that you'll increase your income by ten percent or more. Very likely much more because you'll discover more and better uses for this convenient billing method. Such as taking advance payments for out of town work, and getting advance payments on otherwise hard to collect jobs. The client who balks at sending you a check after the job is complete is usually more willing to give you the credit card number in advance.

A simple way to get a merchant account would be to apply your bank and use their card processing service. But discount rates and other additional fees differ from one bank to the other. There are also other credit card processing services and they will handle merchant account applications. Their rates vary as well. So I would recommend to do some research if you are interested in getting one.

The method a surveyor would use most is the over-the-phone method wherein the customer gives you his information verbally while you write it down. You purchase or lease a transaction software from your credit card service provider. All you need is a PC and a modem. After you install and configure the software on your computer, dialing-in to process cards will be a matter of simple click. The process is easy enough for you to handle yourself, if you have no problem filling out computer forms online.

Be sure to get correct card numbers from your clients first place and not to forget obtaining additional necessary information; expiry date, zip code and so on. It's more difficult than you may think. You will at first make mistakes and not get all those numbers right. It took me a while before I got it down to getting it right first time, every time. It's so easy to get a wrong digit or miss one digit, or forget asking additional information. Using a form is a good idea. I use print-out form that contains boxes for all information to be filled in. Keep them handy near your phone. And process without delay. It will be easier to get back to the client for correct information the same day rather than three days later, if somehow you get "invalid card number" error message.

There is a downside to accepting credit card payments. What you end up with is a double billing system, one for paper transactions and the other for electronic transactions. One is basically no easier than the other. The benefit of card payments is that once you process the transaction, your work is done. There's fewer account receivables to follow up, and that's a big advantage. After the initial hassle, you wonder how you managed to do without it.

Client's Presence

This brings up the point of whether the client should be present during the survey. Many surveyors prefer to work alone, undisturbed, and don't want the client to be present. Personally, I think that is a big mistake. Without the client present the surveyor is losing the opportunity to establish a relationship with his client, and to educate him. With the client in absentia, the surveyor has to rely on the survey report and telephone conversations, whereas if the client is present, the surveyor can explain and demonstrate first hand. Without the client present, you lose the opportunity to direct his attention to where it needs to be.

You also lose the opportunity to educate your client as to some of the reasons why you have limitations in performing your task; you can't explain first hand why you can't see or test something. Most clients appreciate a surveyor who takes the time to review his work and explain things in detail. Most of us, I'm sure, have had the experience of visiting a doctor who seems to be too busy to spend a few precious minutes discussing the reason why we came to see him. He does his job, but he's just too busy to talk to us. Understandably, we leave the doctor's office feeling cheated. We certainly don't want our clients feeling the same way and it's up to the surveyor to make sure that he doesn't.

Of course clients can get in the way and disrupt our work by asking too many questions at the inappropriate moment. The way to deal with that situation is to simply explain to him that you need some uninterrupted time to inspect, review and analyze, that you need to finish your work before you can properly advise him. Then you tell him that at the appropriate time, or at the end of the survey, you'll be most happy to review all your findings with him and answer all his questions. If you don't do this, he's going to be asking a lot of questions at the wrong time, questions that you probably can't answer at the moment, and so you're going to end up looking dumb. You lose both ways. But if you take the time to prepare the client in advance, you smooth the way to a more enjoyable experience for both of you, as well as building his confidence in you.

Which is not to say that you shouldn't, at appropriate moments, take the time to show the client something that he needs to see. Indeed, it's not wise to ignore the client all day long until the survey is completed; when you reach an appropriate breaking-off point, you surprise him by reviewing important findings with him from time to time. He'll feel better that you are paying attention to him. There will be times, such as during the haul out, when there's a whole gang of people standing under the boat looking at it, that you'll be bombarded with questions. If you don't control the situation, you're going to be distracted and overlook things. At this point you need to establish control by diplomatically stating that you need to finish your work and *then* you'll be happy to answer their questions. The novice surveyor is prone to be anxious to please and thereby is likely to allow his work to be controlled by others. He should avoid this at all costs by making sure that those present understand that he needs to be able to work without interruption.

Early on in your career you'll have to work at this. It's wise to frequently review your "bedside manner" and consciously correct your short comings.

Ninety percent of the time these problems can be avoided if you take the time to sit down with the client at the start of the survey and explain what your procedures and requirements are, especially how you expect the job to proceed. Sometimes we are not merely dealing with a client but a whole family who has brought half their friends along. Under those circumstances, the surveyor absolutely must take the initiative to take control of the situation. I don't know about other parts of the country, but in South Florida many clients will try to turn the survey process into a family outing. They bring along the brother-in-law and the neighbor, or Smilin' Jack the Mechanic who services the client's fleet of trucks and who surely knows everything there is to know about boats too! Without intending to so do, clients can turn an easy job into an unpleasant affair —at least for you.

I'll never forget the time nine people including kids showed up for a survey and sea trial on a 30 foot boat and they all insisted on going along. Despite my calm explanation of why I couldn't do my job with all those people on board, with a straight face the client assured me that they would all stay out of my way. I politely pointed out that ten people barely fit on a 30 foot boat and couldn't possibly stay out of my way. The client was adamant, stating that they had traveled long and far to experience this great moment and that they were all going on the sea trial, with or without me. After all, he said, they were family and they were all in this together. Indeed, like sardines in a can.

To make a long story short, they went without me. There was no way I could do my job in the middle of that crowd. I was not about to subject myself to the manifold liabilities that were facing me, including a risk of someone falling through an open hatch that *the surveyor* had opened. Fortunately, this was one of the few times that I have ever faced such an unreasonable client. When people are smart enough to get rich enough to buy an expensive boat, they're usually smart enough to let their hired help do their job. More often than not, clients appreciate your taking the lead as long as you take the time to keep them appraised of what is happening. Fail to do that and there will surely be problems.

Brokers vs Direct Sales

The majority of boats valued in excess of $50,000 are sold by brokers, at least around the major metropolitan areas of North America, and increasingly, the whole world. There's a good reason for this, and it's because direct sales between sellers and buyers often become quite messy. Yacht owners can be quite emotionally attached to their boats, a factor that can turn a hard-nosed bargaining session between buyer and seller into an emotionally charged affair. The role of the broker is to keep buyer and seller separated so that this doesn't happen. Part of his job is to keep things on a businesslike keel and ensure that the process proceeds smoothly.

Brokers often end up making most of the arrangements for the survey to be carried out, including arranging for captains and haul outs. However, the surveyor should not allow the broker to completely control the survey process, nor should he allow the broker to stand between client and surveyor. More trouble results from a lack of communication between client and surveyor than for any other reason, so it's a mistake for the surveyor not to establish communications with the client prior to the start of the survey. This is a situation that can occur frequently in the major yachting centers where many of the surveyor's clients are not local and the client comes to the surveyor by way of the broker. The best thing to do when the referral comes in is to get on the phone with the client and immediately begin the qualification process. *The smoothest relations occur when the surveyor works directly with both the client and his broker in setting up the survey.*

Direct sales, as mentioned, can be troublesome and the same advice can be applied with respect to the seller. The surveyor ignores the seller at his own peril. Sellers are naturally nervous about having their boats surveyed; often they are emotionally attached to their boats and don't take kindly to criticism. Be a good salesman and contact the seller yourself if there's no broker involved. He'll appreciate that and it will establish repoire and good will. After all, you may end up spending a day with him and have to rely on his cooperation. A few kind words can go a long way to making your work a lot more pleasant. You'll also want to find out whether the boat is ready to go and generally learn as much about it in advance as you can. Is there fuel in the tanks? Will the engines start? Will low tides prevent movement of the vessel? Moreover, handled correctly, sellers are often in the market for new boats and are a good source of new clients.

Survey Logistics

This next subject is as important from the standpoint of maintaining good client relations as it is for preventing disastrous or merely aggravating scheduling problems. It is very important that the three basic parts of the survey, afloat, haul out and sea trial, go smoothly and according to schedule. The geographical area in which we work has a lot to do with the way we handle scheduling and pricing. Often times we may have to travel long distances. Or the vessel may have to travel a long distance to a marina for hauling. Or we have to go a long way to get to open water. Sometimes we start out in one location and end up in another, as when the vessel is left hauled at the yard and our car is twenty miles away. There are a lot of "ifs". Oh, how many was the time that I worked a 12 hour day for an appallingly small fee.

It's important to ourselves and our clients to ask the right questions in advance so that we don't waste time and end up working long hours for too little money. If we're on an hourly rate, we'd be well-advised to consider the situation from the client's point of view and not slap him with a bill for a lot more than he expected. We should anticipate these problems and do some advance questioning of the client to find out just how far we'll have to travel, and whether the boat is likely to return to its original location. Or does the new owner intend to leave it hauled at the yard to paint the bottom or do other work, thereby leaving you to call a taxi? It's also a good idea to contact the seller and find out if there's fuel in the tanks. It can really ruin an otherwise good day to run out of fuel in a remote location late in the day.

Very often a client calls to make arrangements for survey and yet he has very few details to give the surveyor. It can be a real mistake to go trudging off to a survey location without first getting a page full of information. Not only do you need pertinent information on the client, you need information on the seller, yard, broker, captain or anyone else involved. Cellular phones come in real handy when trouble arises so it's good to have as many phone numbers as possible. Even though we've already made an appointment with a yard for hauling, calling an hour ahead to see if they will be ready for you is wise. If not, then perhaps you can rearrange your schedule. Many times surveyors have traveled to the yard only to find that the travel lift is tied up with an emergency and is asked to wait until tomorrow! It makes things a lot easier if we take the time to get all the information we need in advance so that both the surveyor and client will be spared a costly experience.

Travelling to Foreign Countries

This topic is included simply because surveyors tend to travel a lot. How much and how far will depend on your individual circumstances. Early in our careers, we are often thrilled to get a call that's going to take us some exotic location. Unfortunately, reality usually has a way of rearing its ugly head to dispel our illusions of the idea of mixing business with pleasure.

It's not easy to anticipate the difficulties associated with long distance travel for surveys, so for that reason I will recount one of my worst experiences with traveling since everything that could go wrong, did go wrong. One of the first things that we fail to anticipate is that we're apt to be exhausted by the time we arrive at the job site. Then we're expected to go immediately to work, and to work continuously until the job is complete. More often than not, that means without food or rest. Some of my worst difficulties have occurred after getting up at 4:00 AM, traveling for five hours and then attempting to complete a survey all in one day. To complicate things further, when traveling to strange places, we have no idea what to expect when we arrive, and therefore scheduling becomes particularly difficult. The third problem encountered with travel is the loss of control over conditions that we experience. The following tale hits some of the high points as to what can go wrong.

A client from my home town, a friend of a friend, engaged me to survey a big Hatteras that was located at what was supposed to be a new resort hotel/ marina in what was then the communist state of Yugoslavia but now Croatia. Located only 100 miles or so past the Italian border, the logistics of getting there were fairly simple. I questioned the client closely and was told that he wanted to buy a Hatteras and also wanted it for use in the Mediterranean. This seemed the ideal choice. The owner and seller was an Austrian who would meet me at the Yugoslav border and arrange to bring me in. I was to fly to Milan via London and thence drive to the Italian city of Trieste. There I would meet the seller and drive to the Yugoslav border. At this point I even called the seller's office in Innsbruck and confirmed the arrangements with the man's personal secretary. My first mistake was in not having the client with me. The second was in not learning that the man did not speak English very well. My third mistake was in not learning the precise details of how I would be admitted to this communist state. I was simply told it would be "no problem." It never is until you get there. My forth mistake was in taking the job; I should have declined it.

In any case, I collected my expenses and my fee in advance, making sure that the check cleared. Time would prove that the fee was nowhere near enough. All seemed to be going well until Alitalia lost my luggage somewhere between London and Milan. Bye bye equipment, clothing and tooth brush. From there a gorgeous drive along the Adriatic coast to Trieste, it didn't take long to discover that no one spoke English in this remote outpost of western Italy. In fact, I was not so sure that they even spoke Italian, which I could at least manage a little. But not here. After 24 hours of continuous travel, a kindly hotel manager, with the use of some wild hand signals and pencil and paper, helped me find my way around to purchase another set of clothing and a tooth brush. The next morning the seller called and said he would not pick me up as planned but meet me at the Yugoslav border. Things were going downhill fast.

True to his word, the seller was waiting for me at what looked like the real checkpoint Charley, replete with barbed wire and crossing gates and guards armed with automatic weapons. He managed to clear me through the stern-faced and very heavily armed border guards with no difficulty. They did not appear the least bit friendly, and I later discovered that just about everyone I met in that troubled land was equally in need of some attitude adjustment. We drove in near total silence, as the seller spoke hardly any English at all, the remaining 50 miles or so to Rejik where the yacht was moored. My discomfort level was increasing steadily. We would not arrive at the marina until noon and I was wondering how I was going to complete a survey in six hours or less. The seller didn't intend to stay the night and neither did I. As beautiful as it was, I wanted out of this dismal place.

All went well until we cast off the lines and headed out into the Adriatic for a sea trial. The owner managed to communicate that he was not accustomed to operating the yacht himself and had no familiarity with the local waters. Fortunately, there were charts aboard, albeit of the Italian variety. He indicated that we were to head over to the nearby island of Otok Krk where he had a luncheon appointment. Great! I'm trying to get a survey done and he's using the occasion for a luncheon appointment! Not to worry, I was to continue my work and he would return in a couple of hours. Meanwhile, from the bridge where I was navigating instead of surveying, I noticed black smoke pouring out the starboard engine room ventilator. We stopped and once the smoke cleared, I found that the engine exhaust manifold was badly cracked and spewing exhaust smoke into the engine room. I wanted to turn back, but the owner insisted that we proceed on one engine. He had his luncheon appointment to keep. Oh, joy.

Pulling into the small port town, the owner jumped off and disappeared into the town square, without even lifting a finger to help with the lines. Had I not tied it up, the yacht would have just floated away, such was the man's arrogance. At this point I knew I was in over my head since the owner showed not the slightest regard for what had happened, and left me alone with the yacht and no idea of what to do if approached by authorities. I had no visa and my passport was not stamped by the border guards. I started to think about all those Robert Ludlam novels I used to read. This seemed like one of those kind of places.

I still had my camera, but no film. I figured that if I didn't have time to survey the boat, I'd photograph the hell out of it. So I also headed off to the town square a hundred yards away to see if any film was available. There wasn't, but I paid a high price to find out. I approached an ancient looking building that appeared to have signs that suggested it might be a drug store. An incredibly old man wearing a long black coat was out front on his hands and knees. He was mixing something in an assortment of buckets which were scattered around on the side walk in front of the store's door. I was attempting to negotiate the obstacle course of buckets and was looking up at the storefront signs at the same time when suddenly a group of old men sitting on a nearby park bench all rose in unison and started shouting at me, shaking their fists. Still walking but now looking in their direction, I suddenly felt the sidewalk turn to mush. Not recognizing what the old man was doing, I had walked into a freshly poured section of concrete sidewalk. Now the old man is coming after me with his mixing stick, slapping me on the back with it, driving me further into the wet cement.

The incident would have been pretty funny but for the genuine hostility I met with from those old men. Needless to say, I never got my film and now my only pair of shoes and socks were covered with rapidly drying concrete. I'll never forget the hostility of the people in this region; it was palpable, even fifteen years ago. I hightailed it back to the boat and cleaned up as best possible. The owner eventually returned and with only a few words passing between us, we returned to the mainland, smoke billowing out the engine room vents. On arrival back at the marina, the owner passed me a note which stated simply, "You are not to say to Mr. Smith (my client) about this." With that he pushed a wad of twenty dollar bills across the table. I pushed it back at him. He got up, left the boat and I never saw him again. Which meant that I was left stranded in Yugoslavia with no way out.

I thought I was in luck when I checked into the brand new hotel across the street from the marina. It looked quite nice. They gave me a room immediately next to the entrance off the main lobby - probably the worst room in the hotel.

Though it was obvious that the hotel was nearly empty, my attempts to get the desk clerk to give me a different room were futile. "No, no, no," he said, making it clear that it was that room or nothing. The bathroom dispensed only cold water at a temperature suitable for keeping fresh fish. If that weren't enough, a group of people held a party in the lobby that lasted most of the night, a very loud party with lots of vodka. By morning it was 48 hours since I'd slept.

With the help of a drunken Italian boat owner at the marina, I made my way back to the border crossing where I spent the next eight hours in the guard shack, having not slept in nearly 60 hours and having eaten little. After an evening of what seemed to be endless phone calls, the dour-face border guards apparently got things cleared up with their superiors (none of them spoke English so I had no idea of what was going on) and they opened the gate and pushed me across the border. I was surprised to find that there were no Italian border guards on the Italian side; apparently they let you in but not out. When back in Trieste I asked about this, the Italians laughed and said that no one ever comes over from that side, so they had no reason to guard their border. Their smirks told me that they knew what I had gone through. I wished I had learned this on the way over instead of on the way out. Had I known, I might have turned around right then!

Arriving back in Milan three days later I found that Alitalia never did find my luggage. An Englishman on the plane laughed when I told him about the luggage, saying that one never checks luggage because if doesn't get lost it will get stolen. He suggested I not waste my time looking for it as it would not be found. He was right. With my shoes still stiff with concrete, I arrived in Heathrow at 8:00 PM, just in time for the airport to close for the night. I had never imagined that one of the world largest airports completely shuts down at 8:00PM, but it did. After 72 hours without sleep, I spent the night sleeping in a fiberglass chair, so tired I wasn't even uncomfortable. By the time I arrived back in Miami I hadn't bathed in four days and looked like a refugee from a revolution.

The object of this little story is to relate just how badly things can go wrong when heading off into uncharted territory without good advance knowledge of what we're getting into. Sojourns to South America have produced some disasters far worse than this. In Honduras I spent a night in a hotel basement to avoid getting shot in a street war raging outside my hotel that night. In the morning the hotel lobby was riddled with bullet holes. Problems like this are not at all unusual when traveling to unfamiliar places, and can often occur in unexpected destinations.

Not only did I lose a great deal of money on the Croatia deal, for which the client refused to reimburse me, but in the week it took to recover from the ordeal, when I could not work effectively and thus continued to lose income. What little I was paid was greatly offset by the increased expenses and the loss of income. Even when traveling within the U.S., unforeseen circumstances can cost time and money. Here's a few rules I've learned to live by when traveling, particularly to third world destinations:

- Never travel under any circumstances when another person controls your destiny.

- Never permit a client to purchase your plane ticket. Always purchase your own.

- Never permit a client or other person to make travel arrangements for you of any kind, not even hotel or car rental reservations. Always make your own.

- Always check with the consulate or embassy about travel visas or work permits for any foreign country.

- Never accept another person's word about foreign requirements.

- Always speak directly to the individual who is in control of the vessel to be surveyed. Never rely on advice from an intermediary.

- Determine for yourself where the vessel is and all the logistics of where it may have to go.

- Determine what your travel costs will be and then double it. Tell the client the difference, if any, will be refunded.

- Always collect your complete fee and expenses in advance. Fail to do this and your chances of not getting paid are very high.

- Avoid checking in luggage if possible. If not, place one clothing change and toilet articles in carry-on bag. Use carry-on to foreign countries whenever possible. Travel light.

- Schedule in adequate time for food and rest. Avoid being pushed into working immediately after long periods of travel. It's best to arrive a day early and charge for it.

- Theft of plane tickets from hotel rooms is a serious problem. Keep plane tickets on your person at all times.

- Never leave valuables, not even your work notes, in a hotel room. If you must, find a good place to hid them.

Every once in a while I get a client who wants to travel with me and wants to make all the arrangements, purchase the tickets and pay all expenses. Do this often enough and eventually you'll find yourself at the complete mercy of a client who has little regard for you or your way of doing things. This can generate some really terrible predicaments for the surveyor and is the reason why I recommend that he always make and pay for his own arrangements. Never put yourself under a stranger's control.

Travelling to foreign countries can be a difficult and very time consuming proposition, one that's rarely as profitable as if you had stayed at home and worked. Unless, of course, you have no work. The worst of it is that you're usually exhausted when you return and often need a day or two to recover, for which you'll not likely get paid unless you figure that in your fee in advance. A marathon trip to Guam and Japan took me four days to recover from. The only reason I did it was because I charged for those four additional days of 13 time zone jet lag.

Another good piece of advice is to always travel as light as you can for long trips. Nothing wears me down faster than having to haul luggage around. This is what usually happens when you have to check out early to save paying for an extra hotel day because of logistics. More often than not, I want to depart as soon as the job is finished, and not go back to the hotel. That means I have to drag my luggage with me to the job site. In the long run, if extra clothing or small tools are needed, it may easier and cheaper to buy them where you are than to haul them around. For these purposes, I buy cheap clothing and don't hesitate to throw them away if they get badly soiled rather than drag them home. One of those fold up cases on wheels that the airline crews use are ideal as long as they're not too big. I use one of those and a shoulder bag and that's it. In the shoulder bag I keep my camera and other expensive gizmos and never let it out of my sight, though it's always fun going through security with multimeters and other unfamiliar electronics. If I do check a bag on the plane, it contains the expendables, the things I can afford to loose, if only because I can't always carry it around with me.

Because I go to a lot of strange places, I'm leery of credit cards, wallets, jewelry and travelers checks. There are many places and many circumstances where these forms of money are not welcome and are worthless. I haven't been anywhere yet where U.S dollars are not accepted or readily convertible, so I always take plenty of cash. In many countries they prefer U.S. dollars but abhor travelers checks. Having been robbed twice, once right in the middle of San Juan airport, I take my cash and divide it in three parts. The first I carry in my sock, the second in my pocket, the rest I hide in my hotel room. Therefore, if

I'm robbed or I lose it, I lose no more than a third of my cash. Remember that there is nothing like cash for easing your way out of a difficult situation. And the people you need it for don't take American Express.

Plane tickets and passports are also hot items for theft. Never leave these in a hotel room or anywhere off your person. I've had tickets stolen twice, once from a hotel room and once from a brief case on a boat. Both now go in my pocket and stay there.

Taxis: Taxis drivers in many third world countries are in the business of robbing people. Many taxis are phony and not registered. Many drivers are stupid and will drive you into places where both of you will get robbed. In Caracas I had a taxi driver take me through one of the worst barrios in the city, straight into a gang war going on in the street. I saw it coming before he did and only my screaming prevented him from driving right into the middle of it. When traveling to dangerous places, and if you work long enough as a surveyor you'll go to plenty of them, you need to make travel arrangements with your contact at the point of destination. It can be very dangerous to just fly into an airport and then take a taxi to your hotel. Always make arrangements in advance for secure travel. Try to have the seller arrange to pick you up. If that's not possible, at least go to your airline ticket desk and ask for information on local travel.

Work Requirements: Just because foreigners come to work illegally in our country by the millions in defiance of U.S. laws, don't expect other countries to reciprocate. I was once refused entry into Canada after answering truthfully to a customs agent's inquiry. It was very embarrassing because I spent the client's money for travel expenses and couldn't perform the job. If you travel to islands or central or South America, be prepared to face a little extortion from time to time by government officials. They don't accept credit cards, hence the need for cash. Keep in mind that you may be asked to do a survey in a place that requires you to have a work permit. Only occasionally have I been challenged, but in every case someone had their hand out for a little grease. I learned this lesson the hard way once by refusing. The result wasn't pleasant. Beware that virtually all of the Caribbean Islands have the work permit requirement, though it can be very unevenly enforced, customs or police officials may take personal advantage. If you read the requirements, you will find that it's nearly impossible to determine what the work requirement means. If you are questioned and intend to lie, you'd better look like a tourist and not someone prepared to go to work.

A bag full of tools is a dead giveaway that you're not a tourist and that you're there to work. This can cause lots of problems. If there's any doubt about where I'm going, I dress like a tourist and don't take any tools, particularly a brief case that always raises eyebrows. While you might wonder how you can do a survey without bringing tools, actually it's easy. What I can't find on the boat, I usually manage to scrounge up somewhere. People are usually very helpful.

When traveling to the Caribbean or South America, I recommend calling the embassy and asking about the work requirements. Tell them that you're just going to look at a boat on behalf of a client. They usually won't quite understand who you are, but to them it will be clear that you're not stealing jobs from the locals. While I've been refused by customs officials who like to flaunt their authority, I've never been refused by a consulate and in a few cases actually received an advance clearance in terms of the work issue.

Many South and Central American countries present some serious travel dangers and conditions can change suddenly. On a trip to Caracas, Venezuela, which I expected to be pretty safe, I returned to my Hilton hotel in the middle of the downtown area, after a day's work, only to find it surrounded by the Army. Terrorists were roaming the streets robbing everything in sight, including hotels, while I had innocently struck out across the countryside on my own, totally unaware of the danger. In fact, everyone I had talked to had denied there is any danger there, both before and after the incident. Uh huh. For information about travel to such places, call the U.S. State Department for up-to-date information. They'll fax you a report or you can get it direct from the Internet if you're so inclined.

Also beware that the Bahamas *strictly enforces their work permit laws.* Expect to be turned away if you announce your purpose. If you get caught doing a survey there without a permit, expect to be arrested and taken to jail. I can tell you from personal experience, Fox Hill Prison in Nassau is not a place you want to be. This is a good selling point to use on the client when explaining your expenses. It's worthwhile to call the Bahamian consulate to see if you can get a deferment, or obtain a day rate permit. Policies change rapidly there but I've gotten them for as little as $50.00 although I'm sure this was more "grease" than an official fee. If you try to sneak in, your chances of getting caught are fairly high.

Because of the tremendous distances when traveling to Pacific Islands, it's downright foolish not to investigate work requirements. Customs on South Pacific Islands can be very rough and it's best to make sure travel arrangements are very secure indeed, as in the form of a visa.

I've painted a pretty gloomy picture of what it can be like when traveling

Fig. 2-1. Surveying old boats can rather quickly become something of a nightmare. A surveyor failed to discover all this rot and corroded fuel tanks within this twelve year old custom wood sport fisherman. Why? Because the area was completely inaccessible. His biggest mistake was in failing to warn the client that such conditions could exist.

overseas, mainly to illustrate to the uninitiated how easily things can go wrong. After learning the hard way, most of my trips are now trouble free. Even so, I work a lot longer and harder on travel jobs and find they're not worthwhile unless I get a sizable fee. The best part of travel, I think, is the people. The trip to Croatia was the only time I ever felt that I was treated poorly. Despite what I hear on TV, I find foreigners really like Americans and I've received wonderful help and assistance in some of the most horrible places. (If you're wondering why a surveyor goes to a war zone, it's because when wars break out, people want to get their assets out, so there's often a lot of boat sales in these places.) Treat your hosts well and you're likely to be treated well yourself.

As a final note, attempting to mix business and pleasure, such as staying over a few extra days on some lovely island, is usually not a good idea. Clients get the feeling that you're vacationing at their expense. Yes, there will be times when the client won't know, or it won't make a difference, such as when they invite you to do so, but generally speaking it's a practice that should be avoided.

A Question of Quality

Throughout this book the term "entry level" boats is used to describe those types of vessels that are commonly purchased by unknowledgeable, first-time buyers. Some of these are fairly decent boats whereas others are not. After a few years experience surveying, it's not too difficult to determine whether a builder has at least made a conscientious effort to build as good a boat as he possibly could for the money, or if his goal was simply to capture market share based on price. There are some boats that are so poorly built that the manufacturer clearly demonstrates contempt for his customers. Mistakes in design and construction are one thing, but wholesale disregard for the safety of the people who buy these products is something else again. There is no more excuse for poorly built boats than there is for poorly built aircraft because they are nearly equally dangerous. Manufacturers have no right to foist such junk on an unsuspecting public. On the other hand, an ignorant, inexperienced public has no business going to sea in a vessel that was ignorantly purchased so it's a two-way street.

There are many occasions when the marine surveyor enters into the middle of this sorry picture by being asked to perform a survey by a novice boater on a vessel suitable only for being sent back to the drawing boards. A survey of the US boat building industry performed by Eric Greene Associates in 1988 revealed that 64% of boat builders surveyed do not have a naval architect or degreed engineer on staff. Sixty four percent! That figure alone should relieve the surveyor of any misguided ideas that the "builder knows best." It also explains why we run into so many design problems. Is it any wonder then why so many boat builders come and go like the changing weather?

Fig. 2-2. All too often, old boats present us with pictures like this. In this case, the boat is quite literally trashed. Here, wiring and plumbing are fouling the steering system, rendering the vessel unsafe for a sea trial. Conducting a proper survey would take at least twice as long as a well maintained boat. Unfortunately, it's difficult to anticipate situations like this.

Up to a point, it is fair to state that quality is in the eye of the beholder. We reach that point when the question of safety at sea is broached. It's the surveyor's responsibility to know when a vessel is safely designed and constructed within certain limits. Those limits are defined by equating what you see in the field with what you know about our system of legal liability. If the surveyor does not keep up to date with the latest court decisions throughout the field of business liability, then that surveyor is operating blind. Every surveyor should disabuse himself of the notion that the builder alone is responsible for ensuring the safety of the design and construction of the vessel. When the surveyor completes a survey, he is assuming a good part of that liability. That's why it was earlier stated that surveyors should think like lawyers.

Unknowledgeable clients who are purchasing inferior quality vessels deserve special handing. Not only do they need your help because of their ignorance, but the surveyor must also protect himself from their ignorance. There comes a time when every surveyor is faced with a client who desperately wishes to purchase a particular boat that clearly is going to lead to trouble. He's the guy with champagne tastes and a beer budget. He wants to go long-range cruising in a papier-mâché boat. If he's concerned about the duration of his career, the question the surveyor has to ask himself is: "Who will the target be when he crashes?" The surveyor, the builder or both?

The only adequate solution is to do what's right by the client, whether he wants to hear it or not. It's not just the sale of that boat that's on the line: it's the surveyor's business, reputation and assets that are at risk.

The First-time Buyer

The client who has never owned a boat before is the most difficult of all, and certainly the most dangerous, to deal with. They're usually the ones who want the surveyor to make his decision for him or to say whether a vessel passes or fails. The wise surveyor knows that in order to head off trouble, he has to educate his client somewhat, even at the expense of spending more time with him than he would like.

One of the best ways for the surveyor to protect himself from the ignorant client is to make sure that he understands the cost of ownership. Quite often, new owners believe that the cost of ownership is a lot less than it really is. It is when he runs into serious financial difficulties that he's most apt to look to the surveyor for economic assistance, so to speak. While it's not advisable that the surveyor should undertake to estimate costs, particularly repair costs, it's a good idea to feel out the client as to his expectations, and make sure he understands, in round numbers, what it's likely to take to put a vessel that is in poor condition back into shape. It's the person with unreasonable expectations, the one who thinks he can get a half-million dollar yacht for $100,000.00, that the surveyor has to protect himself against.

Vessel Age	Annual Average Cost
1 - 5 years	8%
5- 10 years	12%
10 -15 years	15%
16 - 25 years	18%

The above table illustrates annual average cost of ownership (not including mortgage payments) based on the age of the vessel and the purchase price, including dockage, insurance, fuel and maintenance, including major repairs such as engine overhauls averaged over time. I developed these estimates by interviewing dozens of owners and from 30 years of experience over a broad range of motor vessels. It is based on the average sale price of a used vessel and should not be applied to clunkers. While it assumes that the owner will perform all necessary maintenance, as boats get older maintenance is increasingly neglected, and for that reason the cost of ownership steadily increases.

If the client is asked what he thinks the average annual ownership cost is, and his answer is far off the mark, then you're alerted to a potential problem. Say he's looking at an old boat for a price of $100,000 and it needs a lot of work. The realistic cost of ownership is $18,000 annually. If he was fully aware of that, he'd probably never buy it in the first place. He could do a lot better off with a newer boat but most likely he can't qualify for a bigger loan. If the surveyor tips him off to what he's really faced with, he'll be a lot less likely to get dragged down with the client.

Old Boats

There's just no getting around the fact that old boats are big problems unless they're really something exceptional. But old boats are not exceptional, they're usually just old, so this is a subject that I won't mince words over. If you're a novice surveyor, or thinking about becoming one, let me put this into perspective as bluntly as I can.

If we take all of the lawsuits ever filed against surveyors, we'll find that 95% of them involved old boats. The reason is very simple: old boats cost a lot of money, not just to buy, but to own. Most of the people who buy them can't afford to own them. They don't realize that it costs a lot more money to own an old one than a new one. As I said, people buy them because they can't qualify for a loan on something better. That fact alone tells us that they are likely heading for financial trouble.

If you have any doubt at all about what I have said, I'd suggest you take a half day and go tour some of the lower end boat yards. There you'll find dozens of boats whose owners have obvious gotten in way over their heads. There you'll see boats with owners that are being buried by an avalanche of pending repairs and maintenance, but can't begin to afford the enormous costs involved. These are boats that are nearing the end of their economic life that are soon to pass over the horizon

New surveyors are the new guys on the block, and because of that, in the early years most of their work is going to be on old boats because experienced surveyors tend to stay away from them. But whether you're new, or maybe you just like old boats, you're got to learn how to protect yourself. That's one of the reasons that "qualifying the client" is so important. This procedure is really the best insurance policy you can get.

After qualifying the client, the second rule for old boats is to never under estimate their ability to bankrupt people. We all know about Murphy, but did I tell you about O'Tool's law? He's the guy who thought Murphy was overly optimistic. When dealing with old boats, we have to figure that everything is going to go wrong, and it will, in spades. What works today is broken tomorrow. What the surveyor failed to see yesterday is glaringly obvious today. And everything he failed to see or test is going to cost a fortune to repair. Behind the rust and under the paint and under the sludge there are alligators, just waiting to take your whole arm off. And the worst of it is that you don't find out about it until two years later after they've foreclosed on your client's house, his lawyer is sending your nasty letters and you no longer remember a thing about it.

When the lawyer calls you and demands that you ante up, you'll go back to your file and find that your notes weren't very good and in the report there's not a word about the thing he's complaining about. You read over your report and recall that on the day you did the survey the client had six kids climbing all over the boat, plus the seller, his wife and daughter, it was raining and snowing at the same time, a hurricane was approaching, the batteries were dead, the engines wouldn't start and the yard was three hours late in hauling. All in all you had one terrible time of it. And now he's suing you. It always happens like this. Always.

Why will it happen this way? Because you set yourself up for it. You broke all your own rules and did a survey you never should have done. You let the client, seller or broker control the conditions of the survey with the result that it was impossible to do a good job. Or the boat was so old and there were so many things wrong with it that you could take notes for a week and still not cover it all. God, Himself, wouldn't try to work under those circumstances. But you did. And now you're going to bite the bullet.

Does it sound like I know what I'm talking about? Believe me, I do. The good news is that this sorry situation is preventable. With each bad experience, we learn to tighten up our lines, toss the extra ballast overboard, and reef our sails so that we're *never tempted to do it again.* You've got to control your working conditions and you've got to qualify the client to make sure that he's not going to take you down with him. You've got to find out if you're doing business with a fool. Remember that the client is paying you for information and advice, and if he gets the idea that your advice helped lead him into his predicament, you become a potential target for his relief.

It is a mistake to think that we can disclaim our way out of such situations. All valiant attempts to provide a bulletproof report will mean nothing to the client, or his attorney. It's not enough to win a lawsuit, the cost of defense can bankrupt you before you ever get that far. No, what is needed is to learn to spot trouble before it takes your arm off. The only way to do this is to stay away from people who are getting themselves in trouble. Remember that old boats are trouble with a capital T and only fools buy them. People who could afford them don't buy old boats, no matter how nostalgic they are, because they know better. What the surveyor has to decide for himself is whether he wants to risk aiding and abetting a fool. If you are one of those who has great nostalgia for things of the past, balance that against the upper limits of your potential liability and you'll soon find yourself thinking straight.

Here's another consideration. Many of these people buying old boats are well aware that, if you write a report that accurately describes the condition, they won't be able to get a loan or insurance. They'll ask you to "tone down" your report. Do this and you'll deserve to get sued. If you have to take on an old boat, the thing to do is "tone it up." That means going into much greater detail about the nature of the condition and what you could or could not do. Of course they won't be able to get insurance, but that's not your problem. Just be sure you get paid before they see the report. With old boats, it's always imperative to get the fee in advance. You'll run about a 75% chance of not getting paid if you don't.

Even if you've done as close to a perfect job as possible, you can still get clipped. I've had lawyers call me asking me to ante up after claiming that I had overlooked something. In each case I asked them if they had read the report.

Incredibly, they said they hadn't. The lawyer was acting on the word of the client who said that I was a bad guy who cheated him, that I had acted with malice and aforethought, endangered his family, caused irreparable trauma and mental anguish, not to mention at least five million in expenses. I'm not sure I believed that the lawyer hadn't read my report since he was probably just trying to get a quick settlement on a complaint that he knew was groundless. I said I would send him a copy of the report and to please call me after he received and read it. Of course he didn't call back, and so I would call him back and ask nicely, "Now what part of the survey are you complaining about?" They'd usually say something like, "My client is out of town. I'll have to get back to you on that." Case dismissed.

There was another instance when a lawyer called and asked me to pay for the replacement of a fuel tank that started leaking. Not only did my report describe an aluminum tank sitting in bilge water, but it described in detail what could happen if the tank wasn't pulled and inspected. Not only did the client pay no attention to my report, but the lawyer who had it in his hand when he called me apparently didn't read it either. Then the lawyer claimed that I didn't send the report to the client until after the client bought it. That part was true because the client concluded the sale the very same day, before the report was even written. But the client was told verbally and in writing about the condition and he declined to do anything about it. The truth was that the client was angry because with that report he couldn't get insurance with my report. I knew that because the insurance company had called me about it and they declined the application. I told them absolutely that the tank had to be replaced. The client then went out and got another survey that didn't mention the tank problem and he was able to get insurance with another company. I then told the lawyer that if he sues me, and I found out that his client fraudulently obtained insurance, that I would report him to the insurance commission. He was committing fraud because he knew about the condition and intentionally disguised it. That was the last I heard from him.

If you must become involved with old boats, it is necessary to go to exceptional lengths to cover yourself, and always in writing. The risk involved in surveying old boats can be greatly reduced, but it comes with a price; You'll double or triple the amount of time you spend, hopefully for an equivalent fee, but more often not. Bargain basement shoppers are very stingy about survey fees. They may want you to work twice as hard for half as much.

Fast Closing Deals

Perhaps you picked up on another important point that I mentioned above. That was where the lawyer complained that the client transacted the purchase before he had received my report. It may seem unreasonable and unfair that a court would rule in favor of a plaintiff who complained that the surveyor didn't get him his report prior to the closing, even if the closing occurred the same day. But courts have ruled in favor of plaintiffs under these circumstances when the buyer complained that the surveyor misled him about the severity of defects when he was given verbal advice immediately following the survey.

The following case in point reveals how easily the surveyor can become trapped in unsuspecting situations. Back around 1993, a staff surveyor for an insurance company was tasked by his employers to survey a fleet of several charter fishing boats. These were party boats catering to the general public. Like most such boats, they were in poor condition and it took the surveyor several days to go through four of them. The last of the boats he looked at was in such poor condition, that he stopped by the owner's office to advise him that there were serious hazards and that the boat shouldn't leave the dock unit the problems were repaired. The owner as not in his office, so the surveyor informed an associate.

The surveyor returned to his office where he had heavy backlog of reports to write. The written report was not completed and gotten into the owners hands until two weeks later. Note, however, this was an insurance underwriting survey, and not something done and paid for by the owner. However, the surveyor recognized that he probably had an obligation to advise the owner of a dangerous condition, which he did.

It so happened that the vessel operator took a group of people out fishing that very same December afternoon. Of course, no repairs were made, and it is interesting to note here that by the terms of the insurance, this boat was supposed to be laid up for the winter and not operating. They went out anyway and never returned. Four people lost their lives when the vessel sank.

Naturally, a blizzard of law suits followed, one of which was by the owner against the insurance company and the surveyor. The allegation was that timely warning of the hazards was not given. The owner denied that any verbal discussion took place, and there being no other witnesses to the discussion, nothing could be proven. The court agreed that the surveyor had failed to give timely notice.

This story illustrates just some of the potential risks that the surveyor faces, and of which he may be completely unaware, and why it is often necessary to go to extraordinary measures to cover oneself.

Needless to say, after a surveyor has spent a hard day of labor performing a survey, he's probably not in the best mental state to be able to cautiously craft a verbal presentation. Nor does the surveyor even get a few moments to consider and reflect on his findings, which puts him into a very bad situation indeed. This is all the more reason to be extremely wary of old boat surveys. That's why I say it's foolish to take the attitude that if the client is getting in over his head, that's his problem. Obviously the thing to do here is to find out when the client plans to close, and if it's immediately, take the necessary steps to make it completely clear that your survey is NOT COMPLETED until you have written the report and placed it in his hands. If he's going to ignore your advice, send him a letter of confirmation that you advised him not to close until he had read the report.

Repair Costs

Should a surveyor estimate repair costs once the survey is completed? The answer is absolutely not, and yet we do it all the time. This is an unavoidable problem for which the surveyor needs to be well versed. If a boat yard can't estimate the cost of a repair before they've torn something apart, how is the surveyor expected to do the same? Moreover, costs between yards can vary wildly, from Joe the mobile mechanic to upscale yacht yards with fancy conference rooms. It would be nice to just tell the client to take the survey to a yard and ask for quotes on any necessary repairs. Anyone who's tried this knows it can't be done, and the client usually knows it too. If yard people are immediately available after a survey for estimating, this is the best way to handle estimating costs. More often than not, the surveyor will find himself being asked by the client to make estimates. And when you say "no," they won't take that for an answer.

If you've had a lot of experience with estimating you can do this. Because I do a lot of insurance work, I am intimately familiar with repair costs and have no problem with it. However, if you don't know pricing forwards and backwards, don't do it unless you absolutely make the client understand that you're only *guessing* and that your guess may not be accurate. But don't just guess at the whole bundle of work. Take the time to sketch out an estimate with lump sums for each item and total them up. Estimate high: everything costs double of what you think it does. Your totals may surprise you. Read your numbers to him but do not give him anything in writing. Never, never, never do that. Many times a client or a broker will ask the surveyor for copies of his notes immediately after the survey. I ask you, would your doctor or lawyer give you copies of their working notes? Why not? Because those notes could be construed as your full report to the client prior to making an immediate purchase. Take as much time as you need to verbally report after a survey, but never give anyone your notes.

Working Conditions

In order to do his job properly, a surveyor needs conditions that are conducive to doing a good job. Trying to survey a boat that is laid up for the winter under a tarpaulin or under shrink wrap is near impossible. So is conducting a survey in a driving rainstorm, or under conditions of extreme temperatures. The wise surveyor does not permit himself to be pressured by a client or broker who is in a great hurry to close a deal into performing a survey under conditions in which he cannot reasonably do a good job.

Here in Florida, my biggest enemy is the high heat and humidity. Surveying can be brutally physical work and extreme temperatures can seriously reduce the quality of my work. I've measured temperatures inside closed up boats as high as 130 degrees. This is as economically dangerous as it is physically. We shouldn't be afraid to let it be known that the weather is affecting our ability to work and to adapt our work methods accordingly. You can't imagine a physician performing a physical examination under these conditions, but that's what surveyors have to do. One way or another, to do a good job, we have to exercise control over our work, even to the extent of postponing, taking longer breaks, or extending the survey into another day. Not at our expense, but the clients.

Not only does weather interfere with our work, but also conditions of the vessel itself. Live aboard boats are a good case in point, where every nook and cranny of a boat may be jam-packed with the owner's personal effects, and often his family and even pets. Live aboards are my bete noire; they can be almost impossible to perform and I hate to do them. The distractions and hindrances can be endless. Sometimes the owners won't even leave the boat for fear that the surveyor will steal their belongings. Or we may be faced with a vessel that is undergoing repair, that is crawling with workers, or that in any other way is not ready for survey. Although it is quite rare that the surveyor is ever faced with ideal conditions, he should not allow himself to be put in the position of doing a job under poor conditions. That's asking for trouble.

However, there are often times when we cannot escape from working under deplorable conditions and there is a solution for the liability hazards that this problem poses. The first step is to discuss the situation with the client and make certain that he understands how your ability to do a good job is impeded. In doing so, you're letting the client know in advance that the quality of your service will be degraded by those conditions. He is advised that these limitations will be described in the report, and are a condition of the survey, and that the client agrees to them. Then you ask for his consent to proceed. In this manner we have created a fairly effective hold harmless agreement that could go a long way toward absolving us from oversights or errors. Under these circumstances, the hold harmless agreement carries weight because there are legitimate reasons why errors or omissions may occur that any reasonable person would recognize. It's not at all like a disclaimer that says "I'm not responsible for anything."

Dealing With the Seller

Seasoned brokers are usually wise enough not permit the seller to be present during the survey and sea trial. They do not want the seller conversing with the buyer, nor do they want the seller interfering with the survey or getting into arguments with either the buyer or the surveyor. Yet there will be many cases of direct sales that the surveyor will encounter that do not involve a broker to smooth out the survey process.

Whenever the seller is present for the survey, the experienced surveyor knows that he has to put on his statesman's hat and conduct himself in a most diplomatic manner. There will be many occasions when the surveyor will be sorely tested by a seller's behavior and, if he is not prepared for it, could well fall into the trap of saying things he ought not to say. In most instances, the seller will do everything possible to extract as much information from the surveyor about his findings as he, the seller, possibly can. And once the seller does this, he is very likely to start an argument about anything the surveyor is foolish enough to tell him. The surveyor should reverse this and extract as much information from the seller as possible, but learn to keep it a one-way street. One little trick that I've developed is to always answer the seller's question with a question of my own, not impolitely, but to simply divert his attention. This let's him know that I'm subtly declining to answer his questions without having to tell him so. To avoid creating problems with the seller, I've developed a few rules for myself:

- Firmly, but politely decline to advise the seller as to any survey findings. It is proper to advise him that the information is confidential to the client.

- Be alert to seller's attempts to induce the surveyor into making any comments about the condition of the vessel. "She's really in great shape, don't you think?" Don't answer questions like this, you could be falling into a trap.

- Avoid discussing the survey findings with the client within earshot of the seller or broker. Exceptions to this are well-planned presentations at a time when you're ready for them.

- Don't criticize or make gratuitous comments about the vessel at any time. Many surveyors, thinking they were out of earshot of the owner, have gotten themselves in trouble making negative comments because the seller overheard their remarks.

- Treat the seller's property with the utmost care and respect. Always return all equipment and furnishings to their original position. That includes neatly remaking the beds after you've torn them up. Replace all removed covers. Surveyors do beds, furniture and carpets.

- Treat the seller with the same respect. The surveyor is always potentially in harms way if he does something to aggravate him.

The presentation of survey findings should only be made when the surveyor is ready to make them. He should not allow himself to be put in the position of being interrupted to answer questions that he is not prepared to answer. This is not fair to either the client or the surveyor.

This next is an extremely important point. Quite a few surveyors have gotten into very serious trouble because a boat burned or sank shortly after they completed a survey. It's awfully easy to accidentally break something (like a plastic fitting), leave a piece of equipment running, or forget to return a circuit breaker or switch to its original position. This just stresses the importance of sizing up the vessel before you start. Operating electrical equipment poses one of the biggest hazards. We'll discuss this in much more detail in the ELECTRICAL chapter, but the point should be taken here that testing electrics requires utmost care. It further stresses why the surveyor must avoid unnecessary distractions that could cause him to make a serious mistake.

If the owner or captain is present, I always make it a point to go over everything before leaving the boat. I ask him to please double check with me to make sure that everything was left the way it's supposed to be. Often they'll say, "Don't worry, I'll take care of it." Don't accept that; they don't know what you've done and chances are that they won't check. Make him go over it with you. That's part of your insurance policy.

Finally, it's best not to let the client put you into the position of making the presentation with the seller present. It's not the surveyor's job to be an intermediary. Often times we'll get unwittingly drawn into this situation. Only recently I found myself in such a position where I couldn't escape because the boat was on a mooring, there was no place to go, and I was unable to get the client aside. It was eight o'clock at night and I was dog tired. The seller challenged me on everything I said and the situation turned ugly when, in my exhaustion, I lost my cool. To head off these situations, the surveyor needs to get the client aside before it's too late and let him know that the presentation will be between just the two of you. If you do it in front of the seller, you'll find yourself having to justify and argue about most of your findings, at the end of a long day when you're tired and not at your sharpest state of mind. This is the worst possible time to have to deal with a difficult seller.

To summarize, this chapter contains the distilled essence of thirty years worth of my own mistakes, mistakes that I wish someone had been able to teach me about. The great difficulty of so much of the surveyor's work is that he is going blind into so many of his jobs. The process of "qualifying the client" is like learning how to see in the dark. The surveyor who learns how to do it effectively will eliminate about 75% of his most serious difficulties, establish better relations with all concerned and significantly increase his revenues by avoiding loss and wasted effort.

Chapter 3

Sound vs. Seaworthiness

The surveyor's worst nightmare is to one day find out that a boat he recently surveyed went down. Every year many boats are lost at sea. Most of the passengers return to tell their story, but some don't. Most of these boats are lost in deep water and are never found, yet the few that are recovered often reveal the cause of their misfortune. Before we consider the basic elements of the hull survey, let's take a look at the two main terms that are often used to describe the fitness of a vessel for operation.

The causes of loss are many and varied, but chief among them are hull failures or other problems resulting from design and construction defects, as well as inferior design standards that rendered the vessel unfit for the use it was subjected. Not only does this raise the specter of litigation, but also of casualties. Above all things, this we want to avoid. Yet it's hard not to be mindful that the more surveys a surveyor has under his belt, the greater the odds are that sooner or later it will happen. That's the bad news.

The good news is that while he cannot prevent people from doing foolish things with boats, there is a lot the surveyor can do to protect his clients against accidents and loss involving faulty engineering. In fact, faulty design and construction is fairly easy to discover during the course of a typical pre-purchase survey if the surveyor has a good knowledge of the fundamentals of design and construction, knows what he's looking for and why. That's why the emphasis throughout this book is on the discovery of defects and loss prevention, highlighted by many "what if?" scenarios.

Since the hull is the foundation upon which all else rests, surveying the hull is one of the most important aspects of the surveyor's work. The purpose of the hull survey is to ensure that the hull is built in such a manner that, not only will it safely carry the occupants of the vessel over the waters and under the conditions in which it's likely to be used, but also that it does not pose a hazard to itself, or an economic hazard to the owner. Obviously, this statement presupposes that we have some idea of what those conditions are likely to be. But before we get into that, let's take a look at the two terms that are most commonly used to describe the condition of a hull.

Seaworthy -vs- Soundness

Understanding the precise meaning of these terms will go a long way helping the surveyor accurately assess the condition of a hull. Seaworthiness is a term which is often misunderstood and misused. It is an ancient term, one which is essentially a legal doctrine since it is an entirely relative term that has its basis in the courts, but the dictionary definition sums it up very nicely:

The fitness of a vessel for a particular voyage with reference to the condition of its hull and machinery, the extent of its fuel and provisions, the quality of crew and officers and adaptability for the type of voyage proposed.[1]

In other words, seaworthy means that a vessel is in every way fit only for a *particular voyage,* not each and every voyage that it could possibly, or is likely, to make. Application of the term is essentially on a case by case basis. Seaworthiness depends not only on the preparedness and overall condition of the vessel, but also of the crew.

Now contrast this with the definition of soundness:

Healthy, free from injury or disease, abnormality or defect, impairment or likelihood of impairment: not impaired: free from flaw, defect or decay, marked by solidity or firmness.

By this definition we note that, whereas seaworthiness is a relative term, soundness is more nearly, but not quite, absolute. To term a vessel sound it is not necessary to first determine the specific details of how it will be used, manned or equipped. Soundness pertains generally to the thing being observed regardless of circumstances.

To determine whether a vessel is seaworthy is to determine with a high degree of certitude that a vessel can safely make a proposed voyage without the likelihood of loss or injury to the vessel, cargo or passengers. But to determine whether a vessel is sound involves the determination of whether there are any defects, abnormalities, decay, lack of solidity or firmness. While there is an obvious similarity between the two terms, soundness deals essentially with the vessel itself. From this it should be clear that seaworthiness is not a term that the yacht surveyor should use to describe the condition of a vessel unless he has been specifically charged with making what is known as a voyage survey. In conducting a pre-purchase survey it is the term "soundness" with which we are most concerned.

I used the qualifier "essentially" because the vessel does not operate in a vacuum; soundness is not totally absolute because there has to be some reference to the environment in which the vessel operates. Surely it would be foolish to attempt to judge soundness of a vessel completely out of context of its use. If it is impaired, it is certainly necessary to know how it is impaired from performing. If we're to use this term "sound," we are once again charged with making some kind of determination as to the most probable use of the vessel. Otherwise, how are we to determine how, and to what degree, the vessel is impaired? For our purposes, the key word in the definition of soundness is "impairment."

Defect is also relative term. If a boat has a large and ugly scrape along the hull side, that could be termed a defect, damage or probably both. However, that scrape does not cause an impairment from the vessel's intended function, only of its appearance and possibly its value. The soundness of Rembrandt's Mona Lisa would be impaired in both its usefulness, appearance and value were it to have the same large scrape across that lady's amazing face as our boat does. Both are impaired, but again, that impairment must be in context of its use.

What the surveyor should be concerned with most are defects which, in one way or another, affect the safety or value of the vessel. During the course of this writing I was asked by an insurance company to survey a thirty year-old wood yacht in which a quarter-million dollars had recently been invested in modifications and refurbishment. Being thirty years old, my primary interest was in the condition of the hull, not all the fancy interior decor that was newly added. Unfortunately, the owners were more interested in appearance and luxury than the integrity of the hull. They had solved the problem of severe leakage caused by deteriorated structural hull members and loose planks by fiber glassing over the bottom planking, planking that was obviously loose from the frames. Was this vessel unseaworthy or was it unsound? Actually it was both since the safety of the vessel was impaired under any conditions, specific or general.

What about a defect that would impair the safety under some conditions but not others? This can be a hard question to answer. Evaluating soundness has to be predicated on some understanding of the conditions to which the vessel is likely to be subjected. This is a consideration that we have to pay very careful attention to because it is in this vein that soundness is similar to seaworthiness. That means we are going to have to draw some kind of conclusion as to what constitutes "normal" use of a particular type of vessel. What constitutes soundness for one type of vessel may not be sound for another. Canoe, maxi racer, express cruiser, day sailor, megayacht, bass boat are all different classes of vessel that are used in vastly different ways. A canoe may be sound to cross a small lake but not a large one. A high speed motor yacht requires different engineering than a displacement cruiser. Obviously, then, the intended purpose of the vessel has to play a role in making a determination of soundness.

A vessel is not sound if it has not been properly designed to fulfill what should be its obviously intended purpose, precisely because it is impaired from performing its intended purpose *safely,* and because the lack of soundness implies the lack of safety. For that reason, those who claim that surveyors should not criticize design are wrong. A hull that is not properly designed or constructed is unsound by definition and the determination of soundness is the essence of the surveyor's function.

What is a Sound Hull?

This is a question that surveyors are often asked, and one which we should be prepared to answer, although not necessarily in the absolute. The pre purchase survey is the evaluation of a completed product, not the process of construction. We should be clear about this since there is a great deal that surveyor cannot determine about the construction of a hull during the course of a survey. It may be a rather startling thought to realize that in looking at a fiberglass hull, we do not know specifically what materials it is made of. We say it is "fiberglass," but what does that mean?

Thirty years ago, the term fiberglass meant basically one thing. Today there are so many variations of reinforced and non reinforced plastic that the word has been reduced to a generic meaning. In looking at a molded hull, all we may really know is that it is some kind of plastic reinforced with something we know not what. We don't know what resins were used, fabrics, molding processes, laminating schedules, core materials and so on. About the best we can do is to observe the hull, inside and out (insofar as visibility permits), perform our soundings and test operate the vessel. And since destructive testing is costly and legally problematic, it's not really an option and is rarely done.

The fact is that in the normal course of the surveyor's work he cannot absolutely prove the soundness of a hull, for he hasn't the means of proving that a hull is entirely free of defects. There always exists the possibility of hidden defects that show no outward sign or evidence of their existence, such as the beginning state of disbonding of a hull core that eventually progresses to catastrophic proportions. We want it to be clear in our minds then, that the role of the surveyor is proving the negative, not the positive. We cannot prove that a vessel is sound, we can prove only that it is unsound. We can prove the existence of defects, but not the absence of defects. Because so much of the interior of most hulls are inaccessible, it would be downright foolhardy and misleading to make the absolute declaration that a hull is "sound." Yet we can, and should, declare any hull unsound which displays evidence of any defect that threatens the safety of the vessel or poses a hazard of potential failure.

Understanding this should help put the hull survey process into perspective. The surveyor's job is to evaluate the design and construction of a hull to the extent that he is able to, and to report upon any defects, design or construction faults that affect the ability of the hull to perform its function safely. Does that mean that he should evaluate whether a 70 MPH go-fast boat will hold together if the operator drives it full tilt, head-on into six foot seas? No, it does not, because most powerboats are capable of speeds which, if operated imprudently, could cause a vessel's hull to break up. So let's constrain the definition even further.

A sound pleasure craft hull is one which displays adherence to principles of good design, shows an absence of evident defect after a thorough survey, and can reasonably be expected to convey its passengers safely in all conditions of weather and sea conditions under which a prudent boatsman, with knowledge of the vessels limitations, would normally operate that vessel.

The terms "good design" or principles of "good marine practices" are often used rather cavalierly in survey reports without providing any clue as to their meaning, so here's a further definition. Good design simply means that the design has been proven safe and effective based on actual experience in operation under the conditions for which it is intended. Safe means that the structure has been assessed and evaluated to the extent reasonably possible and found to be designed within standards or criteria that are known to be effective. It means that the design will function without *probable* risk of failure.

Where You are Makes a Difference

Since we cannot separate the what from the where, it's important that we pay attention to the caliber of vessel that the client is buying and the area he intends to use it. It was mentioned in the previous chapter on Client Relations that the client should be questioned as to his intentions. A good example, one that I experience from time to time is a client who is purchasing a flimsy sailboat with the intent on sailing it around the world. Clearly, the vessel is not seaworthy for the client's generally intended use. I've had clients express intentions to use unsuitable boats for extended cruising that I wouldn't take beyond coastal day sailing.

Nowhere is it engraved in stone that the surveyor is obligated to advise the client on the seaworthiness of the vessel for such voyages. It's not the surveyor's obligation to try to stop people from doing foolish things. But surely the surveyor owes it to himself to stay out of harm's way which, for our purposes, means shotgun lawsuits that inevitably arise when someone does something stupid, hurting himself and others. The best way to do that is to do the best he can to keep his client out of trouble. When confronted with such situations, one way to deal with it is to write the client a letter under cover separate from the survey report. Without completely raining on the client's parade, the surveyor can say that, based on the client's expressed intentions, it is his opinion that the vessel selected is not adequately designed or constructed.

Situations like these, where it becomes apparent that the client is about to sail off the edge of the earth, do not occur frequently. But when they do, we're usually caught off guard, and unless we're prepared to deal with them, we're likely to be dragged over the edge with him. Here are a few examples of how serious this can be, demonstrating how easy it is to get in trouble.

A Case in Point

Late one afternoon I received a rather frantic overseas phone call from an insurance brokerage house. They had an insurance application pending on a hundred foot schooner that was over sixty years old. The time was early April and the owners were preparing to make a Transatlantic crossing from Florida to Europe. They wanted to leave within the next few days. Since I have been around long enough to know that last minute phone calls for insurance surveys only hours preceding a long voyage usually means trouble, I quoted the broker an unusually high fee, knowing very well I would probably be facing a difficult situation. Little did I anticipate how difficult.

I arrived at the vessel the next morning while it was being loaded with supplies and immediately recognized my problem. There were six young people in their late teens or early twenties on board. The captain indicated that there would be nine crew members, including the 6 young people, all of whom had little experience sailing, yet alone transatlantic crossings. Only the captain and two others even had blue water experience. They were all very excited at the prospect of their rapidly approaching departure, looking forward with glowing optimism toward their transatlantic crossing in early April. All except for one young lady who was obviously terrified and appeared to be sea sick long before the yacht even left the dock. I wondered what she was doing there and soon discovered that a boyfriend had dragged her along.

I was soon to discover that an inexperienced and inadequate crew was the least of the problems. This sixty year-old museum piece was no different than any other sixty year old wooden vessel. Someone could pour a million dollars into her without making a dent on the sixty years worth of deferred maintenance. She smelled like a Pennsylvania mushroom farm inside. Stalactites were forming under the cast iron knee braces in way of the mast partners. She had no working navigation lights, the auxiliary generator was partially dismantled, the wiring was a wreck, and the only bilge pumps were a couple of 12 volt submersibles operating off batteries that looked as old as I am. I was afraid to even look at the rigging for fear of what I would see.

Right then and there I could visualize the news reports and the subpoenas arriving, the meetings with lawyers and eventual courtroom testimony. All of these visions flashed before my eyes. As it turned out, these were no mere hallucinations. I turned to the captain and said, *"Sir, this vessel is not seaworthy. I recommend that you do not undertake the proposed voyage. I am going to send you a certified letter to that effect."* The captain shrugged his shoulders and returned to his business. I finished up making notes of some of the more grievous conditions aboard the vessel and left. The broker was called and advised of the vessel's condition; wisely, he did not issue the policy but the yacht departed anyway.

It would take a miracle for that old hulk to have made that crossing. I sent the certified letter and tried to stop worrying about it. People do stupid things all the time, but this guy had lured unsuspecting and ignorant kids into what could turn out to be the voyage of the damned. And it did. I even correctly predicted the day of the disaster when that evening news' weather report showed a strong cold front moving off the east coast. The yacht broke up and went down several days later, before it even reached Bermuda.

If lawsuits were filed I never found out about them. But I sure was glad that I had taken the time to send that certified letter. Even though the yacht owner was not my client, the certified letter cleared me from any possible claim that I had in any way approved either the vessel or the voyage. Here was a case where not only was the vessel unseaworthy, but three adults and six teenagers were a completely inadequate crew for a 100' schooner. One of the great difficulties that surveyors run into is that people in distress can and will say anything. I've even had client's fraudulently alter my reports in an attempt to avoid culpability. When confronted with such situations, if we don't take care to protect ourselves, and do it in no uncertain terms, it will become almost inevitable that we will be dragged into the abyss.

In another case a surveyor was performing a survey while an owner was installing a bilge pump. The vessel only had one and needed another. While the surveyor was doing his job, the owner was in a dinghy, drilling a hole in the side of the boat to install the pump discharge fitting. The owner said he would finish the job that day. The surveyor didn't write it up and the owner didn't finish the installation. For whatever reason, the owner drilled the hole and left it there, uncapped. Overnight the boat sank. The surveyor issued his report, got paid for it, but the owner never said a word about what had happened.

Well, of course the boat didn't have insurance and when the suit papers arrived, the owner stated that the surveyor told the owner that it was safe for him to leave the boat with the hole in the side. There was not a word in the surveyor's report about the situation and so he was trapped. The problem for the surveyor was that his report did not reflect the condition of the vessel at the time he surveyed it. Was the vessel seaworthy at the time he surveyed it? No, not with a hole in the side. Did his report reflect that condition? No, it didn't. The point here is not whether the surveyor was right or wrong. It is the fact that the surveyor left himself wide open by taking the client's word for it that something would be done. And then it was not done. Whether the surveyor prevailed in that case is irrelevant; it cost him dearly to defend against it.

Don't be Influenced by Reputation

When approaching the survey of a boat built by a builder with a good reputation, it is very tempting for the surveyor to fall back on that reputation, rather than making the same kind of thorough examination as he would if he were approaching a boat that is unknown to him.

A good example of this occurred some years ago when I was called by an owner of a five year old yacht after he noticed an unusual bulge appearing on the bottom of the hull. The bulge on the bottom turned out to be a large area of delamination that was the result of several candy bar wrappers and a lot of saw-dust having been laminated into the bottom. This, despite the fact that the builder had a fine reputation for building very rugged hulls. Thousands of own-ers bought these offshore sport fishing boats and relied on their reputation for integrity. And rightly so. Yet there it was, a hull bottom that was about to split open, probably because some disgruntled employee was seeking revenge against his employer, or perhaps just as a prank. The boat had been surveyed and pur-chased just six months earlier and the surveyor had missed this obvious defect. In all probability, the surveyor had also relied on the builder's reputation and didn't bother to look at the bottom too closely.

In another instance, I had just completed the hauled portion of the survey on a very popular 35' model by the very same builder, a model which also had a fine reputation. A group of us were standing around behind the boat talking. I put my arm out to lean against the transom. As my weight bore against the transom, it suddenly buckled inward, very much like what happens if you were to sit on the hood of a car. It turned out that the laminators forgot to finish laying up the transom of this boat; it had only the skin out mat and one layer of roving in the transom. Backing down while fishing, that laminate, which was barely 1/8" thick, could easily have given way with unfortunate consequences. This defect nearly escaped detection because up to that point I usually neglected to sound out transoms.

Nobody's perfect and serious defects can occur on any boat. The surveyor's job is to execute all reasonable means to find them if they exist. Tapping around on the transom is hardly an unreasonable means. I would have rightfully been held accountable had I not accidentally discovered the fault.

Entry-Level Boats

It is sometimes said that one gets what one pays for. Live long enough and we find out that this is generally, but not always true. The reason why boating is no longer an elitist sport, but a mass recreation, is that builders have found a way to reduce the cost of construction in order to appeal to the widest possible market. Today there are an estimated 20 million or more recreational boats in the U.S.

For the lack of a better term, a large percentage of the boats in existence are what we might call "entry level" boats. These are mass produced boats that are generally designed and engineered to attract first-time buyers, usually those who are so ignorant about what they are buying that quality is not an important consideration in the purchase decision. It's not important because the buyer is not sufficiently experienced to understand the effect of the lack of quality on how well his expensive purchase will hold up over the years. Some builders so shamelessly appeal to the public's frivolousness and ignorance that their products have earned the well-deserved moniker "fur-lined glove," "floating cocktail lounge," or "floating camper." Indeed, some even have "pop tops" and mosquito netting.

Anyone who's been surveying for a few years knows the type of vessel to which I'm referring, and for the most part they do not present the surveyor with any particular problems because it is so easy to see these things for what they are. If asked to perform a survey on one of these creations, it's not likely to be mistaken for a seagoing vessel. The difficulty presented to the surveyor are those entry-level boats that are disguised as seagoing vessels, thousands of which fill coastal marinas throughout the nation.

Several years ago a neighbor came to me saying that his wife was complaining that their new 32 foot express cruiser was noisy inside. She also complained that when the boat was underway, "things inside bounced around." I sort of chuckled at that statement. On what boat don't things bounce around? They had no experience in boating and this was their first boat, one with which they got an awful lot of boat for relatively little money. Too much boat, too little money, ultimately that was the problem.

When we took the boat out for a test run, noisy was hardly the word for what went on inside the cabin of that thing. I intentionally used the word "thing" because in my view it didn't qualify for the proper use of the noun "boat." It was a plastic container into which a means of propulsion and living quarters had been added. It could hardly have been intended to go to sea.

The first thing I noticed was that standing on the cabin sole was like standing on a magic carpet flying over the clouds. As the boat went over a 12" chop, I could feel every wave under my feet. The bottom was flexing so badly that the refrigerator, mounted under the galley counter, was backing out of its hole. The flush-mounted stove top was leaping up off the counter top. The head door wouldn't stay closed, nor would many of the cabinet doors. In the head compartment, the head was visibly moving up and down. Inside the cabin was a deafening din of creaking, cracking, crunching and groaning. It sounded like a collision with a freighter in slow motion. Or perhaps a percussion band without the benefit of a rhythm section. Before my very eyes the interior of this boat was literally falling apart. Overhead cabinets were starting to fall down. Everywhere fasteners were backing out, moldings coming loose, joinery misaligned and working. It was doing the Watusi without benefit of music, just a lot of noise.

But that was nothing compared to what was found once we started pulling things apart. There were no structural bulkheads in the vessel whatever. If I stomped on the bottom, I'm sure I could put my foot through it. Stringers and bondings were fractured throughout. There was so much internal friction from parts working that it's a wonder it didn't start a fire. Had the owners ever attempted to use the stove, it would have. A bundle of wires was routed beneath a partition and as a result of the bottom flexing and pinching the 125 VAC wiring, the insulation was abraded completely away, including the power supply for the stove. In order to disguise the use of some of the lowest grade plywood, and the use of wafer board, the entire interior hull had been lined with carpet which was now water-soaked and rotting. Virtually everything in that boat was the lowest grade material and poorest quality equipment. The list went on and on.

By now you get the picture and this is what is meant by an entry level boat. It's a piece of junk intended to be sold to unsuspecting buyers like my neighbor. They thought they were getting a great deal because this boat was so much bigger than anything else they could get for the price. Yes, they got a lot of enclosed space for their money, but what they got was not something they could safely take to the Bahamas on long cruises as they had intended.

Just out of curiosity, I asked to see the Owner's Manual, wondering if the builder had included any kind of statements limiting usage. There were none. I read the warranty, which was very cleverly worded so that by the time one cut through the legalese, it was apparent that the builder didn't warrant much of anything. It's truly amazing that, because of product liability cases, we find all kinds of bizarre warnings on our common, every day products. As I write, I'm sitting here looking at a warning sticker on venetian blinds that warn that children can get tangled in the pull strings and strangle on them (a rather remote possibility, I think). We're warned not to stick forks in toasters and not to use hair dryers in the bathtub or take 15 aspirin tablets to cure a headache. But when it comes to a 32' boat weighing 10,000 lbs. traveling at 40 MPH there is nothing. I might add that I'm no consumer advocate and do not favor strict governmental regulation. It's not possible that government can protect people from their own stupidity. Product liability laws are already heavily weighted in favor of consumers, but it's clear that product liability lawyers haven't yet found the marine industry as a viable target. Rest assured, one day they will. As the expert standing between the client and the builder, the issue here is what degree of responsibility does the surveyor have. Obviously, the surveyor should not be the one held liable for the fitness for intended service, yet, as we have seen, the issue is not very clear.

Boats like this create an interesting dilemma for the surveyor, particularly after they're a few years old. Does the surveyor assume that the client knows what he is getting into, or does he risk offending the client by attempting to educate him? My own experience has been that some clients are so highly enamored by the glitzy appearance that they could care less about what I'm trying to tell them. They don't want to hear it. I suspect my neighbor is the sort that falls into this category, and had I done a survey on the boat before he bought it, he probably would have rationalized everything I said about it and bought it anyway. This is a potentially dangerous situation that deserves some serious consideration. Ultimately, it comes down to a question of whether the hull is sound. Sometimes the surveyor has to make the tough call and say that it isn't. Or risk the consequences. The old adage says that if you don't want to get shot, don't stand in front of guns.

The way to do this is to make sure that we are never in the position of having it appear that we are in any way approving what is obviously a poorly constructed product. Entry level boats may put the surveyor squarely in the middle of this Catch 22. These are situations where the surveyor has to be extraordinarily careful. The next three chapters deal directly with how to determine the structural integrity and soundness of a vessel's hull, how to locate defects, and whether there exist structural inadequacies that could lead to failure or economic loss. As we have said previously, it's not just accidents that we are looking to prevent, but also economic loss to our clients such as experienced by my neighbor. Despite his efforts to obtain a remedy, he did not prevail. He wasn't willing to go forward with a lawsuit. He experienced a loss of nearly $50,000.00, plus the risk of having to sell an obviously unseaworthy vessel.

An unhappy ending to dreams of fun in the sun.

[1] Webster's Third New International Dictionary

Chapter 4

Procedures

In the chapter 2 we discussed the importance of good communication between surveyor, client and seller or broker in setting up the survey to ensure that all runs smoothly. Once the survey has been set up and we're ready to begin, a new level of planning begins.

Ideally, we don't want to hop aboard the vessel and then immediately have to take off for a haul out or sea trial. We want at least a few hours to get our bearings and start sizing things up. The larger the vessel, the more time it will take to orient ourselves. Those who've been surveying a while will have already developed their own routines. The novice needs to develop a strategy for each type of vessel. A 72' motor yacht that is literally three stories high presents considerably greater challenges than a single level 32 footer. Let's look at what should be done first and why.

The size of a vessel is often more a matter of magnitude than complexity. An 80' motor yacht may not be appreciably more complex than a 40 footer. There's just a lot more of it, of everything, from plumbing to washing machines and bar equipment. On the other hand, some small, cramped boats can be harder to survey precisely because of the lack of space. Or cramming too much in a too small space. Having a plan and being able to follow it minimizes errors and oversights, as well as improving efficiency.

Order and Progression

The best way to work is from most difficult to least difficult, from the most important to the least important. Here we define "importance" in terms of money should you make a mistake. The reasoning here is simple. The longer we work, the more tired we get, so the most important things should be done first. Or, if for some reason time is cut short, we need to be sure that the most important aspects are covered. This means ordering our work in an hierarchy of importance. Cosmetic considerations are left until last; we don't concern ourselves with relatively minor details so long as there are major considerations remaining. Our judgment of significance must always be made in terms of cost to the client.

Every large vessel requires brief preplanning the moment the surveyor walks aboard. Make it a point to perform a quick tour of the entire vessel, not only familiarizing yourself with the layout and where things are, but also taking note of potential difficulties. These can be such things as poor accessibility, bad maintenance and other items of interest such as particularly complex systems. Look for anything that will require special attention or require more time than you anticipated. Is there something that will prevent you from completing the job in one day as planned? Are there systems or equipment that you might need help with? Then size up just how much equipment there is on board that you are going to have to deal with. Some yachts are so extensively equipped that they're going to take a lot longer than expected. Tenders, outboard motors, life rafts, davits, washing machines, dishwashers, compactors and all sorts of appliances, appearing not once but even two or three times. Does the client expect you to be sure that all these things work right? If so, the job will take quite a bit longer than expected.

Now is the time to clean up all these loose ends, making any adjustments in time scheduling or even fixing price mistakes. Most surveyors quote jobs sight unseen if the initial description of the vessel seems reasonable. That's why it's so important to get as much information from the client as possible. However, if the yacht is considerably out of the ordinary, or it was not adequately represented to the surveyor, he shouldn't hesitate to try to adjust the pricing if he can support his reasons for doing so. As a professional, the surveyor should be able to size up a job over the phone and quote a price for late model yachts. If not, then he should make an inspection first and then give the price. If this is not possible, under these circumstances it's fair to adjust your price. There will be many times where a client states that the vessel was in good condition, only for the surveyor to arrive at the vessel and find that it is a disaster. In that case, your are justified in raising your price, rather than working twice as long for half as much.

Working with Captains

The surveyor not only has to be a professional technical expert, but a diplomat and psychologist as well. Yacht captains can be his best friend or worst enemy. It's important to start off on the right foot and turn him (or her) into a friend right away. They can provide the surveyor with immeasurable assistance, or ruin his day, depending on the kind of relationship that is established. Many surveyors have trouble with captains, probably because they don't understand their position, so let's take a look at it.

Nowadays most yacht captains are paid, professional managers. Their boss is the boat owner, and included in their function is the maintenance of the yacht. Along comes the surveyor who, for all practical purposes, is going to be assessing how well the captain has done his job. That's not what he's really doing, but that's going to be one of the by-products of his work. Right away there is a potential for great displeasure on the part of the captain. Few people in this world take to criticism kindly and captains are no different. Even though the yacht's being sold, the captain may be retained as captain for the next yacht, or he may need a letter of recommendation from his current employer. If the captain hasn't done a good job, it is the surveyor who is going to be making that fact known.

What happens to a lot of captains is that they're not given an adequate budget by the vessel owner so that he can do a good job of maintenance. This is a very common complaint. The worst mistake the surveyor can make is either to make critical comments to the captain about the condition of the vessel, or to allow his commentary to others to be overheard by the captain. Do this and you'll have an instant enemy. It's best to completely shield all negative aspects of your work from the captain and make sure that you're not rubbing his nose in his problems. Be friendly, be sympathetic, win him over. But do not discuss findings with him unless he provides you with a receptive opening. Many captains will be completely open about maintenance problems and tell you what and why. Some will even do part of your work for you. But not all; the ones who are negligent in their work may fight you tooth and nail because you pose a threat to their continued employment. The surveyor needs to be aware of this, to size him up and try to allay his fears.

Engine Surveyors

If you're working with an engine surveyor, you should try to coordinate with him prior to the start of the survey. If you haven't worked with him before, you need to find out his time schedule, what he wants to do and when. Some engine guys only want a half-day, but good ones know they need a whole day for a good-sized pair of diesels.

If you got a half-day guy, it's going to screw up your plans for performing a sea trial last. Obviously, if you can coordinate this before hand, these problems will be avoided. Otherwise, work it out at the start of the survey. Maybe he doesn't want to hang around during hauling. The needs of the hull surveyor should take precedence over the engine surveyor because he has the whole boat to think of, the engine guy only the engines. If you're going to be working with these people, it's best to develop a good working relationship. But don't let him push you into doing a sea trial on a dirty bottom.

Opening Up

Having conducted the tour, decisions have to be made about what has to be opened up, furniture moved or special assistance required. A forty foot sport fisherman can have a ton of furniture sitting on top of the engine room hatches and you may not be able to survey the engine room without moving it. This is a good question to ask before you get there. Now is the time to get these problems out of the way, not thirty minutes before you're due at the yard for hauling.

My preference is to open up all panels and remove all drawers before getting underway. I don't remove stairs or open up hatches because someone may fall and I don't want to be responsible for that. But by opening up everything else on the interior (especially in larger yachts) I'll get a better feeling for how systems are routed and where things are. Often, there's nothing behind drawers so that when they're pulled out, the inner hull and systems are exposed. I take all the drawers out and set them on the beds. After I've checked behind them during the sea trial I put them back during the sea trial. Then I'll move the mattresses and look under the beds, also during the sea trial. Why now? Because I want to see these things while the boat's bouncing along, not just sitting at the dock.

It's very unwise to pull up a lot of hatches and leave them open, even if no one's around. Eventually you'll fall through an open hatch yourself if you're at this long enough. If all the hatches are open in a cockpit, or over an engine room, keep people out. If they fall, you'll get blamed. Never stand hatch covers up on end; they're guaranteed to fall over, on your foot or on your head. Nor should we rely on hatch retainers; tie them open with a piece of rope if they're not removable. Never trust the retainer mechanism. If it falls, a hatch cover can cut fingers off like a guillotine.

Where to Start

I start with the engine room first because in Florida it gets awfully uncomfortable after the machinery has been running. March in Maine may suggest a different order of progression, but one way or another the surveyor needs to order his work in a logical progression. I do this even in spite of the fact that the engine surveyor is usually working there also. We are often getting in each other's way, but an advantage is that I have an opportunity to share and discuss findings, his and mine. I'll know what he covers and doesn't. The engine room is a place where one should work at a leisurely pace because it's a very complicated place. It needs a lot of eyeballing and shouldn't be rushed. Which is why it's a good place to start.

As a rule of thumb, it's best to work a survey from the bottom up. This fits with parameter of doing the most important things first since that's where most of the expensive and costly repairs will be, along with all the heavy lifting. Some surveyors try to perform surveys categorically, or compartment by compartment. A surveyor will run himself ragged if he tries to survey by category because he will constantly be going back over the same ground. To some degree, the survey has to be done by compartment, but your notes shouldn't be organized that way because this will result in a report that frustrates the reader.

Defects and deficiencies are best ordered categorically, not by location. If done this way, every category of system will be repeated over and over for each compartment. This will render a report that is very difficult to follow and work with. A well-organized report should to some degree be categorical, but not by compartment. The lone exception is the engine room where most of the machinery is located. If the machinery is more spread around, one may not want to use an Engine Room category because the locations will have to be described anyway.

1	2
Machinerey	Engine Room
Plumbing	Plumbing
Electrical	Electrical
Structural	Structural
Bilge Pumping	Bilge Pumping
Air Conditioning	Air Conditioning
Fire & Safety	Fire & Safety
Miscellaneous	Miscellaneous

The above table illustrates two good methods of categorizing. The only difference in the order is that an Engine Room section takes the place of machinery. It's a convenient order of grouping because everything that pertains to the engines, generators and other machinery can be included here in a logical manner. The advantage of the Engine Room category in the second column over the first is that it will save the surveyor the additional time of having to repeatedly describe the location. If he uses the first column method, then he's got to describe the location of everything. One method simply saves time over the other.

One good way of ordering notes is to take a legal pad and devote one page to each major category. Forms are a good place to record information but they're a lousy place to record notes. I record information and deficiencies and recommendations categorically, always placing the categories in the same order on my pages for every job. That way it's easy to flip to the plumbing section on page four or electrical on five. I know right where it is and I save time fumbling around with paper. On small boats it doesn't matter that much, but for bigger jobs organizing notes in advance will save a lot of time later on writing the report.

Notes

Some day you're going to hate yourself because you didn't take good notes and I'll get to the reason why in just a moment. I can write complete and accurate survey reports without ever taking any notes, except for copying down numbers. Yet I always take notes, though I usually don't look at them much when writing reports. For me, notes are a backup for when I forget. More importantly, taking good notes forces you to do and look at things that you'd otherwise forget. It forces you to look at things more closely, and to think about them as you're writing them. I recommend the writing of detailed notes. I use lots and lots of abbreviations, but I spell out the condition completely. If I don't do this, I find myself not considering things as closely as I should. Then, when I get back to the office, I find that I don't know about something that I should know about and I'm stuck. The novice surveyor should know that this is something that will happen to him repeatedly, and he'll never fully solve the problem unless he learns to take his time and take good notes. Get rushed and you'll find yourself bumbling through your written report.

Good notes are also important from the standpoint of whether you get questioned about something later. While you've described a fact in your report, the notes provide additional verification of what was found. With no notes, the report is just floating around by itself. Be aware that notes can be extremely damaging if a surveyor gets sued, or his file is subpoenaed in some other matter, and the notes do not comport with what was written in the report. If a condition is mentioned in the notes, but not included in the report, the surveyor should record in his notes his reason for not doing so. When depositions or testimony is given, the surveyor will get nailed to the wall for this sort of thing and it will look extremely bad for him. If there are questionable areas for which the surveyor does not have a full understanding, it's best to create a separate heading on the note pad. I put three question marks at the top of the page. This clearly indicates doubts about whatever is said on that page. If I can't resolve those questions, then I know that my report should cast whatever commentary I make with a clear sense that the issue is not resolved. That way, I'm much less tempted to resolve it by going out on a limb.

File Management

While the surveyor may think that it will never happen, believe me, sooner or later one of his files will be subpoenaed and subjected to very hostile criticism. Files should be maintained with the conscious realization that others, including adversaries, may end up looking at them. You may think that they are your personal files and that no one else has the right to them. If you watch TV even a little bit, you've got to know that isn't true. I estimate that during the course of my career, my files have been subpoenaed over 200 times. In the beginning this proved very embarrassing because either I didn't do a good job of file management, or there were things in there I'd rather no one else saw. Or worse, my notes didn't comport with what I wrote in my report, not meaning that I fudged something, no. What it meant was that I'd changed my mind about something, or did some research, changed my views, and yet my file reflected something entirely different because I didn't update my notes.

When the file was subpoenaed three or four years later, I had no recollection of what happened and had a very hard time explaining. That can be painfully embarrassing on the witness stand when a hostile lawyer has a copy of your notes in hand, and is making a fool of you in front of a room full of people.

Every surveyor owes it to himself to do a good job of note taking and file management. It may seem like a trivial thing in the beginning. It may seem to be a waste of time. But remember that boats create a lot of litigation and the chances that the surveyor's work will also end up in litigation is very high. The novice surveyor can't appreciate this until, usually sometime after he's been in business for about five years or so, the subpoenas start rolling in. Only then will he begin to appreciate just how important good file management really is. This is yet another reason that I urge surveyors to think like lawyers.

Memorizing Techniques

Having a good memory is absolutely essential to the surveyor performing his job efficiently and well. When a surveyor has to crawl down into a hole, more often than not he'll not be able to take his clip board with him. That means that when he climbs out, he'll have to be able to remember what he saw down in that hole. That may include a dozen items. If he doesn't have a good memory, he's going to have to in and out of that hole several times.

There's no better way to do this than to just quietly sit down in a particular area and leisurely observe everything around you. Not once, not twice, but again and again and again. A mental note is made of each item that has to be recorded. In this way you learn to create a mental picture of what you see so that when you climb out of that narrow hatch, you'll be able to remember what you saw, along with the ability to write it down clearly and accurately. It is literally like taking a mental photograph; the trick is that you have to get the right exposure. Sort of like time lapse photography, the longer we concentrate on something, the better it will imprint itself on the mind. This method works so well that I can often remember hull and engine numbers months after the survey. I can write accurate reports without ever looking at my notes, and without omitting details. Developing a "photographic memory" is not something anyone is born with. It's a skill achieved with practice that can save hundreds of hours over the course of a year and is well worth the effort to learn.

Photography

A camera can be a very valuable tool on a survey. I drag around with me a camera case containing an expensive Nikon and full array of lenses. Since I provide photos with my report, it only makes sense that I use it for other purposes as well. One of these is making a record of complicated situations for which I don't want to spend a lot of time writing notes when a simple picture will save time. It's particularly adept in recording problems with complex arrays of plumbing or wiring. When unusually costly problems crop up, I photograph them. Having a good photo record on more than one occasion saved me from a lot of grief. Having photographs in the file of a contentious situation has got me out of a hot spot on more than one occasion. I view it as another form of insurance, one that costs me about $12.00 per job.

The Hauled Survey

By the time the engine room is completed, it's usually time to head off to the yard. Unless we know the bottom is clean, the haul out should be first, otherwise we may not get a good trial run. One of the biggest time saving things to do is to contact the yard about an hour before arrival to make sure they're ready for you. More than half the time they're not. Every area is unique and poses different problems so there are no neat solutions to dealing with logistics. Using the radio or cellular can save an awful lot of time if there was some sort of emergency and the travel lift will be occupied for a few hours, or the rest of the day. It might force you to do your sea trial first, but it could be a lot better than to have to come back another day.

Even if there's a broker, I get involved in the selection of the yard. Some yards couldn't care less whether they keep an appointment with you and I want to be sure to avoid them. If I don't know the yard, I make it a big, big point to talk to the manager and insist that they be punctual, telling them that I also promise to be on time, and then make sure we are. Foul ups at boat yards can rip hours off your schedule and we want to do our best to make sure that doesn't happen. But rest assured that if you develop a reputation for not being on time, you'll do a lot of waiting, even if it's not your fault. Make sure others in your party are also prepared to keep the appointment punctually.

The trip to the yard may involve an open water passage or a trip down a no-wake zone waterway. Whichever it is, this time can be used to good advantage. During docking and undocking is a good time to check the engine mounts and slow speed shaft turning. It's also a good time to check the steering gear and parts of the exhaust system, particularly those areas that will be difficult when charging along at full speed. If there's time left over you can move up to the bridge and test any electronics that can be tested at low speed.

If there's an hour or more, this is fill-in time. I'll often work outside on the decks because it's cool while the boat is moving and I won't be standing out in the blazing sun after three o'clock when the heat is the worst. Of course, if it's November in New York you'll have different ideas about that. The point is to schedule your work wisely and make the best use of the time available. It's very easy to get side tracked by beautiful scenery and pleasant conversation. If you do, you'll pay a price for it later.

When it comes to larger vessels, the choice of where and how to haul usually involves the broker and possibly the owner. I've seen an awful lot of foul ups and damage caused to boats by lift operators who have no idea of what they're doing. They may just run the boat in the slings and lift it up with no regard whatsoever as to any damage the slings may cause. It's not a good idea to take an attitude that it's not your problem. Clients and surveyors occasionally get dragged into a dispute about any damage that was caused. I've had sellers blame me for damage saying I wasn't holding the boat right and allowed it scrape against a concrete piling, as if I were responsible for handling. The surveyor can do a great service to all concerned by pointing out any potentiality for causing damage and helping to avoid it. There are three things that I will do to help avoid damage.

- Make note of where the shafts exit the hull and point out to the lift operator if the slings are on the shafts.

- If vessel has external exhaust cowlings, advise lift operator if slings will need special blocking to avoid causing damage.

- Advise lift operator if slings are going to cause damage to weak rub rails.

In no case do I offer advice on how the operator should do things; I just point out the potential for problems and hope that I head them off.

If the surveyor is going to crawl under the vessel and have tens of tons of weight hanging over his head, it makes sense to check out the condition of the lift before getting under it. About 90% of all drops are caused by parted slings and cable clamps so it makes sense to check them out. If the slings show heavy wear, the boat should be blocked before you get under it.

Cleaning dirty bottoms is another point that should be resolved before you get to the yard, and preferably at the time the job is scheduled with the client. There's nothing like ending up with a bottom crusted with barnacles and no one willing to foot the bill to clean it. The bottom can't be surveyed and it might as well not have been hauled in the first place. The surveyor may have no way of knowing this before he arrives at the vessel, but he can avoid this problem by checking before taking off for the yard. If the bottom looks very fouled, he needs to resolve this issue before leaving the dock.

Sea Trial

If the surveyor is going to be checking out the engines, the sea trial should be divided up in two parts: the engines and everything else. If he hasn't allowed himself adequate time, or if circumstances intervene and cut short a sea trial, the job is not complete. One of the worst mistakes a surveyor can make is to allow his time to be cut short, and then represent the job as being completed. How to conduct a thorough sea trial is discussed in the Sea Trial chapter.

The thoroughness of a sea trial is completely at the mercy of weather and geography, over which the surveyor has no control. But he does have control over many other factors that can hinder his performance. Sea trials are often perceived by the seller and the client as an opportunity for party time. This absolutely must be avoided. The surveyor cannot possibly do a good job on a boat that is crawling with people. Once he arrives at the vessel and finds that the boat is loaded with people, it's very difficult to disappoint them all and tell them they can't go. The time to resolve this is during the initial job scheduling. It must be made clear to the client that the quality of the work is dependent on working conditions and that an uninhibited working environment is mandatory. His friends and family will have to wait for another day for their boat ride.

Post Survey

Upon returning to the dock is the time to go back over the vessel and make sure everything is put back in its proper place. This is also the time when the surveyor reviews his work and starts asking himself if he missed anything, the time when he pulls the loose ends together. When putting the interior back together is the time when the surveyor usually discovers things he's missed. The survey is winding down and everyone is thinking about going home, the pressure of keeping a schedule is off. Now we can take time to relax a bit and take a good look around, just as we did at the outset.

If I haven't had time to do a general inspection of the interior, decks and superstructure, this is when I do it. I've saved both the easiest and least important aspects for last. If my time gets cut short now, at least the major parts are completed. If I overlooked a leaky window or the microwave oven doesn't work, at least I'm not likely to get dragged into court over that. After the final going over, I then sit down and review my notes, reminding myself of my work and giving myself the opportunity to fill in any gaps. I'm also getting prepared to make my presentation to my client. Because Fort Lauderdale is the largest yacht market in the world, many of my clients have traveled here from other parts of the country and even the world. They're usually on a tight schedule and they're in a hurry to hear the results. It's a risky business but if I don't have a local client, I don't get much time for reflection, I've got to give a presentation now, when I'm tired and sweaty and least able to perform at my best. That's the way it goes.

Sitting the client down and beginning by telling him that I've just finished a very difficult physical task, that I am tired, and that I've had no time for consideration or reflection on my work, reduces the pressure. I make it clear to him that this is raw, raw, information. Not infrequently, when writing my report the next day, do I discover that I forgot to tell him something. Perhaps I forgot to write something in my notes, but now I remember. I have to make a quick phone call, hopefully before he's signed the papers. If he wants to sign the purchase agreement one hour after the physical survey is completed, as many clients do, he has to know that by the time I write my report I may change some of my views on what I'm now telling him. I reserve that right and I advise him to wait for the report. About 1 in 10 smaller boat buyers take that advice. Buyers of larger yachts are usually smart enough to wait for the written report; rich people don't get rich by being stupid. This tells a lot about the emotional state of the client, despite his outward appearance, and why the surveyor has to try to stay out of the line of fire. You may have a client who's going to rush a decision on a purchase worth perhaps hundreds of thousands of dollars. This is the sort of foolishness that surveyors with many years of experience have learned how to insulate themselves from.

The presentation of survey results is something a whole book could be written about. The long and short of it is that the more skillful the surveyor becomes at delivering a presentation, the better he serves his client and reduces problems for himself. If I couldn't get a handle on the client at the outset, I want to try to complete the picture now. I don't want him falling over the edge and taking me with him. The surveyor should never take the attitude that the client's future problems won't rub off on him. This is not to say that the surveyor should give advice whether to buy or not to buy. He shouldn't. What he should do is to make sure that the client understands the magnitude of what he's getting into. If the surveyor has been considerate and patient with the client, that client is going to find it very difficult indeed to come back on the surveyor and say, "You didn't tell me." He won't be able to find it in his heart to do that. Do you know why? It's because he won't be able to face the surveyor saying, to him "I told you so."

Not only does the surveyor have to be a diplomat, but a psychologist as well. When a client is so emotionally involved with his purchase, it won't do to insult him by insulting his purchase. It's like the man who complains about his wife. After all, he chose her. Clients are apt to lure the surveyor into that trap by saying, "Well, what do you think." The fact is, what they really want is for the surveyor to confirm their original opinion, not to pull the rug out.

There are many times during the course of the survey when the surveyor should point out important problems, things that the client needs to see with his own eyes. Pay attention to this because it can smooth out a potentially rocky road. If, prior to the presentation, we have taken the time to point out most, if not all, of the major deficiencies, by the time we're ready to sit down with the client, most of the presentation will have already been done. At this point all we have to do is remind him of what we have shown him, and then finish up with the rest of the less important details. There is tremendous benefit to following this procedure. First, it takes the load off when you are most tired and apt not to phrase things as well as you might when you were more rested (For surveyors working in hotter climates, heat exhaustion can be a serious problem. Those working in cooler climates will probably wonder what I'm talking about.)

Secondly, the client has seen the item in question with his own eyes so you're not saddled with a personal description. Third, when he asks for your summary opinion like, "Well, what do you think?" you now have a means of referring him back on himself. It's not what the surveyor thinks that is important. After all, the surveyor is not buying the boat. It's what the client thinks that counts. Fourth, you've now worked him into a position where you can help him make his own decision. At this point, it's really hard for him to throw it back on you and ask you make his decision for him. He's seen it, now he's got to decide. He may well just wait for your written report and consider it even further, which is a wise thing to do.

You're now in a position to help him put the boat into perspective. If the boat has problems, with the budget he has, can he do any better? If the boat has some years on it, won't other boats in his price range be likely to be in the same state of repair? At this point, reminding him of what a new one costs, usually at least double what he's paying, brings him in focus. We remind him that the average boat over 5 years old will require 5-10% of sale price to repair deficiencies. This is normal, and unless he wants to pay an exceptional price for an exceptional boat, he's likely to run into the same thing with the next boat he surveys. This is what giving good advice is really all about, helping the client to make his decision, not making it for him.

It's an interesting thing, too, that so many brokers attempt to manipulate and control their clients, distorting the truth and trying to rush the client into a quick closing, even before he's seen the report. Recently I started asking brokers what their closing rate after survey was. Answers ranged from 25 to 50%. In my book, that's pretty bad. What is interesting is that probably over 95% of my clients purchase the first boat I survey for them. It doesn't take much imagination to understand what the brokers are doing wrong. I'm not pressuring them, and when they come to their own decision, they feel comfortable with it. They've been honestly shown what their options are and, in most cases will opt to resolve the existing problems and get on with it, rather than moving on to the next boat that's just as likely to have similar problems. On the other hand, when the broker tries to hustle the client, he gets cold feet and rejects the broker instead of the boat. The fact is, honesty sells more boats than deception.

When boats have numerous and serious defects that are likely to kill the sale, the surveyor may want to use some discretion here about when he reveals these findings. If he points out too much, too soon, the client may want to terminate the survey. Remember, the surveyor has the right to see the survey through to the end and collect his full fee. If the survey is terminated, the client will probably try to negotiate the fee.

The Surveyor's Kit

It's a fortunate thing that surveyors don't have to carry a lot of tools and instruments because whatever he uses, he has to lug around through airports, onto aircraft, across rubble-filled fields, construction sites, across endless yards of parking lots, and down some of the longest and most rickety docks imaginable. Then there are the times when he has to carry it up and down ladders, across bolder-strewn beaches, and into tipsy dinghies.

Because of these conditions, there comes a time when every professional surveyor comes to the conclusion that less is more. The most important thing I've found is that it's not so much a matter of how much you carry, but how you carry it, meaning the containers you put it all into. Air travel mandates containers that travel cases will withstand the antics of airport baggage handlers, along with their associated thieves; you can't carry on a tool kit - you'll never get past security. The important point here is that the case will not crush and wreck my electronic instruments.

After many years of trying every kind of inexpensive soft container imaginable, I finally realized that I was going to have to make an investment in something more substantial, something that was durable, and had good sized wheels on it. Ultimately I discovered the Sampsonite fiberglass overnighter shown below. After much searching, though I found many nifty tool cases, none were equipped with wheels, and all were dedicated to tools of specific trades, like computer repairman. So, I ended up locating several large

blocks of cut-foam material to house my tools and instruments within the Sampsonite case, which needed to be modified from what was basically a suitcase into a tool travel case.

The other important feature of these travel cases is the pull-out handle that allows you to stack yet another case onto it, which I do and more. By the time I've got the thing loaded up with all I need it looks like a pack mule. Tool case, lunch box, thermos bottle, rags, all these and more get strapped on with bungee cords. And across the parking lots and down the docks I go.

Having two cases works out well since the attache case-like box is fitted out specifically for small tools, each with an individual holder. Having a place for everything and ensuring that everything is in its place is the only way I can avoid loosing tools on every job. It also avoids the problem of having to haul the heaviest case off the boat before or after hauling. It's no fun trying to jump off a boat in a travel lift slip with a big overnighter in hand. Thus, the smaller tool case has everything in it needed to survey the bottom.

Though my work vehicle is well stocked with just about every kind of tool I could need, my basic kit is more limited. Here's a list of my basic essentials:

- Screw drivers - A selection of small to very large. Buy only Craftsman or those with square shanks. Can't use a wrench on a round shank driver.

- Sounding Tools - Though most surveyors use plastic hammers for sounding, my preference is for the ball-tipped handles of large Craftsman screwdrivers. For most purposes, the smaller tip does a better job. In addition to that I carry a large rubber mallet for checking for bottom or side delamination.

- Scrapers - There's no end to the usefulness of a varied selection of quality scrapers. Go for those with heavy blades.

- Pocket Knife - Good sturdy fold ups come from China for only $15 or so. Keep one in the tool kit so it will always be there.

- Screw Gun - Turn screws by hand long enough and you'll become intimately familiar with the joys of carpal tunnel syndrome. A top quality screw gun is a must, along with a complete selection of driver bits, including the square Roberts head bits for Hatteras boats.

- Infrared thermometer - This essential device is the most versatile tool in my kit. It is available from EPD Technology, Elmsford, NY 1-800-892-8926.

- Pencil Magnet - For dipping and checking gear boxes and other machinery for wear metals. Available at Sears.

- Brake Rotor Dial Indicator Kit - This device has a locking flexible shaft that camps onto any surface that can take a vice grip clamp. Used for dialing shaft runout and checking engine movement. Available at automotive tool suppliers. Tip: Don't ever oil the flexible arm because after that the arm will never lock in place. You just have to let the darn thing rust and get ugly.

- Moisture Meter - Choose the type with a number graduated read out.

- Portable GPS - Indispensable for checking speeds. It's best to have your own unit rather than relying on the unit on the boat. I use the Garmin III Plus because the unit is triangular has a rubber base, and one can read the display without having to have the unit in hand.

- Camera - Can be used as a portable secretary. Instead of taking notes of a complicated situation, just take a picture of it. A quality camera with built in flash is preferred. Messing around with clumsy flash units in this environment isn't cool.

- Small Socket Kit - Deep sockets are preferred.

- Compression Tester - The kind sold at Sears is fine. Gauge uses ordinary bicycle tire valves and you'll need some extras. If you do outboards, buy two because sooner or later you'll drop one in the drink.

- Adjustable Crescent Wrench - is necessary for turning screw drivers when opening lower unit oil drains.

Digital -vs- Film Cameras

I debated and waited a lot of years before taking the plunge with an expensive digital camera. Most of the problems that I had anticipated with it turned out to be worse than I imagined. The pre purchase surveyor does not have to have a camera at all, but if he doesn't he's missing out on what is an important tool for most surveyors.

The advantage of the automatic 35mm film camera is that it is almost fool proof. It is also more durable and less prone to damage. Another huge advantage is that picture filing and storage is quick and easy. I just write the file names and dates on the envelope and file them in a shoe box. Its main drawback is that you have to deliver the film for processing and then go pick it up. That takes time.

Now, with the digital camera, you may think you'll save that time, but the reality is that you'll probably spend more time managing your digital camera images than you save in development time. First of all, your camera saves the picture with a number name. That's no help because you have to open the graphic file on the computer to see what it is. For picture management you have two choices: either set up file folders on you hard drive to store the images by a particular category, or tediously rename the images. Even if you have an image browser, by the time you've got merely a hundred photos, examining all those thumbnails gets very laborious.

Moreover, printing digital images can get very costly, even if you use only plain paper rather than photo paper which is outrageously expensive. Ink jet cartridges begin to disappear every couple weeks or so, and at $25-30 a pop you may be looking at a $700 annual ink cartridge bill, not to mention paper and batteries.

While the digital camera is more versatile in low light situations, it is far less versatile in bright light where the image monitor can't be used at all. You're stuck with a viewfinder comparable to an old Instamatic. Its biggest drawback is the lack of versatility resulting from the view limitations of the standard lens.

Used for business, a digital camera with autofocus and telephoto and flash will consume batteries like crazy.

Chapter 5

The Hull and Its Structures

In order to survey a hull, a surveyor needs to have a basic understanding of the engineering principles involved. This does not mean that the surveyor himself must be an engineer, for many of the people who design and build boats are not themselves engineers or naval architects. This chapter will review basic composite boat building and structural principles in considerable detail in order to provide the prospective surveyor with a solid foundation that will assist him in recognizing some of the many structural faults that he will be faced with.

It's not the surveyor's job to analyze the structural engineering of vessel upon which he is performing a pre-purchase survey. After all, it is a survey that we are doing, not an engineering analysis. However, as was discussed in Chapter One, it is the surveyor's responsibility to be able to recognize the symptoms of structural faults when they appear.

Background

Design Faults and Why They Occur

Despite all the talk about high technology, high tech materials and advanced techniques, major design and structural faults continue to plague the boat building industry. There are manifold reasons why this is true, and it will be helpful to us to have an understanding of why this is so.

In this age of mass consumerism, modern manufacturing techniques and quality control methodology has resulted in extremely high levels of product consistency and freedom from defects. In large part, this is due to things like robotics and computer controlled manufacturing where much, if not all, of the human element of manufacturing has been eliminated. If the design is right,

Fig. 5-1 This 30' open fisherman under construction reveals some major design faults. Note the uneven spacing of the stringers and excessive spacing of transverse frames. Stringers are glass over 1/2" plywood and are too tall relative to the height. Also, that the the outer stringers in forward section are almost completely cut in half by the holes drilled for the 3" PVC control cable conduits. Stringers will surely fracture at these points.

and the process is right, then the machines will turn out thousands or millions of exactly identical product.

It is the economy of scale, the marketing and sale of product in huge numbers that makes all this possible, for such machines are enormously expensive. Unfortunately for the boat building industry, the market for pleasure craft is rather small, particularly when compared with the auto industry. There are approximately 350 million motor vehicles in the U.S. Over the last decade, the number of pleasure craft has held rather stead at slightly above 21 million vessels, with total annual production running around 600,000 vessels. Divided by approximately 1200 boat builders in the U.S., the annual average production numbers per builder is minuscule compared with almost every other major industry. The one major difference for boats, of course, is the average cost per unit, which is very high.

The U.S. boat building industry is the largest in the world, but in monetary terms of production, it pales in comparison with most other major industries. The significance of this is that these numbers point up the essential problem of the boat building industry: it does not have the necessary economic resources to be able to perform the kind of research and development that is needed to achieve a reasonably high level of product reliability. In fact, boat building has a long history and tradition of the trial and error method of product development, a method that remains largely prevalent today.

This problem is compounded by the fact that boats, owing to their low production numbers, are mainly hand made products. There is very little about boat building that is automated. Because of this, it might seem reasonable to assume that boat defects occur mainly due to human manufacturing defects, but this is not the case. The vast majority of boat defects result from design and material application errors, and not the fault of the people who actually do the work of making a boat.

The old adage about sausage making applies equally well to boat building: If you could observe the entire process, you'd never buy one. Yet another historical problem of the industry stems from a lack of professionalism, and the fact that it requires relatively little in the way of capital investment to become a boat builder. To put it bluntly, this has resulted in a lot of unqualified, undereducated entering the industry. It wasn't all that long ago when boat molds in Florida were traded around like kids with baseball cards. Just about anyone could buy an old beat up mold and start cranking out boats. Could and routinely did.

The surveyor who intends to have a long and successful career remains prudently aware that with this kind of background to the industry, he is always presented with the possibility, even the likelihood, that he will encounter boats that have serious structural problems. Though there has been progress in reducing design errors, what little progress that has been made has been arguably offset by the introduction of large amounts of new materials, notably foams and putties. The lack of R&D and product testing continues to be a serious problem, and major hull and structural faults continue to plague the market.

An Embarrassing Example

A good example, one that proved to be a major embarrassment to a materials manufacturer, occurred in 1988 when I attended a product demonstration put on in the shop of the builder of high end sportfishing yachts in the million dollar category. The demonstration was highly promoted and attended by a fairly large group of builders. The product was a foam core material, bonding putty and a special application machine. About forty people stood around on scaffolding around the mold of a sixty foot hull while the bonding putty was

Fig 5-2. The incomplete bonding of the core to the outer laminate shown here demonstrates how difficult it is to achieve complete contact and bonding with the bonding agent. This is a common problem when builders attempt to force large sheets of foam into an area with compound curves. Less than 50% bonding was achieved on this hull.

troweled onto the partly finished laminate. Then a large sheet of scored foam was set in place over the putty and the demonstrators went to work with their special machines.

Once they were finished, the lead demonstrator grandly told the assembled crowd that he would prove the effectiveness of the bond between core and laminate by now pulling the core off. This he and his cohorts proceeded to do, much to their chagrin and the incredulous looks on the faces of the audience. You see, once the core was pulled off, it was immediately clear to all present that at least 20% of the core had failed to even make contact with the bonding putty. See Figure 5-2 that shows how this problem manifests. After a few moments of hemming and hawing, the master of ceremonies recovered his aplomb and calmly told us that this was just a "quickie demo," but if *you* do it right, you will get perfect results every time. Which left a lot of us scratching our heads: if he, the product manufacturer couldn't get it right, how on earth was a $15/hour laminating crew that wouldn't have nearly the motivation that he does, manage to get it right every time? The answer is that they can't. Today, this same builder uses foam cores in his hulls, but vacuum bags them. The materials manufacturer and his equipment has since passed into history. Unfortunately, the boats that were built with those products and system are still out there. When laminates fail to adhere to cores, this is often referred to as "never bonds".

Marketing and Price Pressures

It is said that every good hath its evil, and one of the evils of the free market is price competition. Low cost products are great, up to the point where cost reduction pressures end up creating shoddy products. This is particularly true for boats that, because of their nature, need to be strongly built as well as durable to withstand some of the world's harshest environments.

Not only do we face the problems associated with undereducated and untrained designers, but also those of the bean counters. In fact, foam cores have come into widespread use not because they make the product better, but because they replace heavier, more expensive materials with lighter and cheaper materials. The never-ending drive to reduce costs usually has the effect of reducing overall quality, which continues to be a growing problem with boats.

Moreover, it may well be that after forty years of fiberglass boat building, unacceptably large numbers of defective boats are still being produced precisely because the increases in technology and vast array of new materials which find their way into boat building without being subjected to adequate product testing.

My point here is not to give a gratuitous critique of the industry, but to provide a background assessment of the industry who's products we evaluate, in order to better understand the influences that cause those products to be what they are. Although the vast majority of boats do not have serious design faults, the number of boats that do is sufficiently large that the surveyor needs to be alert for them.

Basic Structural Principles

Before we go directly into reviewing the kinds of problems encountered by the pre-purchase surveyor, it's important that we first review the major principles of hull design. From an engineering standpoint, fiberglass boats have similarities to both bridges and aircraft.

Boats are similar to bridges in that the hull must have a framing system to support it. Both a boat and a bridge provide a span over a fluid substance, air for the bridge, water for the boat. Gravity, of course, exerts a downward force on both, and for the boat, water offers uniform support for the hull, assuming that the boat is loaded evenly, which it never is.

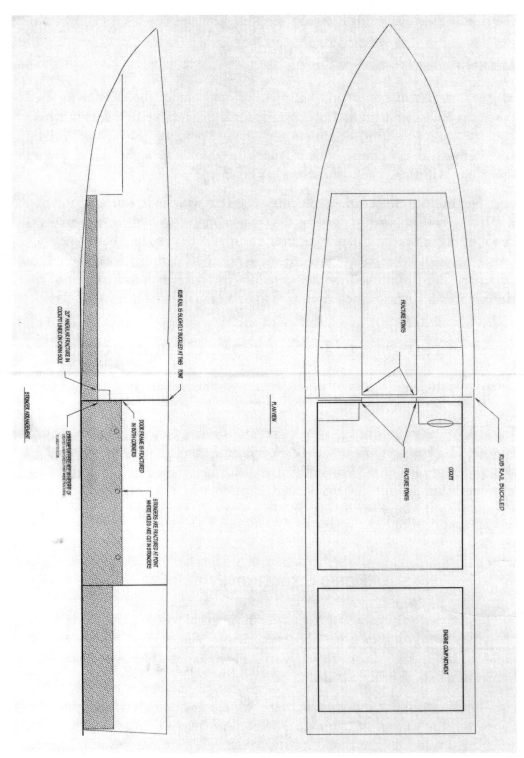

Fig. 5-3. Cross section and plan view showing faulty stringer design in a 41' offshore hull that began to break apart.

When a boat is hauled out and set on blocks, often with only one block at each end of the hull, then that boat hull becomes literally like a bridge (and the primary reason you need to worry about crushing on keels). Unless a hull has an adequate system of girders and framing, like a bridge it may buckle and collapse.

Now try to imagine the forces acting on a boat hull as it speeds along on rough water at twenty, thirty or forty knots. It frequently becomes airborne, multiplying the effects of speed as a result of slamming. As anyone who has ever done a belly-flopper off a diving board knows, water can become as hard as a rock when impacted squarely by a relatively wide, flat surface. Thus, the forces acting on a hull are far more than just a matter of mass and velocity; it includes a mass in motion coming to a sudden stop.

When a boat is banging along on waves, the impacts that the hull sustains are never uniform along its length, but will tend to be localized to a limited area of the hull bottom and/or sides. The impact may be only on one side of the hull, in which case the result will be a tendency toward torsional stress or twisting, or at one end of the hull, such as the bow, where the stress will be in a longitudinal direction that will work to buckle the hull like bending and breaking a stick. In this later instance, one can see that unless the stringer system is truly massive, the strength of the hull alone will not be sufficient to resist this force and longitudinal bending will occur. The effect will be like placing a five pound lead ingot at one end of a shoe box, and then trying to pick that box up; the box will crumple because it is not strong enough to bear that load.

Examples of Structural Design Defects

Boat hulls are rarely ever capable of sustaining all the stresses that they are subjected to without the help of reinforcing structures. Returning to our shoe box example, if we take that very same box, place the weight in it, and then securely tape the lid in place, chances are that we can now pick it up without the box crumpling. Why? Because in taping the lid on, we have added another structural element to the box. Instead of a three-sided structure, the box becomes like a box beam with the lid taped on.

This illustrates the structural function that decks can provide when they are properly designed. Not only decks, but any raised structure attaching to the deck, such as house sides and raised coamings will add strength. Perhaps you've heard the term "monocoque," which refers to the method of modern aircraft construction whereby the fuselage of the aircraft is designed in such a way that the outer skin is the framing system. With autos, this is known as unibody construction. Fiberglass boats can and are being built employing this principle of monocoque construction. The use of grid liners is but one form.

Untrained designers are often unaware of these engineering principles and so we end up with boats that are so poorly designed that they begin to break apart. One good example is a case I was involved in several years ago with a forty-two foot offshore or "cigarette" type boat that was, in fact built by that famous builder. Typically these high performance hulls have an aft cockpit and a huge expanse of foredeck. These decks are not just "hull covers," instead, this deck is designed as a major part of the overall structure in the manner of a box beam. The longitudinal stresses on these hulls are so great that a stringer system alone would not prevent the hulls from buckling.

Stringer Design Error

In this instance, the designer made a major error with his stringer design, which is illustrated in fig. 5-3. Maximum effectiveness of stringer or girder design mandates that the stringers be of uniform height throughout their length, but in this boat the stringers had a number of large steps both up and down. In fact, the stringers were at four radically different levels in different parts of the boat. Now, imagine trying to build a bridge with girders like that! Even an untrained designer would know better. Any trained designer or engineer can look at this drawing and immediately predict where the structural failure is going to occur — right at that huge step down that takes place at the amidships bulkhead.

Fortunately, a massive hull failure did not occur, for the problem was detected before massive failure occurred when the symptoms of trouble became glaringly obvious. These included the rub rails popping off, buckling starting to show up in the hull sides, deck fasteners backing out, and severe gel coat stress cracking showing up on both the deck, cockpit and interior liners.

A cursory survey of the hull did not immediately show up the cause because of the fact that all the liners completely obscured the stringer system. It was not until the cockpit deck was opened up that it was determined that the mid section stringers were three times the height of the stringers forward of the mid bulkhead that it was known for certain that improper stringer design was at fault. The essence of the problem here was that unequal loading on the hull was working to break this boat in half longitudinally.

Bulkhead Failure

This next example, figure 5-4 is of a diesel motor yacht and points up the important role of bulkheads. Note that the engine room is approximately amidships. If this were a sixty foot hull, that would mean that the entire length of the drive train (engines plus shaft length) would be at least twenty-five feet long. That makes for a very long shaft, and it should be pretty obvious that unless the hull is absolutely rigid in both the transverse and longitudinal planes, then the drive train will not remain in proper alignment. And in this case, that was exactly our problem.

This nearly new yacht first began to experience problems with excessive drive train vibration, followed by broken engine mounts and then transmission failure. When I was called in by the yacht's captain, the first thing I did was suggest a sea trail. We ran the boat up to cruising speed and then put the yacht into a modest turn. The normally high vibration substantially increased. This was followed by putting the boat into a hard turn. At this point, the vibration was so bad that it affected one's eye sight and the engines slowed down significantly.

By this time I was pretty certain that I knew what the nature of the problem was, and began to examine the framing system. It soon became apparent that there were only two full structural bulkheads in the yacht. I stress the word "were" because one of them had been partly removed at the behest of an owner and interior designer who had redesigned the interior layout. Having only two main bulkheads planned by the original designer was not enough, but one of those was subsequently 50% removed to create more open space in the forward quarters. This resulted in transverse twisting of the hull that threw the shafting

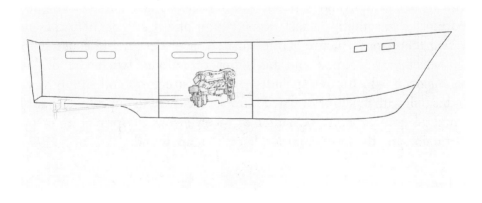

Fig. 5-4. Profile of 60 ft. motor yacht showing total length of drive train.

out of alignment by a matter of inches. Other symptoms such as stress cracking at the intersect of house sides and foredeck were also beginning to appear, along with badly leaking windows and obvious interior disturbances.

Thus, we can see that the issue of proper hull design is no small matter. Often times chronic problems with boats, such as transmission failures, engine mount and other such alignment problems can go on an on for the life time of the boat without anyone ever discovering the real cause.

These examples illustrate how the major structural elements of a boat work together to strengthen the whole, and how a fault or weakness in one element can negatively affect the whole.

Design Elements

The four major elements of structural hull design are hull skin, stringers, bulkheads and decks.

Although there are only four major structural elements involved in hull design, the varieties of design and materials encountered in boat construction is nearly endless. The following discussion covers those most commonly found, the methods of design, materials used, along with some of the more common faults.

Decks

It seems to be a little-realized principle of how important decks are to a boat hull. As mentioned above, the four major elements of structural hull design are hull skin, stringers, bulkheads and decks. Each of these elements is as important as the other; a defect in the design of any one of them can end up affecting the whole structure. Unfortunately, poor design and construction of deck shells is very common, and this is most often found when a builder simply takes his deck (which often includes an upper structure) and simply screws it onto his hull with machine or wood screws. Decks are so important, that I have devoted an entire chapter (Chapter 8) to reviewing the principles of proper construction and the most common faults that are found.

Stringers

In power boats, stringers provide the majority of the longitudinal hull re-sistance to bending in conjunction with the deck. The apex of the vee at the bottom or keel adds to it. This is qualified by whether the deck is also designed

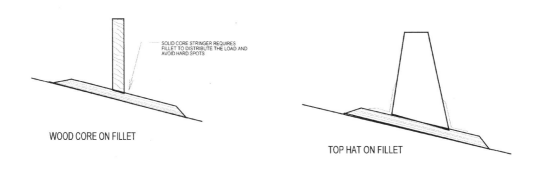

Fig. 5-5. The two primary methods of stringer design.

to give the hull longitudinal rigidity. Depending on design, some decks, particularly on motor yachts with very short decks and lots of windows, are so small that they add very little additional strength. On the other hand, the typical flybridge sport fisherman with its long foredeck, relatively small windows and strong house sides, adds a great deal of rigidity to a hull. So it is that we can now understand why there is a lot more to the strength of hull than just the framing system. In monocoque, or semi-monocoque construction, the whole structure must be considered. And it is precisely here that so many untrained "designers" who lack a solid background in engineering, make their mistakes.

Mistakes involving stringer design and installation are legion, about which a whole book could be written. And yet the principles for creating an effective stringer system are very simple and easy to achieve. Surely there are not many designers or builders who do not understand this. Or are there? Problems usually arise as a result of other design and marketing considerations, such as the efforts of the bean counters to cut costs. Or it may occur when a designer wants to create a small boat with 6'6" headroom or wants to install unusually large engines.

In order to get the 6'6" head room or make high profile engines or other equipment fit, the principles of proper stringer design are often sacrificed. It's common for builders to reduce stringer height, and therefore strength, in order to achieve headroom. Bulkheads are often eliminated to achieve large interior open spaces. In other words, the principles of sound hull design get sacrificed for marketing considerations and the surveyor needs to be constantly aware of this fact. It's the primary reason why, in this day when just about all is known

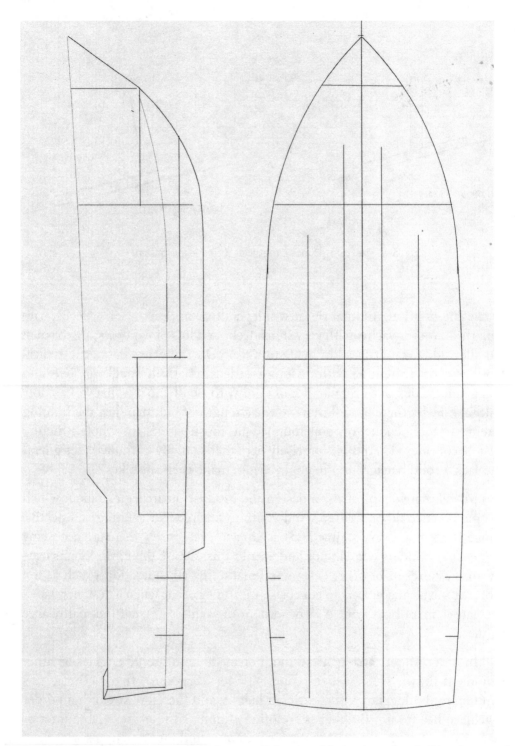

Fig. 5-6. Typical framing plan of 40 ft. sport fisherman. Notice how few bulkheads extend from keel to gunwale.

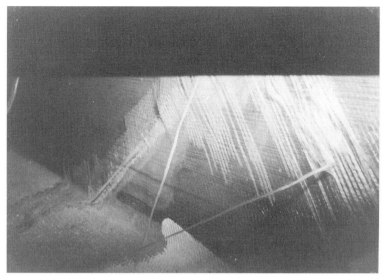

Fig. 5-7. What can happen when a stringer system isn't designed right. This builder tried to get away with a three stringer system instead of four. Saved the cost of the fourth stringer, but not after he was forced to take his broken boat back.

about how to build a good boat, bad boats are still being built.

The principles of good stringer design are simple. They must run uninterrupted from one end of the hull to the other. They must be of adequate height-to-width ratio, i.e., structural modulus, to resist impact loading on the hull skin, be of sufficient strength to carry the engine load, be stabilized against lateral movement if high profile, and be securely attached to the hull so that they don't break loose. The profile, or top of the stringer, should run in a straight line. If there are any changes in the profile, then special design reinforcements must be added.

These principles are often compromised by designs that utilize dog-legs, step downs, step ups (meaning an inconsistent profile along their length), perforations with large and ill-placed holes, inadequate section modulus and numerous other faults. In nearly all these cases that I have seen, there is no compelling reason why these faults should have occurred. What these design faults unfortunately suggests is that the designers really don't understand the basic engineering principles. Yet in most cases of failure that I have seen, the builder could have had his cake and eat it too by giving a little more thought to the design issue. What is compromised in one way can always be built up in another. There's always an alternative solution. The builder just didn't bother to find it.

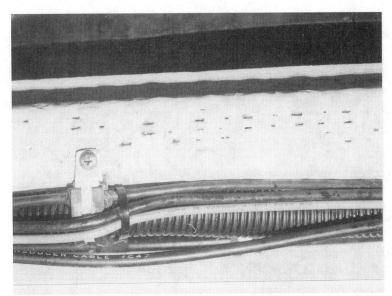

Fig. 5-8. What you see here looks like small staples in the top of this stringer. Actually, these are gaps in the weave of roving not filled with resin. The gaps are discolored by the brown fluid seeping from the rotting wood sringer core. A typical problem of incomplete lamination of a wood stringer or any other wooden component.

There are four primary stringer types in use today: solid glass which usually appear in the form of structural angles; top hats which are premolded independently and then glassed into the hull; the wood core stringer which is the most common type; and the foam cored stringer.

Top hats are probably the most effective type, and are most often found in high end boats, particularly sport fishermen, mainly because they're considerably more expensive to construct. They tend to be problem-free with only rare instances of bond failures.

Solid glass stringers have also proved expensive, are rarely used, and tend to be defect free.

Wood core stringers are well-known for problems of deterioration of the wood. Unfortunately, this very effective and lowest cost method gets all the blame when the real fault belongs to the builder for not using rot resistant wood, or failure to fully encapsulate the wood. The most common material is, of course, plywood. There is nothing wrong with plywood so long as the builder is not using junk plywood, which many of them do. Good quality plywoods such as fir have a life span of decades, even when continuously exposed to water.

Foam cored stringers tend to be widely misunderstood by boat owners. The foam is not really a "core" but a former or male mold over which glass is

Fig. 5-9. This 3/4" plywood bulkhead fractured because it was the only one in a 34' Boat and couldn't quite handle the load.

laminated. The foam itself serves no structural purpose. Many boat owners are aware of the problems associated with wood core stringers when parts of the wood is exposed, such as around limber holes. This same stigma gets transferred to foam cored stringers. Exposed foam and potential water absorption does not pose a deterioration and resulting structural weakness problem and does not need to be treated with the same concern as the former.

Bulkheads

Bulkheads serve two very distinct functions. First, bulkheads act as transverse frames.

More importantly, the bulkhead is the structural element that prevents torsional stress or twisting of the hull. Unified with a stringer system, they form a structural web and a truss. Remove the bulkheads and it's rather like removing the trusses from a bridge or a roof. The overall strength can be reduced to the point of structural failure. And because of the efforts of interior designers to produce small boats with the appearance of wide open interior spaces by the elimination of full, and even partial bulkheads, that hull structures begin to fall apart.

One builder that produced a 34 footer which had only one partial internal bulkhead - an engine room bulkhead that was only slightly more than half the height of the freeboard of the hull - resulted in massive structural failures of the entire model line. You probably know the boat, the 34 Wellcraft San Tropez. In this model line, not only did major hull skin and stringer failures occur, but in many cases the single plywood bulkheads fractured from side to side.

Even companies with reputations for building very rugged hulls occasionally make silly mistakes, such as the instance of some of the early Bertram 46's when Bertram decided to make very large cut outs in the centers of plywood bulkheads to save weight. They unthinkingly removed all the strength from the plywood bulkhead with predictable results; the bulkheads fractured.

It should be obvious how engine room fore and aft bulkheads constitute one of the foremost structural elements of medium size yachts, and yet we've witnessed what happens the builder unthinkingly decides to cut a big hole in the bulkhead and install a door without accounting for the weakness he has caused. For whatever reason, it did not occur to the builder or designer that he was destroying the structural integrity of the bulkhead.

To do their job, bulkheads must be adequately secured to the hull bottom, sides and underside of the deck. Judging by 30 years of inspecting fiberglass boats, it's a fair statement to say that many builders don't think that this is very important considering the large number of bulkheads that surveyors find to be broken loose. Probably at least half of all boat builders don't tie the bulkhead to the deck, and often for good reason. The bottoms of their boats are so flexible that the bulkhead will telegraph the deflection of the hull into the deck, causing damage to the deck. Therefore, if they leave a gap at the top, at least it won't tear the deck apart, just everything else that the bulkhead is attached to, or is attached to it.

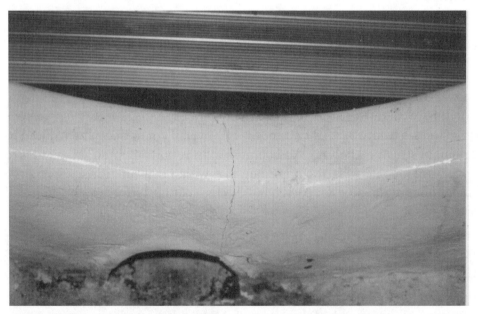

Fig. 5-10. This beautifully finished frame is all looks but little substance. It cracked because it is made entirely of mat.

While we've been talking so far about structural bulkheads, bulkheads come in several varieties, including full, partial and nonstructural partitions. While I know of no published rules on the subject, my own rule is that to be classified as a full bulkhead (1) it must span the width of the hull; (2) span no less than 75% of the depth of the hull and be attached to the bottom and sides; (3) have no openings larger than 50% of the height of the bulkhead; and (4) such openings must be centered in the vertical plane. For example, an opening that effectively cuts the bulkhead in half is not a full bulkhead but a partial. For maximum effectiveness, the bulkhead must be attached to all four sides of the hull.

Partial bulkheads are really nothing more than frames and do not serve any greater function than frames. It is a mistake to call a hull partition with two doors in it a bulkhead, for it is really only a partition, or a partial bulkhead at best. Surveyors often mistake partitions for bulkheads. Remember that to be classified as such, a bulkhead must be serving the purpose of tying the four sides of the hull together (bottom, deck and sides). If it's shot full of holes and openings, it's not achieving that purpose.

Partitions simply serve the function of separating one space from another while providing little, if any, major structural strength. Builders often make the mistake of thinking that partitions are structural bulkheads and this is because they don't have any trained engineers or designers on staff. And just because a partition may be taped into the hull does not mean that it's structural; the taping may be there just to hold the partition in place, not the partition to hold the hull together or strengthen it. Sail boats and some smaller power boats often have plywood partitions that are screwed to bosses on an inner liner. These should not be mistaken for bulkheads. This type of fastening cannot begin to withstand the forces acting on the hull since we're again dealing with screws into fiberglass. Fortunately, this type of construction has mostly passed into history.

Frames

Frames serve the purpose of stiffening panels between bulkheads and stringers. Fiberglass boats often lack frames where they are needed. Obviously, if a panel is flexing too much, additional framing would prevent that condition. Some builders scrimp on frames because frames create additional detail work and adds more to labor cost. Fortunately, where excessive panel weakness is discovered, adding frames after the fact is usually fairly easy to accomplish and effective. So long as there is accessibility, correcting panel weakness is usually not too difficult or costly.

Internal Structural Materials

Recent years has seen some builders almost completely eliminating wood from the structures of boats. The most common method of construction of fiberglass boats utilizes glass over plywood for the basic framing system such as stringers, with plywood for bulkheads, partial bulkheads and various types of frames. Plywood works very well as a basic material so long as it is made of a good quality wood such as fir. It's not uncommon to see quarter century old Bertrams or Pacemakers with a fir plywood framing system that has been exposed to water and which has no rot in it.

Unfortunately, in the interest of producing low cost boats, many builders have resorted to using cheaper and cheaper plywoods so that rot in primary structures, even when it is fully glassed over, has become a major problem. These days it's not uncommon to find ten year old boats with major rot in stringers and bulkheads, a situation that poses major risks to the surveyor should he fail to find such problems. This is particularly true with "price" boats, boats that are marketed based primarily on their lower price than comparably sized others.

The first thing to do is to try to size up the quality of the wood used. This can be done by checking out the bulkheads, cabin soles and other plywood components in concealed areas where there is less likely to be any finishing material on the surface of the wood. Poor quality ply is notable by having a rough surface finish, often with major imperfections such as splinters. It may have exposed knots or large, exposed seams, edges with large gaps. Generally it will look like roof sheathing material. If you find this grade of wood, it's a tip-off that you're dealing with non-marine grade, substandard materials. There will be the need to check things over extra closely.

When non rot-resistant woods are used, the boat doesn't have to be ten years old for problems to show up. Deterioration can begin to occur in three to four years. Pay extra attention to plywood surfaces that have been painted over with gel coat. It is common to find plywood edges that have been painted with gel coat as a means of sealing it. Unfortunately, gel coat fails as a sealant; gel coat is so porous that water will penetrate it. When that happens the wood swells and will crack the gel coat.

Encapsulated wood stringers can pose problems when the laminating is not thorough. We often see this where a wood stringer is covered over with a single layer of roving and there are gaps or holes in the weave, ends and edges that aren't covered, and most frequently drain or limber holes which were cut after lamination. Another indicator can be fasteners into the laminate that is allowing water penetration. Beware whenever you see rust trails below a fastener.

Also watch out for the effects of fasteners such as screws and bolts into and through stringers. These pose a risk of water ingress and can result in deterioration in unexpected places. Water and rust trails around fasteners serves as a red flag that core saturation is likely, so be sure to check extra carefully when these signs appear.

Another point to be alert for are box beam stringers of the sort that Sea Ray uses. These create closed compartments that can fill up with water. Quite a number of Sea Rays have been found in which the mid section of the outboard hull stringers were completely rotted out. The problem is that, being boxed in, it's very hard to locate this kind of damage. First, determine if box stringers exist. Then check the outer surfaces for signs of weepage, water stains, abnormal mildew growth and so on.

Also, watch out for leaks from above, particularly as these may affect bulkheads and partitions. Aft house bulkheads, both above and below the deck, are prone to rot problems. When working in the engine room, don't forget to look up, being sure to check around the air intake vents as well as the point where the aft bulkhead meets the deck.

Amidships bulkheads can be affected by deck leaks from things like loose stanchion bases or leaking windows. The rope locker bulkhead is yet another target for rot from rope locker hatches that don't have any gutters, or the locker itself that may not be adequately drained. A pile of wet rope laying against the bulkhead for years can work wonders on plywood.

Tabbing

This is the term for the method of attaching wood structures to the hull by means of fiberglass strips. Cracked, broken or otherwise damaged tabbing is the most common hull defect found on surveys. This usually occurs because a wood component hasn't been installed properly or the basic structural design isn't right. To properly evaluate the significance of damaged tabbing requires a bit of experience, and even then it is not easy. Generally speaking, if the amount of breakage is slight, the problem is either minimal or, if the boat is fairly new, the problem is just beginning. If it's an older boat, then it has lived with the problem for a long time and is not likely to be serious.

In cases where a larger area of tabbing has become disbonded, this usually indicates a secondary bonding fault, in which case all bonding should be considered suspect, mainly depending on the age of the boat. Cabin soles taped into the bottom of the hull frequently display breakage or disbonding. Examine the design here and you will usually find that the cause is the result of flexing of the hull skin, in which case repairing the broken tabbing will just result in it breaking again. Whenever in doubt about the severity of such breakage, it's best to recommend repair.

Materials, Shape and Strength

Shape Affects Strength

Most powerboats today are of a basic hard chine design. Round bilges have largely gone out of fashion because of their propensity for rolling and the need for a deep keel to keep them stable. We are well aware of why an egg is easily punctured by an impact but is very strong when a more uniform pressure is applied to it. This is the principle of why a curved surface is generally stronger than a flat surface, and why changes in shape of a surface can add strength to it. It all has to do with the direction in which the stress is being applied and whether contours are designed to resist those stresses.

As a general rule, vee bottomed hulls are not as strong as round bilge vessels by virtue of their shape. Some simple illustrations show why. Say you place a flat fiberglass panel between two chairs and then stand on it. What happens? The panel bows under your weight. But what happens when you place a curved panel between the two chairs? It will also bend, but to a lesser degree. But perhaps what you didn't notice was that as the panel flattened out, the width of the panel increased. Now, if you were to place the same curved panel on the floor and nail down two blocks to stop the edges, would the panel still bend when you stood on it? Why not? The reason is that the curved surface is transferring the load to the edges which, in turn, are resisting movement. The flat panel bent downward because there was no transference of load to another structure. Same material, same thickness, same load, the only difference is the change in direction of the load caused by the shape. Conversely, the *width* of the flat panel between two chairs that you stood on *decreased* because of the bending. If that same flat panel were rigidly attached to two uprights and then you stood on it, depending on the strength of the uprights, the uprights would also bend because the change in shape is pulling on the uprights. Here, again, part of the load is being transferred to another part of the structure.

This example illustrates some of the stresses to which a boat hull is subjected. The important point to take note of is how loads from one member can be transferred to another, as for example how stress on a hull bottom is transferred to the hull side and then the deck. This is one of the reasons why we so often see hull side cracking occurring above the chine. And while we probably have a basic understand of framing systems, let's review some of the basic principles.

Fiberglass Laminates

As a material, basic glass can be quite strong. We tend to think otherwise because ordinary glass windows are not very impact resistant and when they do break, they shatter. Higher quality glass, such as the tempered specialty glass used in skyscraper construction however, is amazingly strong. It has to be able to resist the wind pressures so high up in the air. Moreover, many types of glass are capable of bending far more than we might imagine. Glass has tremendous tensile and compressive and shear strength. It is, as we all know, very brittle and little impact strength. When spun into filaments and bundled together, stranded glass is incredibly strong.

Fiberglass reinforced plastics have most of the characteristics as basic glass. They are highly resistant to most stresses and are most vulnerable to impacts. Like its cousin plate glass, glass reinforced plastics are prone to shattering. The components of basic fiberglass hull construction are woven glassfiber cloth in its various weaves and polyester plastic resin that is catalyzed with the addition of a chemical catalyst and may be hardened with other hardening agents. The most common fabric weave for the basic hull laminate is woven roving, a coarse weave of flat, banded fibers, each bundle about 1/4" wide. Because of its coarseness or the high profile of the weave, roving does not bond well to itself and often leaves air voids or small pockets of resin. All heavy fabrics entail this problem. For that reason, light layers of chopped strand mat are laid between the layers of heavy fabric. This generally prevents voids or pockets of resin, but not always. The ideal fiberglass-to-resin ratio is 65/35%. Fiberglass laminates are strongest when closest to this ideal ratio. Vacuum bagged laminates will have an even higher glass ratio, often approaching 75/25.

When laminates have a lower glass-to-resin ration they're said to be "wet," meaning that there is an excess of resin above the ideal When the ratio is higher, they're said to be "dry." A dry laminate is far weaker than one that is wet or over saturated with resin. Resin starvation is often an initiating factor in delaminations or fractures. Resin rich laminates are weaker but not prone to delamination and does not normally affect overall strength unless the laminate is borderline weak to begin with.

There are two types bonding that occur in a lay up, primary and secondary. Secondary bonds are those that occur after the resin has cured. The strength of any secondary bond is primarily that of a glue joint. Primary bonding occurs when a lamination is laid over one that is not fully cured. As a result, the resin commingles and becomes more or less a unified part. Even if the first layer is still tacky, a primary bond will occur because to some extent the solvents in the resin will partially dissolve the curing resins in the base laminate and thus there will be some degree of chemical bond that is far stronger than a secondary bond. This accounts for why secondary laminations so often fail while primary laminations don't.

The most important factor in determining the general strength of a fiberglass hull is its design and laminating schedule. A laminating schedule is the planned number and sequence of how the various layers of material are worked into the mold. For example, lacking a proper skinout mat, roving laid directly against a sprayed on gelcoat will result in "Print-through," the weave pattern of the roving telegraphing through the gelcoat. Print patterns on the outside of a hull are the result of the improper selection of materials. The strength of a hull is dependent upon the relationship between the framing system and the thickness of the laminate. Proper design is predicated on the laminate being a certain thickness between the spans or distance between reinforcing elements such as stringers and bulkheads.

Glass reinforced plastic is quite resilient; it bends fairly well and tolerates large numbers of stress cycles. It begins to break down when the modulus of elasticity is exceeded, the scantlings are inadequate, or the laminate has been impacted, shattering to some degree the plastic to fiber bond. Surprisingly, despite the complicated and very messy business of laying up a hull, very few manufacturing errors occur in the lay up of boat hulls. Most errors that lead to problems or failures occur in the design stage.

Manufacturing defects can occur, for example, when a layup is started on Friday, the layup crew goes home for the weekend while the carpentry crew works over the week end filling the shop full of sawdust. The laminating crew returns on Monday, finishes the layup which has now become a secondary bond, in addition to being contaminated with sawdust. Errors can also occur as a result of incorrect metering of catalyst in the spray up equipment, resulting in too hot a cure, or incomplete cure. This is quite rare because it is usually discovered before the hull is completed.

In recent years new fabric designs have appeared with names such as unidirectional, biaxial, triaxial and stitched bundles. Unlike woven roving and cloth, most of these are specialty and not general purpose fabrics. Unidirectional and stitched fabrics tend to have strength in only one or two of three directions, and for that reason require special knowledge in their proper application. Increasingly boats are turning up where these materials have been misapplied, resulting in failures.

Common Structural Failures

Whether failures of the outer skin of the hull, or damage or disturbance of internal structural components, structural failures occur from a wide variety of causes. While we might think that manufacturing errors or faults in the layup process are common, actually they are not. The most common cause of hull failure is poor design, a fault which can involve anything from a poorly devised layup schedule, framing plan or failure to account for the effects of high speed.

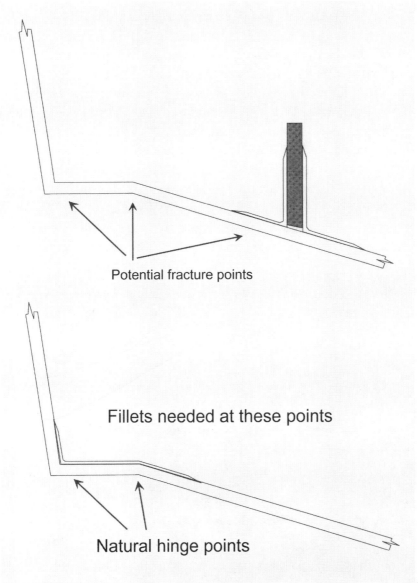

Potential fracture points

Fillets needed at these points

Natural hinge points

Fig. 5-11.

Of these, the most common is fracturing, stress cracking or delamination caused by insufficient skin thickness relative to the framing plan. Whether a laminate thickness is adequate or not is always dependent upon the framing plan just as the strength of a beam is dependent on the width it must span and the load it must carry. With a hull skin, the closer the framing, the thinner the skin can be without resulting in a degree of flexing that causes the laminate to crack. Up to a point. Since resins and reinforcement are expensive, there's always an inducement for builders to reduce the amount of costly material that goes into the making of a hull. When a hull skin becomes too thin, it begins to flex excessively and can result in cracking or delamination.

Fast power boats regularly fly through the air and slam down on the surface of the sea with great force. Not only is the weight of the boat involved, but the forward velocity increases these forces. The greater the speed, the greater the potential impact force. These forces are first sustained by the hull skin and then transferred throughout the framing system. Moreover, these loads are often sustained unequally by only one part of the hull. A hull may come down on the crest of a wave so that the impact is sustained only at the midsection, or it may nose-dive into the backside of a wave, taking the load on the bows. While nearly everyone understands the essence of slamming, few are aware that a hull is subject to the opposite force, a vacuum. This occurs as a hull is leaving the water or rolling or pitching severely. Similar to the function of an airplane wing, there occurs areas of very low pressure which pull the hull skin in the opposite direction, away from the framing. Therefore, the stresses acting on a hull consist of both pushing and pulling, compression and tension.

Flexing of the hull skin, in and of itself, is not usually damaging unless it is extreme. Quality laminates are reasonably flexible. Stress cracking and lami-

Fig. 5-12.. This builder tried to tab in all his structural members with mat. It didn't work and they all broke loose. Also note that the tabbing overlap in many places is extremely narrow.

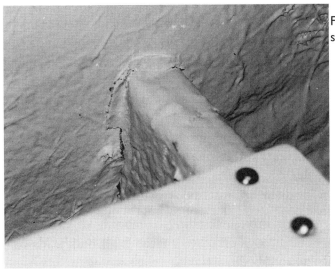

Fig 5-13 . Improper glassing stringer to bulkhead intersect.

nate failures generally occur at "hard spots," the point where the laminate is anchored to a frame or bulkhead. This is sometimes referred to as the "hinge effect," the point where rigid laminate becomes flexible. The reason failures usually occur at this point is because the radius of the bend is much greater at this point than over a wider expanse of panel that is gently bending. However, the "oil can" effect greatly increases the forces of interlaminar sheer (shearing forces parallel to the axis of the laminates) that radiate in all directions. Oil canning forces the laminate into a compound curve. Rigid materials resist bending into compound curves, thus the effect of "oil canning" is to cause severe delamination or breakup of the resin to fiber bonds. The worst of the damage usually occurs at the perimeter of the oil can dimple because this is where the greatest angle of bending occurs.

Because of the close spacing of stringers, oil canning rarely occurs in power boats and is most often found in sail boats which rely mainly on bulkheads rather that stringers for primary hull structure. Convex curved panels are most prone to oil-canning. If they appear at all, they usually appear on the bows of power boats which is the one location where oil canning is likely to appear. Square panels are more prone to oil canning than rectangular panels. Panels in power boats are usually rectangular, not square. Stress cracking appearing in the bottom paint and gelcoat are the first sign of excessive panel flexing. It appears about 95% of the time paralleling stringers and rarely does it show up transversely along bulkheads. Only if there is a condition of both stringers and hull skin flexing does stress cracking along bulkheads appear.

Structural Weakness

Rarely has a structurally weak hull been built that did not begin to exhibit evidence of that weakness sooner rather than later. The symptoms of a weak hull are many and varied, particularly on high speed vessels. Weak bottoms have been known to flex in such a way that will exhibit no signs of a problem on the bottom but will inevitably show up on the interior. Because interior structures such as cabin soles, modular units and cabinetry are usually attached to, or resting on bottom structures, flexing, twisting, wracking action of the hull is bound to show up as damaged or disturbed internal structures.

The most common of these is broken bonding or tabbing of structural members and other components directly attached to the hull, bulkheads or frames. Broken tabbing is easy to spot because the fiberglass taping usually lifts or moves from the bonding surface once it becomes disbonded. If there is any doubt about the bonding, a little tapping around with a hammer or a coin will quickly reveal the delamination by the sound.

Lose bonding of internal frames, bulkheads or other components does not, of itself, signify a serious condition, except when occurring with stringers. Rather, when broken tabbing is found, it needs to be evaluated in context of the larger hull structure. One side of a bulkhead that is loose may indicate nothing more that a bad laminating job. On the other hand, if it is found in conjunction with stress cracks appearing on the bottom or other interior disturbances, the condition is probably more serious. Observation during sea trial in a sea way will usually answer any questions as to the severity and significance of defects found on the interior. For example, if loose tabbing on a bulkhead is found, but in a moderate sea the hull does not pant or flex in the area of the disbonded bulk-

Fig. 5-14. Proper installation of bulkheads is tedious work but the superb detailing of this custom Merritt sport fisherman is plainly evident.

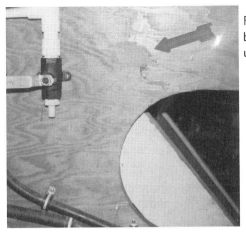

Fig. 5-15 . Trying to save a few pounds in weight by making this big cutout, the bulkhead ended up fracturing.

head, in all probability the breakage is not due to a general weakness but a poor bonding job or perhaps a one-time slamming off a large wave. Thus, whenever internal disturbances are found, the best way to evaluate them and give good advice to the client is to inspect the internal area thoroughly during a sea trial under sea conditions that will provide enough stress to the hull to show up any potential weakness. If we get stuck doing a sea trial in dead calm seas, as we often do, we can at least run back and forth over the vessel's own wake. Should you find that the hull is panting or interior structures moving, then you'll know beyond a doubt that the problem goes far beyond just a bad bonding job.

Bulkheads, floors, frames and stringers all deserve careful inspection. As the many photos in this chapter show, early signs of serious problems can show up in small ways. Stringers, because of their generally low profile and long length, can usually withstand very substantial deflection without showing up symptoms. But transverse members that intersect stringers can withstand very little flexing because hull panels usually flex along the longitudinal axis, perpendicular to the transverse member. Further, normal tendency toward flexing of bottom panels causes the stringers to shear against the resistance of the transverse members, either fracturing the bond at the interface, or causing the stringer to crush the opening of the bulkhead through which it passes.

Bottom Strakes

Angled strakes on the bottom of the hull provide for a prime opportunity to create a hinge effect if they're not constructed properly. Bottom strakes can either be open or closed as seen from the interior. Ideally, they should be closed to best resist hinging. On boats over 30 feet the strakes are usually filled and glassed over, but for smaller boats they often are not. This accounts for why stress cracks are so often found on the inside radius of the strake. Cracks at this location should be taken seriously and investigated from the interior. If the cracks are pronounced or weeping fluid, destructive testing and repair may be in order. See Chapter 7 for a complete discussion on stress cracking.

Bulkheading

Generally speaking, hulls that have localized weakness will only manifest localized faults, while generally weak hulls will show up symptoms throughout or in more than one location. Inadequate bulkheading is increasingly becoming a problem as a result of interior designer's desire to create large, open spaces that are unencumbered by such niceties as a good bulkheading system. Numerous express models of low to median price range thirty footers are fraught with these problems. Designs that incorporate a completely open forward cabin area often have only one or two bulkheads in the entire vessel. The result is usually a hull that when you put the wheel hard over, the bow twists one way and the stern section another. Combined with a lack of hull side framing and poor hull/deck joints, the result is very much like our earlier example of a shoe box with a lead ingot in it. Bottom, hull sides and deck bow, bend, twist and flex in every direction. The surveyor should make an effort to determine whether a boat has adequate bulkheading. If it does not, he should begin checking for signs of working and associated problems.

Bulkheading that is subjected to excessive stress due to inadequate framing system will suffer from a variety of symptoms, including delamination (plywood and composite) disbonding and fracturing. Bulkheads are often found full of holes drilled for routing of wiring and plumbing, Frequently we find so many holes drilled in a straight-line pattern that it creates what can be called the "postage stamp effect," a line of perforations that seriously weakens the bulkhead or frame. Fig. 5-15 shows a plywood bulkhead in a 46 Bertram where the builder decided to create large cutouts in the center of the bulkhead. It was so weakened that even in this otherwise well-built boat the bulkhead fractured.

A common cause of bulkhead disbonding results from improper or nonexistent preparation of the bonding surface. It's very common to find glass tabbing applied over veneered wood surfaces such as teak. Not only is the veneer face weak, but with oily woods such as teak, a solid bond is never achieved. Veneered surfaces have to be ground away to establish a good bonding surface to the substrate. It's even possible to find prepainted bulkheads that have been glassed right over the paint.

Another cause of failure results from the attempt to bond woven roving or unidirectional fabrics directly to plywood. The coarse texture of these fabrics makes for a very weak bond unless a layer of mat is first applied. But no matter how good the preparation is, if the bonding surface is too small — as with taping that is too narrow — or only a single layer is used and is thereby too thin and weak, the bonding is likely to fail anyway. Of all the common failure modes, the use of a single layer of roving is the most common.

The quality and type of plywood also affects the strength. Non-marine and structural grade plywoods, which are widely used in low cost boat construction, may have a high pitch or pine sap content that makes solid bonding all but impossible. And because wood is so good at absorbing moisture, high water content will achieve the same result. Even when painted, low quality plywoods are usually identifiable by their rough surfaces, gaps and knots so that when failures occur, it's a good idea to look over the component and identify the quality of material used.

When broken bonding of bulkheads is found, we need to find out why. Is it poor tabbing or is it a more serious structural design fault? Determining whether there is excessive flexing of the hull skin is one check. Another is to peel back a part of the laminate failure and examine the fracture surface. A secondary bond failure due to inadequate or no surface preparation will usually reveal a smooth surface on the tabbing. A bonding failure caused by excessive stress on the tabbing should reveal fuzzy surface with loose fibers as opposed to a smooth, glossy surface. Another consideration is the orientation of the taping fabric. 90° woven roving should be laid as close to the 45° axis of the joint as possible, not at angles approaching 90° that would end up relying only on one direction of fibers. On the other hand, be alert for stitched unidirectional fabric being laid with fibers parallel the joint. There is no strength in this tabbing at all. Finding one bulkhead with a small area of loose tabbing is one thing, but a boat that exhibits loose bonds in more than one location may be trying to tell the surveyor that there is a larger problem at issue.

One final point. Quite a few builders, particularly of smaller boats, have learned to solve their loose bulkhead warranty problem by covering them up. Literally. How else to explain why so many boats are found with carpeting lining every visible square inch of the exposed inner hull, even on the bottom where it clearly ought not to be. The practice of lining a hull with heavy fabric may be a tip-off that the builder has little confidence in his product and is attempting to conceal potential problems. It's a good idea to peel back some of the carpet and take a look, even at the risk of angering the seller.

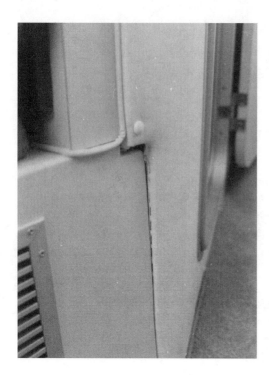

Fig. 5-16. Shifting and misalignment of interior components is often symptomatic of a working hull as it was in this case.

Stringers

For boats under 30 feet, the wood core stringer is most commonly used; in vessels over 30 feet, the pre molded, top hat style stringer is most common. Both types perform very well when properly designed and installed.

Even in older boats, wood core stringers generally don't suffer from problems of rot unless someone has indiscriminately drilled them full of holes or the workmanship is very poor. Wood core stringers most often exhibit problems when the builder, in the interest of profit, has selected a very low grade plywood. Even then, actual stringer failure is rare. However, improperly designed wood stringers can have serious effects on the hull skin when not cut properly and then butted solidly against the hull, thereby creating hard spot that eventually results in stress cracking. Proper installation of a solid core stringer involves shimming the core up at least 1/4" before the laminating process begins so that the solid wood is never hard up against the hull skin. It is the tabbing or taping that should transfer the load from hull skin to stringer core. The exception to this rule is when a fillet has been applied to the hull to help distribute the load and thereby eliminate the hard spot of hinge effect.

This principle of proper stringer installation is routinely ignored and accounts for so much of the stress cracking that we see on the bottoms of smaller boats. Worse, there is nothing that can be done to correct the problem except to repair the failed area. For top hat stringers, this is not a problem since the double wall of the hat section disperses the load over a wider area. Further, there is usually enough flexibility in the side walls of the top hat to absorb very heavy shock loads. Generally speaking, only the most poorly engineered and installed top hats ever fail since this type of stringer is very forgiving of errors.

Unusually tall or thin wood core stringers tend to be vertically unstable. Attached to a vee bottom hull at an acute angle, the normal stress load creates a tendency to bow or buckle. This is especially important around engine foundations where stability is most important to maintain proper engine alignment. Tall stringers should have a sufficient number of web frames between them to prevent them from flexing. Fig. 5-1 is a good example of tall stringers that are not well stayed and buckled under a pounding load. In that case, the bonding of the few transverse members is likely to fracture.

Premolded top hats have the advantage of offering a double vertical frame without the tendency to create a hard spot and are very forgiving of poor workmanship. But they do have a disadvantage for builders who want to create an unusually light hull. The taping on both sides of the hat section creates a hull laminate that will be considerably thinner in the center of the top hat. If the hull laminate is too thin, flexing in a narrow band will occur that can cause cracking. If stress cracking paralleling a top hat is found, most likely this is the problem, one which can't be diagnosed from the interior but only by drilling holes and measuring laminate thickness both in the center and flanges of the top hat.

The other main problem with top hats is poor bonding of the taping. Disbonding of stringers can occur from the center outward with little or no outward evidence that disbonding has occurred. Particularly in way of engine beds, I like to tap around along the taping lines with the tip of a screwdriver just to ensure that all is well. The high pitch sound of a delaminated taping is unmistakable.

Stringer design errors that result in problems occur from faults that are easily discoverable. The first and most frequent of these is the top hat that is too shallow and thereby offers very little resistance to bottom loads. With vee bottomed boats, of course, this is most always the outboard stringer and usually results from headroom considerations solved by placing the engine as low in the hull as humanly possible. Of themselves, low profile stringers rarely fail. Instead, they tolerate substantial deflection while constantly bouncing around, throwing the engine out of alignment. Stringers with a very shallow profile should be checked for deflection in a sea way with a folding rule or straight edge. Shallow stringers through which limber or other holes have been made should be carefully examined for evidence of fracturing. Within the last decade, most boats with shallow stringers are usually found to be import boats from the orient, and it is not unusual to find engine mounts that look as if they're almost mounted on the bottom. Beware of these for they nearly always mean serious trouble.

Dog legs are another common problem which is appearing with increasing frequency as untrained designers get caught up in today's freewheeling design trends and take liberties with structural principles. If you want to know what a dog-leg in a stringer means, try building a bridge with a dog leg in a girder. Or step on a barrel hoop. Stringer, girder, barrel hoop - a load applied to a nonlinear structure transfers that load in a different direction. Stringers should run straight from end to end and whenever there is a deviation from this principle, that's the spot to look for signs of trouble. A dog leg will create a hard spot so look for signs of stress cracking.

By far, the most serious design fault found with stringers are stringers that have vertical steps in them. The linear span of stringers should ideally be a straight, horizontal line. If transitions in height are necessary, that transition should be as gradual as possible, preferably a shallow curve, bearing in mind that when the height of a stringer changes, so does its strength. A stringer that has an angular change in height, such as a 90° step-down, is very likely to fracture at that point. Go-fast boats are often found with stepped-down stringers that fracture at this point.

Frequently we find import boats, particularly from the Orient, and occasionally domestic boats, that have fuel tanks mounted on legs or supports sitting directly on the hull skin without any effort to disperse the load of hundreds, if not thousands of pounds of water or fuel. The failure to provide a proper foundation for such tanks can result in hull damage, damage to the tanks or both. A starburst pattern on the hull bottom is often the result of an improper tank mounting. Tank foundations need to be inspected to insure that the load is being adequately distributed, and that there are no cracks appearing in the foundation area.

Primary Symptoms

Excessive bending, twisting and flexing of a vessel's hull or localized components on newer vessels may not show up as damage or disturbance to the hull. Whether it's a motor yacht, sport fisherman or trawler, some part of the interior, such as cabin soles, modular components like liners, shells or cabinetry, are usually attached to some part of the hull that is working and will therefore show up symptoms somewhere in the interior. Listed below are some of the things to look for.

- Accumulations of fiberglass or wood dust, shredded wood chips or other debris indicative of working action that is causing friction

- Badly misaligned doors, drawers or cabinets. Try inserting a flat screwdriver blade in the upper gap between door and frame while vessel is

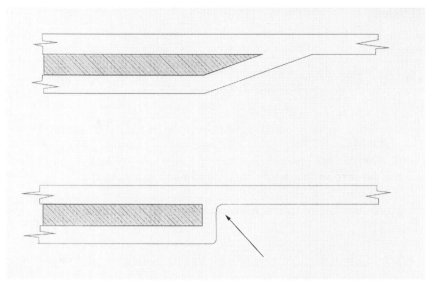

Fig. 5-17. The right and wrong methods of core design. The proper method (top) is to feather the edges to avoid the inevitable the hard spot created by the angle in the lower drawing.

underway. If screwdriver jumps up and down and falls out of place, interior components may be working excessively.

• Loose moldings, nails or fasteners backing out of woodwork, particularly around door frames and bulkheads.

• Friction scraping on finished wood parts, particularly moldings, at locations where perpendicular angles are formed on components abutting the hull sides.

• Gaps and misalignment in partitions, liners and shells, counter tops abutting hull sides, shower stalls.

• Small piles of dust caused by friction inside of cabinets, especially on express style cruisers where cabinets are attached directly to hull sides.

• Fractures in fiberglass or wood movement in lower door sills in express cruisers or particularly fast boats.

• Cracks and fractures in fiberglass liners, particularly around the cabin sole.

• Interior decks or soles that are crowned or uneven, unusually misaligned deck hatches, split deck beams or hatch carlins.

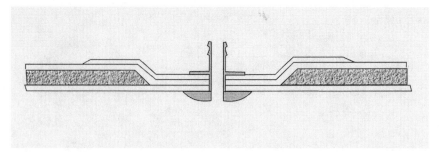

Fig. 5-18. The correct method of installing a through-hull in a cored hull blanks out the core so that water can't migrate into it around the fitting.

- Unusual number of cracked windows, numerous leaking ports or window frames.

- Excessive number of gelcoat cracks in superstructure, particularly at angle of deck to house sides.

Go-fast boats with very high length to beam ratios are often subject to longitudinal bending. Hulls that lack adequate longitudinal strength will usually manifest severe internal disturbance and dislocations, including a fairly large number of the symptoms listed above. If longitudinal weakness is suspected, the surveyor should also pay special attention to the hull deck joint since buckling and loosening of these joints, including bending of the rub rails and loose joint fasteners, are likely to occur.

Bottom strakes offer another opportunity to make a hull stronger or weaker. Adding a rib to any flat panel will make it stronger — if in fact it is really a rib. But a bottom strake is a hinge rather than a rib if it is not properly laminated. To be properly constructed, the strake must be filled and closed off on the inside. If this is not done, then it becomes a natural hinge which only weakens

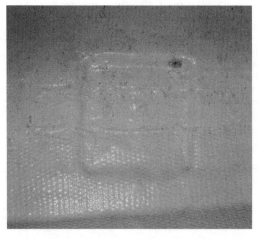

Fig. 5-19. This is how a core blank willl actually appear in a boat. This builder has thoughtfully provided several extra core blanks for future installations.

the panel and may end up in failure. The surveyor should be on the alert for open strakes (showing up as an open V on the bottom) when crawling around inside of the hull. This design error is most common in smaller boats.

Cored Hulls

A core is any type of material used in a laminate other than the basic glassfiber/resin combination. It can consist of anything from balsa, plywood, foam and varieties of honeycomb and putty. Ostensibly, the purpose of using cores is improving strength, cost or weight savings. However, when it comes to improving strength, we have to be careful to be sure that we know what we're talking about. Yes, cores can improve strength in some directions, but not others. Cores generally improve torsional or bending strengths. But when it comes to impact or shear strengths, sandwich construction is substantially weaker. Certain types of materials used in curved surfaces also do not perform well. There is no question that cores used on flat surfaces can improve strength, if the design is properly engineered. The difficulty with engineering and the proper application of cores is that boat hulls do not consist mainly of flat or uniform surfaces, but combinations of highly irregular surfaces. It is this factor that causes the most problems with the selection and application of core materials.

Balsa

End grain balsa has been used as a hull core for over forty years and has proved to be an exceptionally strong material because it bonds so well with resin. Its primary weakness is, of course, that it is wood and will absorb water. Lots of water. Fortunately, balsa is fairly resistant to rot but will rot over time. Cores can degrade considerably from the chemical stew that develops once a laminate absorbs water. I've seen old Hatterases that have had saturated cores in their superstructures for decades without causing serious problems, but that's typically because the outer laminates are quite thick. Thin laminates with rotted cores will not fare so well and will signal the existence of a rotted core by exhibiting excessive deflection of the outer laminate.

One of the most common places for this to occur is in way of through hull fittings and pedestal seat bases on flying bridge decks where the leverage of the pedestal shaft stresses the fasteners to the deck and creates leaks. Sounding will reveal a dull thud as opposed to a core separation that will have a much higher pitched sound. As with all materials, it largely depends on how well the overall structure is engineered. Even some very poor materials, when intelligently applied, can perform reasonably well. Consequently, we should be careful about condemning a material without evaluating the overall structure. Structural design faults may be at fault rather than just a material failure.

Balsa should never be used below the water line. That is a lesson that should have been learned over thirty years ago, yet today there are some builders that have failed to learn the lessons of the past and are once again using balsa on boat bottoms. Surveyor beware! Surveying such boats presents a minefield to walk through.

When surveying a cored hull, I always try to find out where the core terminates. If it's below the water line, then all through hull fittings have to have a pre-engineered blank or fillet, an area for penetrating the hull where there is no core (as shown in Figs. 5-18 & 19), so that a leaking fitting won't put water into the core. Anytime a fitting is installed directly through a cored laminate, there is a high potential for leakage and water saturation of the core, regardless of the material. If there's no evidence of a blank, then the client should at least be advised of the potential problem.

Balsa has the highest cleavage strength of all cores. Cleavage strength is the strength of the bonding of balsa directly to a laminate. The reason, of course, is the ability of the end grain wood to suck up resin far up into the wood cells.

Fig. 5-20. And we thought they were fiberglass boats! These are samples obtained from seven different damaged boats following a hurricane. Each has a different color or type of laminate filler.

Fig. 5-21. An example of a putty core bonding problem. The bond of the outer skin, which was entirely CSM, was almost nil, and could be easily pulled off.

Balsa also has the highest shear strength, so that failures are almost unheard of. Balsa core bond failures in hulls are very rare, and when they are found it is usually the result of incomplete bonding during layup. It's not my practice to fully sound out entire hull sides[1], although recently a customer requested that I do so on a brand new boat. I was appalled to find over 50 areas of incomplete bonding ranging in size from a few inches to several feet. Had this hull had fairly thick outer laminate, I would probably never have found those voids because a thick laminate wouldn't show up much, if any difference in sound and nobody would be the wiser. In this case, the outer laminate was very, very thin and void spaces rang out loud and clear. The question we faced was obvious: Was this hull at risk of the incomplete bonding progressing into large areas of delamination? Since this was a high speed vessel capable of nearly 40 knots, the answer had to be "yes" and that it was my opinion that the hull was not structurally sound. Interlaminar shear caused by high speed pounding was very likely to result in complete hull side delamination.

Foam Cores

By far, these have been the most problematic core materials. Balsa is balsa but there are dozens of varieties of foam, some better than others, and some very bad indeed. Foams come in many different varieties of plastic and cell types. There are open and closed cell types, as well as varying degrees of density and rigidity. Further complicating the matter, no one type performs equally well in all applications. Some foams perform best on flat panels and poorly on curved panels. Some are more impact resistant and better for use on decks than others. Some types bond better than others while yet others are subject to constant load distortion or "creep," especially those that are vulnerable to heat such as Airex.

Fig. 5-22. Made up of only one structural laminate, a single layer of roving on the inside (all the rest being putty and CSM), this hull literally shattered on impact. Note how easily the outer skins have broken out.

One of the newer types to hit the market, on which I have done some testing and have been impressed with is ATC Corecell, a high density, high strength material which has superior bonding capabilities. It is being widely used by custom and "high end" builders.

Unlike balsa, most foams are fairly resistant to water absorption. An exception to this is when water intrusion results in hydrolysis with the release of solvents such as styrene that then causes chemical degradation of the foam. This accounts for why it is occasionally found that water intrusion can turn a foam core to mush. It apparently occurs from the same chemical reaction that creates the fluid in hull blisters. But like balsa, once the laminate is breached, the grid pattern of gaps between the blocks of foam will conduct water all throughout the laminate. Thus, foam cores can absorb nearly as much water as balsa cores are capable of. Moreover, when water enters into a cored bottom, hydraulic action can also destroy the foam much the same way rivers can carve channels through rock.

On a recent tour through a small boat builder's facility that produced fully foam cored sportfishing boats, I picked up a piece of the foam that they were using. Working my thumb nail into the material, I found that it crumbled with incredible ease. Why, I wondered, would anyone use a material like this? When questioned about it, it became immediately clear that the production manager had no idea of the properties of the material he was using, or even why that material had been selected. Somewhere along the line he had heard that coring a hull was the "thing to do" and so he was doing it. It was just that simple. And thoughtless.

Here was yet another builder who had been sold a bill of goods by a salesman. I asked him if he had any cutout blanks around. We found some in the

Fig. 5-23. The effect of bending, compression and ply creep on cored laminates.

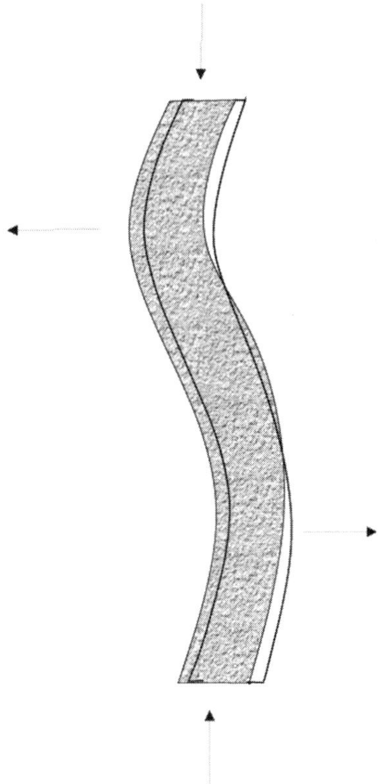

dumpster out back. His eyes nearly popped out when I inserted my fingernails into the foam and pulled the laminate apart with just my fingers. Hopefully I sold him on the need to perform some minimal R&D, or at least attend a few materials seminars. The point for the surveyor here is that he should never, repeat, never, assume that a builder knows what he is doing. Unless, of course, he doesn't mind getting tagged for not finding the builder's mistakes. Builders, particularly small ones, often have very little knowledge about the materials they are using.

Foam core failures in hulls and superstructures are legion and occur for a variety of reasons. Most prominent among these results from the low cleavage and shear strength of foam and the cavalier way they are used. Cleavage strength is the strength at which a core will bond to a glassfiber laminate. Shear strength is resistance to tearing parallel to the central axis. The manner in which resin bonds to balsa versus foam is comparable to the difference between super glue and school room paste. The long-grain cells of balsa make for a very strong bond because the resin wicks into the open ends of the long wood cells. Foam has semicircular cells that are not conducive to making good bonds with resin. For balsa, if incomplete bonding occurs, the residual strength of the remaining bond is usually sufficient that the lamination will not continue to separate under load. Not so with foam which requires wide area bonding to maintain strength. This is because of the inherent weakness of the foam bond itself. (To understand this, just take a piece of foam and dig your thumb nail into it; it readily tears apart. Now try the same things with balsa. The difference in strength is immediately obvious.) This problem is clearly depicted in Fig. 5-2. When incomplete bonds occur, such as gaps and voids, working of the inner and outer laminates can fairly easily cause breakage of the resin or paste (bonding agent) glue joint, bearing in mind that the bond is really nothing more than a glue joint. My evaluation of dozens of failed cored laminates makes it clear that why this happens.[2]

Most foam applications utilize a bonding agent[3], basically a thick adhesive paste to make up for the difficulty of foam to form compound, and particularly compound concave curves. Balsa is strongest parallel to the grain, but most compressible perpendicular to the grain, making sheets of balsa easier to bend in a compound curved. This rigidity of foam in all directions makes it more difficult to work it into a compound curve, hence the need for the bonding agent to take up the slack. As a thin putty, the bonding agent is supposed to be worked into the open foam cells and gaps between the blocks, whereas resin is too thin and will run when applied thickly. As photo 5-2 shows, incomplete bonding during layup often occurs over very large areas. This creates areas of localized stress that accelerates the disbonding process.

Another problem occurs because hulls flex, and because sandwich construction creates a very thick overall laminate. Unlike solid laminates, cored laminates do not take kindly to bending and the reason is the differential of the radius of a curved surface between the inner and outer glassfiber laminate. When a cored laminate is bent, there is a considerable difference in the radius of the curve between the inner and outer laminate. It's the same thing that happens when two race cars circle a track, one on the inside curve and the other on the outside curve. One car has to go faster than the other for the two cars to maintain the same pace. When the cored laminate is bent, the outer laminate has to stretch more than the inner. What causes core separations is when the curve is not a regular arc but a compound curve of a hull side. When a compound curve is stressed, the two curves are working against each other and cause tremendous interlaminar shear. This causes the fiberglass skins to shear against the core, and it is this irregular interlaminar shear that separates the core from the laminate.

Fig. 5-24. Water entered this bottom core as a result of poor core bonding which is almost non existant on the uppper surface. Water then migrated along the gaps between foam blocks, depicted by the blackened areas.

Another way to understand this is to take a cored laminate in the shape of a very shallow "S" as shown in Fig. 5-23. Put that piece under a compression load and visualize what happens to it. Not only do the outside curves want to pop outward, the inside curves bend inward, but shearing forces are set up that act to try to shear the core internally. This combination of stresses is exactly what happens to a hull side that is panting when a vessel hull is pounding. The stresses do not occur perpendicular to the central axis where the sandwich is the strongest, but axially where the sandwich is the weakest. The deep "S" curve of sailboat hulls accounts for why we find so much disbonding in foam cored sailboat hulls.

Foam cores, far more than balsa, are prone to peeling or disbonding that starts from a propagation point of incomplete bonding, or from impact damage. Common propagation points occur around hull openings, port hole and deck hatch cutouts. I've watched workers cutting out hatch openings in cored decks with a saber saw. The upward pull of the saw blade started the core separation at the hatch opening which then progresses over time as a result of induced stresses. Therefore, when particularly thin cored hulls are encountered, it's wise to fully sound them out. If scaffolding is needed, and the client is not willing to foot the cost, then the surveyor should make note of that in his report. It should be pointed out here that the thickness of the outer laminates makes a tremendous difference in the overall strength simply because the thicker laminate better resists bending. Determining the thickness of an outer laminate of a cored hull is a matter of gaining experience at sounding. How do you get that experience if you're a novice? Easy. Every time you walk through a boat yard, pull a quarter out of your pocket and go tapping along down a line of boats. You'll quickly learn which are thick and which are thin.

No boat has total 100% bonding of the core to outer laminate, meaning that nearly every boat has some degree of incomplete bonding. So how do we know how much incomplete bonding is too much? The answer is that you should not be able to find more than a half-dozen small voids per side not larger than a couple inches. Any more than this, and any larger than this, increases the potential for serious delamination to occur. To illustrate, a recent survey of a new 42' sport fisherman turned up over forty detectable voids in the hull sides ranging from about 1" diameter to over one foot. These areas of incomplete bonding tended to turn up in concentrated areas. Because of this fact, it had to be concluded that the number and concentration of voids seriously threatened the structural integrity and the client had no choice but to reject it.

Bulkhead Installation with Foam Cores

It's commonly believed, as demonstrated by actual practice, that the installation of bulkheads does not require special treatment because of the core. This
is erroneous. This practice is probably carried over from balsa core hull methods, which does not require special treatment. The mating of plywood bulkheads to balsa cores does not require fillets or special treatment because of the
high compression strength of balsa that foam does not have. Foam cores, however, need to have a fillet or boss to carry the load and prevent crushing. When
plywood bulkheads are butted directly against the inner laminate of a foam
core, the compression loads on the hull bottom can cause the foam to crush
under the hard edge of the plywood. When this happens, it's very likely to
initiate a propagation point of core crushing and laminate failure. Check for
this condition by sighting down the hull sides or bottom and look for depres-
sions or dimples that follow the contour of the bulkhead. When dimples are
apparent, that's a sure indicator of a crushed core. At this point, the potential
for serious structural damage needs to be considered and investigated.

Water Ingress

As previously stated, when cores are used in hull bottoms, it becomes nearly
inevitable that sooner or later, the outer laminates will be breached and water
permitted to migrate throughout the bottom. The great difficulty with coring a
hull bottom is the high degree of attention to detail during design and construction that is required to prevent water ingress. This extra design detailing and
labor required to do it right is a strong incentive for builders and workers to cut
corners and accounts for the high failure rate. As previously pointed out, a hull
traveling in a seaway is subject to pushing and pulling stresses which work to
both compress and pull the laminates apart. Once the core is breached, the
stresses on the hull act like a hydraulic pump and work to distribute the water
through every crevice and gap of the sandwich.

Breaches in the water tight integrity of a cored hull can occur from a variety of causes, the foremost of which is through hull penetrations improperly
installed by the builder, followed by post construction penetrations necessitated
by the installation of additional equipment by a boat yard or owner. Recently I
observed a cockpit extension project on a high production 46 foot yacht. When
the transom exhaust port flanges were removed, it was revealed that the hull
was balsa cored down to the chine. Virtually all of the through hull fitting holes
were cut straight through the balsa core that was laminated without benefit of
proper blanks. As the caulking around the through hull fittings aged and worked

Fig. 5-25. An unidentified thin foam material used as a core in this small boat could not withstand a relatively minor impact with a 4 x 4 piling.

loose, water worked its way into the balsa core and migrated up the hull sides as much as three feet. When the through hulls were removed, water poured out of the core for days and dripped for weeks.

Checking for water saturation on cored hull sides is easy. On the interior, find a place where the bottom terminus of the core is accessible, such as the engine room. Drill a small hole in the inner laminate and see if water runs out. Or use a moisture meter if otherwise dry.

When hulls are cored on the bottom or even down to the chine, it is imperative that all through hull openings be preplanned with proper blanks. The correct method for accomplishing this is shown in figure 5-18. Whether or not this has been done can usually be determined by examination from the interior. The blank should show up as a recess around the through hull opening. Or there may be evidence that a doubler of some other material such as wood or putty has been laminated into the hull, although this is not a particularly good solution. If there is no evidence of special treatment around through hull fittings, that condition, along with its ramifications, should be described in the report.

Post construction installation of through hull fittings such as transducers, swim platforms, bilge pumps and generators often account for the source of water ingress into a hull. So too does drilling holes in the hull from the interior of the hull. It's amazing how often I find screws driven into the hull from the interior. Sometimes even the builder will do this. Here are a few things to look for:

- Determine if a hull is cored and, if so, whether it is just to the chine or if the entire bottom is cored. Look for through hull blanks on the interior or the core-to-solid-laminate transition zone at shear line or near the chine.

- Look for areas of unpainted laminate on the interior where light may shine through. Are there any areas that show unusual darkening or discoloration of the core? If so, the cause is likely to be water saturation.

- Try to locate the boat's owner's manual. Check the hull section for advice on hull construction or special instructions on installing under water equipment.

- Look for bilge pumps screwed to the bottom of the keel, equipment screwed to the hull in places where water collects such as outboard of stringers. Look for screw holes deep in the bilge where equipment has been removed and the holes not filled. These are prime areas for water ingress into the core from the interior.

- Look for unusual bleeding or weeping of liquid from anywhere on the inside of the hull laminate. Sometimes saturation can be determined from weep streams of fluid from screw holes or other laminate breaches.

- Look for bleeding or weeping anywhere on the hull bottom or sides that looks suspicious, around through hulls, transducers, bolt and screw holes and struts, etc. Bleeding from stress cracks, as they often do, probably means something serious and should not be treated lightly.

- Sounding out a hull is not likely to reveal water saturation; this method should not be relied upon to reveal anything more than delamination or ply separation of thin hulls.

The seriousness of water migration into a cored hull should not be underestimated. Once the water is in there, there is no easy way, if any way at all, to get it out. To make matters worse, the problem might not even be correctable. A discussion of survey methods will be found in Chapter 6.

Other Core Types

Coremat

Yet another type of core is represented by Coremat, which is a thick, fibrous fabric — about 3/32" thick — that resembles the absorbent pads found on the bottom of meat packages at the supermarket. This type of material generally works well when fully wetted out precisely because the material does contain strong fibers and easily bonds well to uneven surfaces such as roving. In the jargon of the industry, it is used to "build bulk," which means it's sort of a hamburger helper for plain old glass and resin.

e yet other types that look like a thin packaging foam. How
works is clearly shown in Fig. 5-25 where this small boat
4" dock piling. Here we can see that the cleavage strength
ely poor, so much so that the outer laminate is easily
way. I have no idea what the trade name of this material is,
en it since, but this points up the fact that there's just no telling
id of materials someone might try to build a boat with.

Putty Cores

The use of putty, usually a polyester mixture of filler and no fibers, as a core or filler in supposedly all fiberglass hull sides had been going on for years before I found out about. Most often it is simply sprayed into the molding process. I was subjected to a rude awakening following a minor hurricane in 1999 when I had occasion to tour a field full of hurricane damaged boats that were being sold as salvage. Here I found dozens of broken up hulls that were built as early as 1992 with a sprayed-on putty as a filler in the hull sides. All of these were boats 32 feet and under, but included such names as Sea Ray, Regal and Wellcraft.

Unfortunately for the surveyor, he really has no way of knowing what a hull is made of in this age of "composites" short of destructive analysis or getting an opportunity such as this one to find out what really goes into a "fiberglass" boat. Here I got the chance to check out a late model boat that had been badly damaged, in this instance a 30 foot Sea Ray on which the hull side was fractured from deck to chine, exposing the "laminate." See fig. 5-21 & 22.

In looking at the boat, I had to wonder how this hull side ended up so badly damaged, as it did not show evidence of having been badly battered. It had a few punctures in it, in addition to being fractured. On close examination I was amazed at what I found. First, the hull side was less than 1/4" thick. Of this, the putty made up 50% and the rest consisted of ONE layer of woven roving on the inner laminate, and two layers of chopped strand mat on the outer, plus the gel coat. I hope you grasp the significance of this, that this hull side had only ONE structural laminate, the roving. No one would consider mat as a structural fabric.

If that weren't enough, the bonding to the putty core was extremely weak, so much so that I grabbed onto the outer skin an literally pulled the entire skin off the side of the boat. The obvious question here is one of whether this situation involved some kind of laminating defect. The answer was proved when I managed to do much the same thing with several other similar boats. Not only was the bond to the putty extremely weak, but the putty itself is very brittle. One can take pieces of it in hand and easily break them up.

Yet another interesting feature of this boat was that if you look at the hull from the interior, what you see is a hull that looks like it is laminated up with woven roving. What you don't know is that this is the only layer of roving in the entire laminate. Since this discovery, I have taken to sounding out smaller boat hull sides with a heavy rubber mallet and have found three boats with massive disbonding in the hull sides. In none of the three was the owner aware of even the slightest problem, though two of the boats displayed severe gel coat cracking.

This situation is not widely known within the industry because the builders who use these materials do not advertise that fact. None of the builders whom I have since found use this material even make mention of the fact in any of their literature. In my opinion this makes for an unacceptably weak laminate and a situation that the surveyor has to be doubly altert for.

[1] Meaning to cover the entire surface area with as many as 5-10 taps per square foot.

Chapter 6

Surveying the Hull

Surveying the hull of a yacht should consist of three distinct parts: interior, exterior and sea trial. This is necessary because the overall survey process proceeds in three distinct steps, and does not provide the opportunity to complete it all at once. The exterior portion, of course, is done at the haul out. In the previous chapter it was suggested that the examination of the hull from the interior while the vessel is underway is essential in determining whether a hull is truly sound. This chapter will explain why.

Procedure

The order in which the various elements of the survey are carried out is important but not always under the control of the surveyor. The ideal scheduling would be to open up the interior and make the internal hull inspection first, followed by hauling and then the sea trial. The reasoning here is that any indications of problems showing up on the internal and external inspections could then be evaluated during the sea trial as to their net effect on the actual structural stability of the hull during operation, rather than merely guessing what the effects would be.

It's always best to approach a hull survey with a coherent plan in mind rather than on a helter-skelter basis. Having a set of plans is most helpful but a rare occurrence. Even so, more and more yachts builders are providing a variety of plans and diagrams packed into their owners manual. These can be very helpful in gaining a better idea of where things are located, rather than tearing the inside of the boat apart trying to locate what you are looking for.

Before getting started, I like to make a general tour of both the interior and exterior. On the outside I look at whatever part of the hull sides I can see, along with briefly examining the hull/deck joint. Here I'm looking for any signs of disturbance which might suggest that the hull is working or wracking. Guard rails that are buckled or exceptionally loose, cracks along toe rails, stress cracking on the superstructure, unfairness or bulges on the hull sides, all of these things may be indicators that all is not well. Signs of trouble on the exterior can alert us of where to look on the interior, save time and avoid errors.

On the interior there is a lot more to look at even before opening things up. In the heyday of wooden yachts, it was de rigeuer for surveyors to examine the interior for evidence of hull working. Wracked hulls always showed up signs of disturbance on the interior. Today, these techniques are still useful. How doors line up to jambs, loose moldings, buckled wall coverings, counter tops with large gaps, evidence of pieces of wood or other materials that are working and abrading, unusual gaps in woodwork or paneling may all be signals that the hull is not as stiff as it should be. When we find such evidence, this is our que to pay extra attention once we pull up the hatches and start crawling around in the bilge.

Hull Numbers

Boat thefts occur with greater frequency than one might imagine. I know of two surveyors who received complaints because the boats they surveyed were stolen boats, their clients purchased them, only to have the boats seized at a later date, a very costly loss to the client. Because of this it's a good idea to check hull numbers and machinery serial numbers. The molded in hull identification number (H.I.N.) is put there by most builders simply by using a plastic tape label gun and making a reverse mold of it. It's so easy that thieves can use exactly the same process to alter the hull numbers. During the course of my career I have discovered two stolen boats and have had several other suspects. For me, that's good enough reason to always check closely.

Fig 6-1. A suspicious looking hull Number that turned out to be fraudulent.

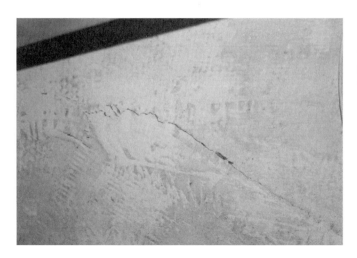

Fig 6-2. Major disbonding of internal members may show up as small cracks like this.

The two altered numbers that I found were very obviously altered. Others may show a patch of new gelcoat on top of old, faded gelcoat. Or one or more of the numbers may be altered, such as turning a 3 into an 8, or a 1 to a 7. To avoid falling in this trap, examine the number closely, then try to find the hidden hull number (in the forepeak or on the inner transom) or try to reference the number back to owners manual, registrations or any other documents. Many times the short hull number (such as 126) will be found written with marker on cabinetry items such as drawers by the shop carpenters. If the boat is stripped clean with no reference material, if the H.I.N. looks suspicious, it's a good idea to warn the client that he should have a title search done. With state registered boats this can usually be easily accomplished by a call to the titling agency. For documented vessels, the client will have to obtain a title abstract. This takes time and will cost about $75.00 from a documentation agency.

When we run across a hull that's been repainted and the numbers are mostly filled in and are illegible, it's a good idea to make note of this in the report. Technically, the boat is in violation of federal law that requires these numbers to be present. There will also be cases where the number was obliterated but then restored by the owner. We ignore these situations at our own peril; one way or another, the situation should be checked out or at least disclaim any effort at numbers verification in the report.

Many states have provisions for providing hull numbers to "homemade" or extensively rebuilt boats with a special designation. The number prefix will be the two letter state designation plus the letter "Z". For example, Florida boat prefixes will be FLZ. This facility has been greatly abused by thieves and insurance fraud artists to obtain legitimate numbers for illegitimate boats. The surveyor should be extra wary when he encounters one of these.

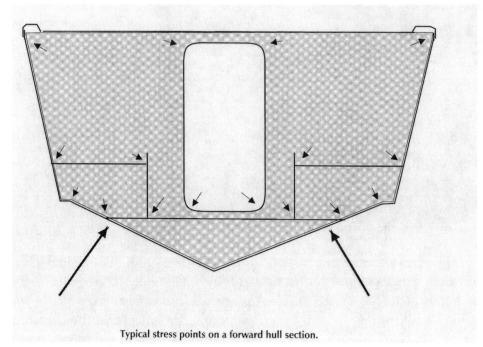

Typical stress points on a forward hull section.

Fig 6-3. The primary stress points on a forward bulkhead. These are the points at which evidence of stress or weakness may show up.

Internal Hull Inspection

To do the best job possible, it's necessary to open up as much of the interior as possible. For time saving and efficiency, there's nothing like carrying a powerful screw gun with a full set of bits since there are usually a lot of panels that can be easily removed and that will give more visual access. Taking up carpets, moving furniture and mattresses and removing drawers is a part of the job that I like to get out of the way all at once. Keeping in mind that we want the interior opened up at the time we do the sea trial, we can take this opportunity to leave behind on the dock anything that will get in the way.

A word of caution about hatches. Be aware that falling through an open hatch can cause very serious injuries. Open hatches are dangerous and if we go through the boat and leave all the deck hatches open, it's possible that someone will fall through one of them. For my own protection, and that of others, I always carry a magic marker and some tape so that I can tape a sign in the door warning that hatches are open. Then, when I'm finished with a hatch, I close it so that even I don't forget and accidentally step backwards into an open hatch, something that's happened more than once. Another thing to remember about hatches is to never stand a hatch upright. We tend to forget that boats roll and the wake of a passing boat can cause a hatch that is standing upright to topple over. Many years ago I was training an apprentice and warned him never to rely on mechanical hatch openers, but to always use a piece of rope to positively secure the hatch open. Or to remove a hatch and lay it down flat. Less than one hour later the man had four fingers badly mangled when the hatch retainer slipped and the hatch slammed down on his hand. Hatch retainers are dangerous and unreliable. If you don't do this, sooner or later one will get you.

Primary tools for the internal survey are a flashlight, screwdriver and plastic mirror. I use a large size Craftsman screwdriver which has a rounded tip on the handle that is used for soundings. It's easier to manipulate in tight spaces than a hammer and serves more useful functions. I hold the blade end and use the handle as the striking surface when sounding out laminates and tabbing. The mirror, of course, is useful for looking into places that one would not otherwise be able to see.

When I crawl down in a hole, clients often ask me, "What are you looking for down there?" What a great question! The short answer is "looking at everything there is to see." The purpose of the internal survey is to inspect everything there is to see. Recalling that the surveyor's essential function is more a matter of proving the negative than the positive, we are looking for evidence of defects or damage. The primary concern is to inspect bulkheads, stringers, frames and the inner skin for evidence of damage or defect. Hulls may be either painted or gelcoated on the interior. Obviously, we can tell more about a structural laminate if it's not painted, but, even so, paint or gelcoat can show signs of disturbance or stress cracking, especially if those coatings dry to the point where they are brittle. Stress cracking showing up on the inside coating is important evidence indicating deflection of bottom panels.

Uncoated surfaces are even more revealing. Stress cracks and even minor degrees of disbonding tend to show up very clearly. Tabbing and taping that is in the process of disbonding will show milky white through the laminate. Since the forward half of the hull takes the worst pounding, this is where most structural weakness will show up. The base perimeter of all structural components should be closely inspected at the point where they are attached to the hull. Most boats will reveal some degree of disbonding at random locations. Generally speaking, I would draw the line at about 10% of the entire bonding surface showing white or milky. It should be kept in mind that partial disbonding is not necessarily a progressive condition. Disbonding can be the result of a one-time occurrence such as slamming off a big wave. Certainly minor disbonding weakens the structure, but as long as the disturbed area is random and does not reveal a general pattern of disbonding, I ignore it. It is only when a line of

Fig. 6-4. There is no end of the strange things surveyors encounter. Here a stringer terminates just after passing through a bulkhead. Notice that the builder glassed the tabbing onto a varnished bulkhead, realized the mistake and then added these aluminum clamp-blocks to prevent it from breaking loose. The boat is a 20 year old 46' Bertram. Odd though it may be, the arrangement worked.

taping indicates that it is starting to peel, as in pulling up from the central axis of the structure, that there is cause for concern.

For painted tabbing and taping, physical sounding is the only means of checking. If I don't have a good reason for doing so, I usually don't make an effort to sound out more than easily reached areas. If there is obvious taping that has disbonded and lifted, then there's good reason to suspect that the disbonding may be more extensive than the eye can detect and I then begin to sound out as much of the internal structures as possible.

As alluded to in the previous chapter, evaluating the effect of disbonded tabbing and taping can be difficult. Finding a relatively small area of disbonding may or may not be the precursor of a larger problem. It is the surveyor's job to perform this evaluation and give the client the best advice possible. It is quite often the case that localized disbonding is the result of a localized flaw and may never extend further than the area immediately affected. For this reason, the surveyor needs to carefully examine or sound out as much of the surrounding structures as possible.

Another thing that we commonly find is fracturing of the laminate at the point where stringers pass through bulkheads, a point where stresses from opposing angles all meet at the same place. (See figure 6-4) It's almost inevitable that some degree of cracking will occur at this point, so that we have to judge the condition carefully. As with all such evaluations, the age, speed of the vessel and severity of the evidence all plays a role. If cracking at one intersect is found, all intersects should be examined. Is the condition local or generalized? Does the cracking indicate just a disturbance, or is it the beginning of a major failure? As with any such condition, if the hull is young and the condition generalized, there is cause for concern.

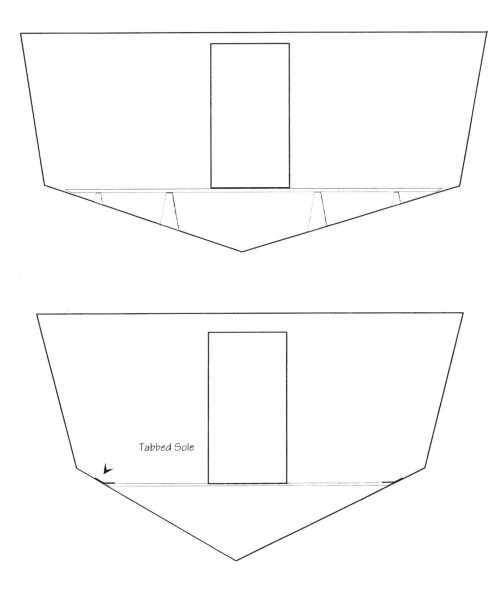

Fig 6-5. Two methods of attaching cabin soles in larger boats. Smaller boats may have fiberglass liners.

Moisture Meters

While I'm not a big fan on using moisture meters on the exterior of a boat, they can be very useful at diagnosing water intrusion problems in wood cored stringers and cored hull sides. If you want to try a meter on a cored bottom, you have first to make sure that the area of inner bottom being tested was not recently wetted by some other means. For example, you wouldn't want to use a meter after a sea trial or on a bottom with salt residue.

The subject of the use of moisture meters is difficult and complex. It would take an entire book to deal with the subject thoroughly, and for that reason is not covered in detail here.

Evaluating Structural Design

Not until we have crawled through the better part of a hull can we begin to get an idea of how well built she is. As we work our way through, we should be constantly assessing the manner of design and construction methods. We covered the basics in the previous chapters, and these are the basic principles of good design that we are now evaluating.

By the time a hull structure is twenty years old, it will be well tried and tested. On the other hand, relatively new hulls have not proven themselves through long years of use, so that they require even more vigilance. While our basic function is not to evaluate and report on the design, knowing what makes for sound construction can tip us off to potential problems when we find poor construction techniques. A new boat that has stepped down stringers, for example, is a strong indicator of potential trouble and provides us with an opportunity to warn the client. It also warns the surveyor to check more closely for evidence of impending failure.

We are apt to get sidetracked when surveying the interior by all the other components we have to inspect, and for that reason it's better to break up the internal inspection into two parts, one exclusively to survey the hull, the other the remainder of the components. If we don't do it this way we are likely to go off on a tangent and overlook things. True, it does mean that we'll have to go through the hull twice, but this method is most thorough.

The real test of hull construction is whether it performs its function without breaking apart. Construction techniques can be sloppy, unconventional or just plain wrong and yet still function satisfactorily. The surveyor's point of view should be tempered by objectivity and not biased by disdain for the unconven-

Fig. 6-6. This dust was caused by the friction of a loose bulkhead

tional. Our job is to look for evidence that a hull may not be sound, predicated on the definition that unsoundness is any condition that may impair the safety or value of the vessel. Inherently in that definition is included any condition that might cause a financial loss to the client. This is where our ability to evaluate design and construction techniques comes into play. The central question is, will a fault or defect in the method of design and construction of the hull be likely to result in a structurally unsound condition? If so, our job is to advise the client accordingly. Being able to competently evaluate design and construction techniques provides us with the ability to make those kind of judgments and provide the client with the highest level of service. It also helps the surveyor avoid potentially serious errors and omissions claims. This can occur as a result of failure to detect a condition, or as a result of giving erroneous advice about a condition that does exist.

The Great Unseen

Large areas of the internal hull are often not accessible and can constitute enormous risks for the surveyor if he doesn't handle these situations properly. The only way the surveyor can protect himself from problems that are hidden is to describe those areas fully in his report. The best practice is to verbally describe the location and size of all such areas that are not visible. Follow this up by giving an assessment of the overall percentage of the interior hull that cannot be seen. This makes it clear to the client how much could be inspected and how much could not. Then the client can decide for himself whether he wants to purchase something that can't be thoroughly evaluated. Having done this, the surveyor will have fulfilled his obligation to fully inform the client.

Why is this so important? An example will serve to illustrate. A man paid $350,000 for a new 41' boat that was delivered to him a distance of about 400 miles by water, on its own bottom. The fellow was smart enough to hire a surveyor for a new boat check out. The survey revealed numerous stress cracks on the bottom. The interior inspection revealed disbonding and incomplete laminations of tabbing and of major structural members, as well as a hull/deck joint that was so poorly made that it was breaking loose all around. Most of these major structural defects were only discovered because an extraordinary effort was made with the extensive use of mirrors to see behind areas that were otherwise obscured. Here we had a brand new boat that was literally breaking apart after only a few hours of operation. Or at least we thought it was a new boat. It turned out that it was not a new boat, but a reject that the builder had taken back from its first owner and resold as a new boat to my client.

Fortunately for myself, I was already aware that the builder had a reputation for pulling these kind of tricks, but had I been a little less diligent, I might have missed most of it because it was so difficult to see behind fiberglass liners.[1] But it was the stress cracks on the bottom of a new boat that was the real tip off that something was seriously wrong.

Sawdust and Debris

Weak hulls, or even weak portions of hulls, usually are not isolated conditions. The effect of any part of a hull that is structurally weak and working is likely to be transferred to other components. A good example of this is the manner in which interior decks or soles are installed. Installing a cabin sole in the forward section of a hull is a difficult proposition in mid to large size yachts. If a plywood sole is bonded to the hull sides, it can only be taped in on the top side of the sole, not the underside, so that all the weight has to be born by the taping. Furthermore, most hull sides pant at least to some degree. These two factors account for why we find so many cabin soles with the hull side taping broken loose.

Other options for the builder is to install shelving on the hulls sides on which to lay deck beams across, or he can lay deck beams down on top of the stringers. None of these are really great options because any amount of flexing of any part of the hull will be transferred into the cabin sole. And since the forward half of the hull takes the worst beating, this is where things are most

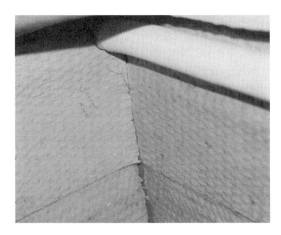

Fig. 6-7. This is an intersect between a stringer and a transverse frame. Note that the glassing does not wrap around the intersect but stops short, resulting in no bond between the two parts.

likely to start coming apart. Figure 6-5 illustrates the two common methods of installing cabin soles in the forward sections of yachts. Study these drawings and imagine what happens when the bottom pants. Since most internal structures are built onto the sole, any movement of the sole transfers into the internal structures. If the cabin sole moves too, then things which are attached to it will move also.

When bottoms and hull sides pant, the cabin soles, deck beams, taping and tabbing are all likely to be affected by crushing and friction. This is why forward quarters are usually so noisy in a seaway. All this crunching and grinding (it happens in most all boats) will create sawdust and debris throughout the bilges which, for the surveyor, are a great telltale of what is going on down there. One can be fairly certain that he's dealing with a very well built hull when there's no trace of debris caused by friction, especially after the boat has a few years on it. Of course, a lot of boats have left over construction debris in them, yet friction debris can usually be distinguished by a rather distinct pattern of where it came from and how it got there. Sometimes one has to look closely, but with a little

Fig. 6-8. Main and intermediate stringers in a high performance outboard boat. Note how tall stringers are tied into transom to support the motors.

experience one can usually tell the difference.

When soles are taped into hull sides, the tabbing needs to be inspected as closely as possible. Reglassing broken tabbing usually doesn't work because it doesn't solve the original design problem. We often see repaired tabbing that has again broken loose. When extensive broken tabbing on cabin soles is found, it's usually better to look for alternative solutions. On larger yachts heavy appliances may be installed in the forward quarters such as washers and dryers or refrigerators. It's a good idea to check the soles from the underside since they are often not adequately supported to carry the weight of these appliances.

Deck beams laid across hull stringers make for a prime indication of whether or not a bottom is flexing. The movement of the bottom will cause the stringers to crush up into the bottoms of the deck beams. This condition should be widespread before any serious conclusions can be drawn since there may be just a very heavy weight above one or two deck beams. Whereas if most of the deck beams are crushed, with much splintering evident, it likely indicates a floppy bottom and that all internal structures should be examined closely.

The examination of hatch carlins (frames) can also indicate how well the internal structure is holding together. When framing joints are loose or pulling apart, it's usually a good indication that the sole is working excessively. It may be that the sole is just poorly constructed, or it may be a sign of excessive hull panting.

Bulkheading

Plywood remains the material of choice for bulkheads, and with good reason. It has the strength necessary to do the job, is relatively inexpensive and easy to work. Marine grade plywood used for bulkhead applications is remarkably resistant to rot. Even though they are exposed to bilge water at the lower ends, it is quite rare to find deterioration. The exception is when low grade ply is used, as is often the case of oriental imports or in low cost, entry-level boats. When surveying imports, it is wise to suspect all bulkheads and at least poke around at the low points or anywhere water collects. On low cost, North American built boats, look for plywood that is rough and poorly made. If it has knots, gaps, curling plies or the surface is very coarse, chances are it is CD exterior or roofing grade plywood that does not resist rot or water saturation well at all. An exception to the above is boats used in fresh water. Sea water tends to act as a preservative to wood because of the salt, whereas fresh water promotes the kind of fungus and bacteria growth that causes wood to rot quickly.

Fuzzing of a wood surface is a condition where the surface appears woolly.

This is little understood condition that is not the result of fungicidal rot but rather the recurrent wetting and drying cycles of sea water. When sea water evaporates, the dissolved salts crystallize in the surface wood cells . As the wood is wetted and dried again, more salt is added. As the size of the salt crystals grow, they start splitting the wood cells. It is this activity that results in the fuzzy condition of the surface. The solution to this is to either stop the leak or sand and paint the wood.

Bulkheads should be inspected for evidence of deterioration, cracking, disbonding or delamination of the wood plies. Moreover, the surveyor should count the number of full and partial bulkheads and draw a conclusion as to whether there are a sufficient number of properly spaced bulkheads to ensure that the hull is sound and not subject to excessive flexing. If there are not an adequate number of bulkheads, then the potential for twisting and wracking of the hull becomes very real.

Don't be fooled into thinking that, because the builder has a good reputation, there is no possibility of a major design error. During a sea trial of a popular production sixty foot sport fisherman, I was down below checking meters of the generator output. At cruising speed, the captain put the yacht into a hard turn. Suddenly the yacht was vibrating so badly that I couldn't even read the meters on the panel. Right away I knew something was wrong. Yet it was another two days and another sea trial later that the source of the vibration was finally discovered. It turned out that this yacht had a custom, or at least a newly configured interior layout that eliminated all but one of the forward structural bulkheads. This was all for the benefit of creating more open space in the interior quarters. The lack of sufficient bulkheading caused the hull to twist so badly that the shafts were binding up in the bearings, and this was what was causing the extreme vibration when the vessel was put into a fast turn. Only by tearing out the interior and adding more structural bulkheads was the problem finally solved.

Stringers

Inspection and evaluation of stringers is much more difficult since only small segments of the stringers can be observed at one time. Even so, every effort should be made to ensure that they are properly designed and installed. The method of attachment to the hull should be examined with care to ensure that they are both secure and not creating hard spots that facilitate the hinge effect. Look for step-downs, cut outs, dog legs, disbonding and stress cracking of the hull laminate parallel to the stringers.

Pay special attention to the outboard stringers, to see if they are of adequate height to resist bottom flexing in way of engine beds. It's fairly common to find outboard stringers that are so low profile that they do little to strengthen the bottom. Flexing of the bottom panels in way of the engines can result in engine mount and transmission damage. Damaged or loose engine mounts are often indicative of unstable stringers.

On outboard boats it is extremely important to check the point of stringer attachment to the transom (Fig 6-8) so as to ensure that the weight of the motors is not pulling the transom off. It is very common to find either poor bonding, or almost no bonding at all at the junction of stringers and transom. Fractures and disbonding of tabbing at this point tells the story.

When vessels have unusually tall or thin stringers, check to see that they are vertically stabilized. Too much height and too little thickness, combined with a lack of cross-framing makes for floppy stingers. Long spans between transverse members, i.e. frames or bulkheads, spells potential trouble. Flexing of the bottom and stringers may result in the stringers bending or delaminating. Whenever any kind of structural question arises, make a mental note to check the behavior of the stringers during sea trial. The proof is in the performance: If they're not moving, then they're doing their job.

Cored Hulls

These have always presented the surveyor with the serious problem of attempting to prove the integrity of the composite. The biggest threat comes about when a builder decides to core the bottom which, in my view, is a very foolish thing to do. A cored bottom yields very high risks and no real benefits, so why do it?

The problem with all cores is the potential for both water ingress and ply separation, or in some cases what is called "never bond," meaning that a good bond was never established in the first place.

Because core problems can be horrendously costly to rectify, if they can be rectified at all, it's best to approach cored bottoms with extreme caution with the awareness that failure to find a serious problem is very likely to come back at the surveyor.

Any cored structure essentially creates void spaces that are capable of filling up with water. Unlike hull sides, a bottom is immersed to a depth that creates significant water pressure on the laminate which, as we already know, tends to be porous. Moreover we frequently see bottoms in which through hulls have been installed directly through the core, either by the builder, or by someone else at a later date, unaware of the risk of creating a water entry point. And though the core material itself may be impervious to water, no composite is impervious to the hydraulic action that will occur while the boat is underway with water in the core. And hydraulic action of water in a core is what ultimately will cause the most damage, in some cases turning an entire core into mush.

Surveying a cored hull poses the problem of determining whether there has been water entry into the core. Moisture meters usually are of no help since we're dealing with a hull that has just been pulled out of the water and will read wet in any case. One possible option is to use the meter from the interior, but this presumes that one has good access from the interior which, in many cases there isn't. Physically sounding a hull may reveal potential problems such as ply separation, but this is of no help unless the outer laminate is particularly thin: thick skins will not reveal water saturation or even ply separation. Very substantial areas of ply separation are often revealed by sighting a clean bottom and noting any significant unfairness as a serious ply separation almost always results in a surface deformation.

Through-hull openings obviously pose the greatest threat to water penetration, especially sea cocks which often don't get the kind of design attention that they require. Close examination of valves from the interior is the first step. Through hulls can be installed in one of two ways: the core is cut back from the opening and filled with putty (less good); or there is a preplanned termination of the core in way of the opening, (I call it a reverse fillet) meaning that the

Fig. 6-9. Termites or wood boring ants in a fiberglass boat. It may be unexpected, but it does happen. Not untill after probing and scraping was this damaged revealed. The surveyor needs to be familiar with the teltale signs of the presense of these nasty critters.

through-hull penetrates only solid fiberglass (best and nearly foolproof).

The problem with so many cored bottoms is that some valves do not have load bearing doubler plates under the inner flanges. If the space between the skins is filled with putty, then any leverage applied to the valve and piping can cause putty disbonding and breakage, which inevitably results in leakage. Consider just how narrow the flanges are on a valve, and when you add a little leverage in the form of piping or strainers, it should be easy to visualize why the use of putty is likely to fail.

Clearly, the thing to do is to view with suspicion any instance where valves or other hardware directly penetrate a cored bottom. Be specially suspicious of any kind of transducer which may have been improperly installed by a yard, electronics firm or owner. Make it a point to apply pressure to sea cocks and try to rock them. Are they rock solid or are they loose? Another fault occurs when the valve flanges, due to the cut back of the opening, are not bearing on the inner and outer skins, but only on putty. This is a case where the valve installation will ultimately fail and you can speed it along by applying pressure to it, possibly breaking it out. Yet another instance of poor design, valves with recessed outer flanges involve countersinking the outer flange into the outer laminate. In some cases the countersink will go completely through the outer laminate, leaving the valve flange bearing only on the core or putty.

Thus, any instance of looseness, cracking or green corrosion trails, inside or out, are likely an indication of serious trouble.

By far the best method to check a cored bottom for water penetration is to take a test boring from the interior with a 1/4" drill bit. The problem with this is that you either need to get the owner's permission — and he's not likely to give it — or to do it surreptitiously, which is not advisable. If you get the owner's permission, seek the lowest point on the bottom toward the keel. Usually you will be able to see where the core terminates somewhere near the keel line. Since the inner skin is usually much thinner than the external skin, the bit will go through quickly. You may get either a stream of water pouring out, or you may just come up with wet or damp tailings. In either case, you have an answer and now your only problem is how to patch up a wet hole. I carry small containers of two-part epoxy and a putty knife with which I fill the holes that I have drilled. But to use this method, you'll have to be prepared to deal with the owner if the hole turns out wet since you can't now fill it.

How many holes do you drill? I try to keep it down to two per side, and try to do it fairly close to a through hull fitting and downstream of the fitting. I inform my client that what I am doing is only a very basic check, and that just because we didn't find any wetness in the test areas, that doesn't preclude the possibility that it exists in other areas. I tell him that short of cutting the boat up, this is the best we can do. The important point here is that at least you did *something* to check. The only remaining option is to leave the boat hauled for a week or so and come back and do moisture meter testing after it dries out. Otherwise, if he wants to buy a boat with a cored bottom, this is a risk that he'll have to assume, so be sure to cover yourself one way or the other.

Cored hull sides pose much less of a problem, in part because they are not immersed. Because of the fact that they are vertical, all water intrusion will collect at the bottom where it's much easier to discover, especially with a moisture meter. If the inner skin is thin enough you may even be able to feel dampness. However, ply separation (delamination) is always a potential problem. Ply separations occur either as a result of in-service failures or what we call "neverbond," meaning a failure to bond during lay up. Reasons why such failures occur are legion; fortunately, our only concern is merely to find them if they exist.

Hull Bottom and Sides

To do the most thorough job possible, it's a good idea to poke around the bottom with hammer and screwdriver handle or blade. Ply separations, particularly on cored hulls, can occur on the inside that may not be detectable on the outside. While I make no effort to sound out the complete interior, I do poke around in the slamming areas forward and particularly around the engine beds. I'm especially alert if I see stress cracking.

Other points of particular interest are the running strakes, if any, chine flats, chine radius and strut mountings. All these areas should at least be given a cursory glance for signs of weakness and stress cracking. Recently I found a

Fig. 6-10. Sighting along the length of this hull, and using available light to best advantage, these blisters stick out like a sore thumb. Not shown is large inset in the bottom that showed up a structural weakness.

Fig. 6-11. Dialing the shafts is a good idea but the problem is that there is often nothing to clamp this tool onto.

boat where the inner laminates on one side of the hull had sagged during lay-up while the resin was still wet, There were big wrinkles along the chine that were hollow and filled with water. There were also stress cracks along the chine in this area, so obviously there was a potential structural problem that required repair.

Hull sides are likely to be completely obscured so that almost no part is visible, yet the surveyor should be vigilant and try to find as many openings as possible to have a look see. The potential for extreme panting is easily determined by pounding on the exterior, but on the interior we can at least look for signs of bulkhead disbonding, evidence of repairs and friction debris or other damage caused by panting. A careful look within the rope locker will usually tell us how the deck is attached to the hull.

Termites & Other Pests

Believe it or not, I find termites in approximately 5% of all boats I survey. I probably would not of even thought of this subject for inclusion in this book were it not for the fact that on the morning of this writing I was on a boat that had serious termite damage. Though there are true termites, the term most often is used generically to mean any number of ant-like insects that eat or bore through wood. True termites are subterranean, live in the ground but eat wood. The types of termites found in boats are usually various types of ants that both nest in, eat, or just bore serpentine tunnels in wood. Once introduced into a boat they can be devastating. Bull ants are one variety of dry wood borer found throughout the south. They are nocturnal and do not show themselves during the day. Bull ants bore large tunnels through wood, particularly love plywood and places where it is wet. Unlike termites, their tunnels often breach the surface of wood and are usually quite obvious. The distinguishing characteristic of bull ants is that they are messy. They drag in saw dust, fabric fibers and other debris to make their egg nests and often leave trails of this debris. They are easily killed with ordinary fumigating sprays. Yet another type is very tiny, so small they are hard to see. Some will create telltale external tunnels to link one area with another.

Wood termites are the most devastating wood destroyers whose activity usually lies below the surface of wood. They will usually hollow out the center of a piece of wood. On painted parts, they're known to eat everything but the paint, leaving a hollow paint shell that, if you touch it, will crumble. Termite damage is easy to miss if one is not looking for it. Termites eat wood and excrete enormous quantities of very tiny dark brown pellets that, when wetted, make very dark stains, even darker than rust. Such mysterious stains are often signaling the presence of termites.

It is also hard to believe that an expensive yacht could be infested with rats or mice, but they occasionally are. Considering where boats go, however, this should really be no surprise and the surveyor should be on the look out for these terribly destructive animals. Small rats (not river rats but the kind that look more like pets) and mice make nests with things like paper, filler from mattresses and life jackets and the like. They signal their presence by both droppings and the nesting debris. Or one may observe soft goods that are chewed up, usually on the bottom side where it is not obvious. In Florida, where out of state owners often store their boats for long periods, these vermin are a problem. In several cases that I know of vermin caused thousands of dollars of damage to yacht interiors. In one case, mice ate through an entire case of aluminum Coca Cola cans.

The Hauled Survey

Having worked in the insurance claims business a long time, it's a fair statement when I say that every boat yard drops a boat on average once every five years. Some more than others, but the average is still there. A few surveyors have had close calls and it's a miracle that so far no surveyor has ever been under a boat when it dropped, at least that I know of. However, I was inside one when it did.

One of the best rules a surveyor can make for himself is to never get under a boat until it has been blocked and the weight is eased from the travel lift straps. If the weight of the boat is only half, or less than half, of the lift rating an accident is a lot less likely. But when the weight of the boat approaches the maximum capacity of the lift, this is when most accidents occur. I am particularly alert to old and poorly maintained equipment, and when encountering these I always request that the keel be blocked before I will go under the boat.

Since most boats are hauled on a travel lift, I like to watch what happens as the hull is being lifted by the slings. The sights and sounds are often revealing. For example, if you know that a boat has too few bulkheads, watch what happens as the hull is squeezed by the slings. Are the sides being compressed? Does the keel bow or do you hear cracking and popping noises inside the hull? Are poorly attached rails being bent or torn off as the nylon slings stretch? All of these things may be clues to serious structural problems.

Larger yachts present the problem of being unable to reach the hull sides areas when they are hauled. The surveyor will need to consider whether scaffolding will be necessary, and arranging for it in advance. Using a ladder and having to move it numerous times can become very time consuming as well as wearying.

In addition to the usual poking, prodding, hammering and scraping that goes on during the hauled survey, sighting the hull is one procedure that is often overlooked. Old-timers often exclaim that the eye is the surveyor's most important tool, and nowhere is that more true than when conducting the hauled survey. In one operation, sighting a hull can reveal a lot about a boat's quality and construction. Experience tells us that the most finely crafted boats are also the fairest because it costs extra money to make a hull strong and fair. Bulges, bumps, wavy lines and general unfairness are strong indications of sloppy construction. Have there been repairs made to the hull, and if so does the repair appear to be effective?

Sighting a Hull

Sighting a hull is a procedure in which the surveyor stands in a position end-on to a hull surface - say the hull side - so that he can look down the length of it in such a way that any unfairness is magnified to visual perception. It's like holding a board up to your eye to determine whether it is straight. Except in hull sighting we're looking for irregularities in the hull. Why? Because this can tell us a lot about the condition of the boat. To sight a hull, the hull must first be clean. Salt spray on hull sides and a dirty bottom inhibit and even prevent sighting. It's best to first check the hulls sides as she first comes out of the water. If hull sides are freshly waxed or new, water will bead on the surface and prevent a clear sighting so you'll want to try sighting before the pressure washer is applied. But, if sides are oxidized and salty, washing down with fresh water will give them a sheen that then can be successfully sighted. The bottom is best sighted while it's still wet. When dry, irregularities are much harder to see.

Sighting requires looking down the length a hull surface in such a way as to detect surface irregularities. To do it you need to use the available light source to best advantage to highlight the surface being sighted. This means a lot of standing, stooping, bending and craning your neck in order to get the right angle, while at the same time being watchful not to step of the end of the pier or trip over a piece of wood and make a complete fool of yourself.

Sighting the bottom and hull sides can reveal a multitude of problems ranging from delamination, improperly installed bulkheads, repaired damage, weak and misshapen hulls, as well as hard to see blisters. It can even show up hot resin cures that results in laminate shrinking or puckering, an effect that often leaves a washboard effect, or looks like a repaired area. Sighting long wise on the bottom will also usually reveal whether there has been a blister repair job since grinder marks and other irregularities are likely to appear. The important point to realize is that long wise sighting shows up irregularities that straight-on, visual inspection is not likely to reveal.

Sighting the keel line is also important as this will show up abnormalities in the keel, including a hull mold that isn't straight. Yes, you might be surprised to learn how many molds are not symmetrical, particularly older and custom or one-off boats. On a recent survey of a 58 foot custom yacht, sighting of the keel showed it to be visually out of true. But when a line was strung and it was measured, it turned out that this keel was a whopping six inches out! Needless to say, steering this boat was a bit of a problem. Any time you let go of the wheel, it automatically made a right turn!

Sounding out a hull is de rigeur, but how far one should go, how much tapping around one should do, is a matter of experience. A busy surveyor can exhaust himself if he tries to completely sound out the entire surface of every hull that he surveys. He can also wreck his knees from duck-walking and get carpal tunnel syndrome in his wrists from the constant banging. The profes-sional surveyor needs to draw a fine line between doing a good job and preserv-ing his body. I do enough to satisfy myself, and how much banging around depends on what I know about the builder and his boats. If I don't know any-thing about the builder, I'm going to check a lot more closely. If we know a builder has an excellent reputation, I'll cover only the most important areas, sounding out the forward half of the bottom, around the strut bases and making sure there is no crushing on the keel. But we still must recognize the potential for builder errors and always cover the basics.

Fig. 6-12.

Because I've found that the hammer is much too hard on my wrists, I've graduated to using a screwdriver handle since, unlike a hammer, a screwdriver can be swung from any direction since it has no point of reference. It does just as good a job and is much easier on the wrists. The large Craftsman screwdriver is great for this because the handle has a convenient ball on the end. Whenever there is any question or doubt about the integrity of a hull, such as potential ply separation, I keep a heavy rubber mallet in the trunk of my car just in case I feel it's needed.

I've watched a lot of surveyors perform hauled surveys and have yet to see one sound out the hull sides and wondered why, since the sides are easiest to reach. Please take a look at the above photo and it will become very clear why this should be done. See also what I have to say about putty cores in the previous chapter and Fig. 5-2(chapter 5). The entire side of this boat was delaminated in the mid section and would have been easily picked up during a survey. But no one discovered the problem until it completely failed. Cored hulls are especially vulnerable to large scale delamination and ought to get at least a cursory sounding out. This means about two or more taps for every square foot of surface area. If there's any major delamination, this should find it. Take note, however, that if the outer skin is particularly thick, you should use the heavy mallet. It takes about 15 minutes to sound out a 40 footer so there's really no excuse for not doing it.

Fig. 6-13. Sea trials can be tough when encountering conditions like these.

The Keel

Vee bottomed boats don't usually present much of a problem but boats with keels deserve special attention. Yards often resort to the terrible practice of blocking a boat with one block on each end, literally suspending the hull like a bridge. Not only does this stress the hull, but puts enormous loads on the keel. If you've ever watched a hull being laid up, then you know that the keel is an exceptionally difficult area to achieve good workmanship. Laminators practically have to stand on their heads to work the fabric into the keel cavity.

Poor laminating and improper blocking are likely result in the keel crushing at some point; poorly accomplished repairs is yet another reasons why keel blocking damage occurs. Either way, when handled in this manner, keels have been known to crush from improper blocking. When this happens, the next problem stems from the difficulty of making effective repairs to the keel since it usually cannot be reached from the interior for laminating from inside. This means that the repair is going to be inherently weak. Therefore, the keel should be closely inspected for signs of irregularities and also fully sounded out. Any sign of cracking or irregularities should be written up, regardless of whether there is any apparent problem. This will cover you in the event that problems arise in the near future.

The Running Gear

This term refers to props, shafts, struts and rudders. It is usually best to conduct the haul out prior to the sea trial so that any faults in the drive system, such as bent props, can be corrected in order to obtain proper speed trials and gauge engine performance. This section is included in this chapter because it occurs at the haul out. However, the complete drive train is covered in a separate chapter. The following points should be covered at the haul out:

1. Gauge alignment of propeller blades. This is easily accomplished by using a stick laid against the rudder and then rotating the prop.

2. Check condition of cutlass bearings by lifting up on shaft to check for any slack.

3. Check rudders for excessive lateral slack or play.

4. Check vertical alignment of rudders for bending, toe-in, toe-out.

5. Check that shaft is properly aligned with center of shaft alley and that there is no metal-to-metal contact.

6. Test struts for looseness. I do this by banging the strut with a shoring block which is always present around a haul out slip. If the strut is loose, you will likely see water squirting out around the strut base as it moves.

7. Some surveyors attempt to mike the shafts. I've always found this to be a rather futile effort since it's hard to get a clean surface to obtain a reading from. If you try to mike the very end, the threads and cotter pin are always in the way. Instead, it can be done at the engine end where you'll get clean metal and something to clamp the micrometer onto. Keep in mind that a shaft that is bent at one end will wobble at both ends, so you still get a good indication.

8. Check for slack in propeller & shaft keys by rocking the props hard.

9. Corrosion inspection - all underwater metals to be examined for corrosion.

This short list highlights only the running gear. Of course everything else on the exterior is to be inspected, but most of those points are self explanatory. In addition you will record both propeller sizes along with shaft diameter. Don't short change prop sizes because you'll occasionally not only find boats with the wrong size props, but boats with two different size props which will account for why the engines turn up to different speeds.

Stern Drives

You don't need a lot of technical knowledge to survey a stern drive unit, but you do need to know what to look for. The main points are corrosion, internal wear, external wear and damage.

Age is the major factor when assessing the extent of corrosion to drive units. Over time, the original paint finish will become damaged, the aluminum exposed, and probably just slopped over with antifouling paint. Over time, corrosion will occur naturally, meaning unrelated to electrical problems, most particularly in sea water. These drives will not last forever, and ten years is probably a good average. When drives are old, I advise clients that they shouldn't expect trouble-free service. If they're corroded on the outside, they'll be even worse on the inside in places you can't see.

1. Check the gear case oil by backing the drain plug out. Check for water contamination and use a pencil magnet to check for excessive wear metals.

2. Rotate propeller rapidly to check for bend shaft. Bent shafts will be visible to the naked eye. The propeller hub should rotate perfectly concentric with the drive housing. If not, either the shaft is bent or the prop is out of round and balance which, in either case makes for a problem.

3. Raise drives and check exhaust and drive shaft bellows.

4. Rock the drives back and forth to check for wear in gimbal and pivot bearings.

5. Be alert to hidden patches of corrosion holes. On more than one occasion I have found sellers that have gone to considerable lengths to attempt to conceal serious corrosion with putty and paint.

6. Zincs should be free of excessive oxidation and pitting. Otherwise, replacement is recommended.

Stray current damage on drives is usually easy to spot. Normal salt water corrosion will be a dull gray usually with white oxides present. Stray current occurs rapidly and the pitting will usually show some bright metal with very rough or sharp edges. In its beginning stages it may show up as white, powdery residue on large parts of the drive, particularly if it is painted black.

Drive units are often found with broken skegs, yet the loss of a skeg is really of little consequence and may result in a slight reduction of steering response, but that's about all.

Some Things You May Not Have Thought About

1. Check location of fuel tank vent. Is the fitting of a type that will keep water out? Is it installed right?

2. Check hull sides closely for stress cracks.

3. The spreading use of putty bonded liners to the hull sides can lead to problems such as unanticipated stress that causes dimple, distortions, and even stress cracking. All the more reason to sight down the hull sides closely.

4. Poor paint adhesion. Hull was not properly prepped prior to first coat, so

that all subsequent coats are going to flake off. Most clients won't be thrilled should you fail to inform them that the bottom needs a costly stripping of old paint.

If it has one, don't forget to look at the bottom of the keel where there is often a lot of damage under a crust of barnacles.

The Deck Joint

Inspecting the deck joint while looking up at it can detect problems that otherwise might not be seen. This is particularly true when rails are coming loose or they're crushed and pushed into the hull side. It can also turn up bad design that leaves large gaps that allow water to enter the hull/deck joint. The deck joint is one of the major structural elements of the hull and should not be overlooked. Therefore, make it a point to walk around the hull, looking up at the rail. It may reveal damage that cannot be seen from above.

Attachments

We covered the topic of the running gear and struts in this and the Drive Train chapter but the importance of testing the stability of the struts is reiterated here. The huge, massive struts found on quality builders like Hatteras and Viking speak for themselves and it's the lesser animals that concern us here. There's a very easy way to test the struts and that is to pick up a big shoring block and give it a good, solid whack. There are two things to look for: (1) whether the hull flexes when the strut is hit, and (2) whether the strut is loose and water is bubbling out of the joint. Struts that shudder too much aren't adequately stabilized and can be the cause of vibration, alignment problems and excessive wear on bearings. When struts are not properly designed and installed, this can place undue strain on the hull laminate and cause failure or delamination. It's always best to thoroughly sound out around the strut bases and check closely for stress cracking.[2]

Now is the time to check over all other attachments to the hull, including such things as trim tabs, swim platforms, transducers, tank vent fittings, all through hull fittings and deck scuppers. All fasteners that penetrate the hull should be tested by attempting to tighten them. This will determine whether they're loose or possibly corroded. Bubbles or blisters of iron oxide appearing around stainless fasteners is a sure sign of crevice corrosion and indicates that all fasteners should be pulled, rebedded and possibly replaced.

Swim platforms, particularly after market add-ons, may not be properly installed. Common faults are improper bolting and backup, dissimilar materials, weak brackets, bolts installed without bedding and no bonding of brackets. Test the platform by pushing up from underside and looking for signs of looseness or water bubbling out of fastener holes. Like all other underwater metals, brackets need to be bonded but they usually aren't. Tubular stainless brackets with flattened ends retain water inside the tubes. They are prone to crevice corrosion on the flattened ends from within the tube. That's why so many of this type shear off, not from electrolysis but internal crevice corrosion. Bonding does not help this condition. It's easy to tell the difference between crevice corrosion or galvanism or electrolysis. The latter will usually attach the edges of the stainless part, whereas crevice corrosion occurs with a joint or concealed area such as a bolt hole.

Check stainless exhaust flanges for signs of corrosion and put a screwdriver in all fasteners and test them for tightness. If loose, pull them out and check for corrosion. Glassed or faired-in flanges or pipes should be checked for signs of cracking, gaps or leaking. At this point, I shine a strong light up the exhaust to check for possible broken baffles in the muffler, or possible overheating of the system.

Trim tabs cylinders can be tested both by operating and by pulling down on the trim plane. If it doesn't take much pressure to pull it down, the cylinders are weak and worn and should be replaced. It's also possible that the system has a leak or is out of fluid. Screws holding the tab hinges on are very prone to crevice corrosion and should be checked. Again, bubbles of brown oxides are clues to internal corrosion. Are the tabs bonded? Often times they're not.

Mr. Blister

The reader may be disappointed to learn that I am not going into a lengthy dissertation on this subject, the reason being that the more I learn about it, the more I realize that nothing can be said with much certainty. There are probably as many theories and opinions about blisters as there are people to have them. I have my own, and I'll leave you to develop yours, since so few "experts" are even in agreement. Yet there are two facts about blistering that we can state with certainty: blisters are the result of low quality materials and laminate design, and that they constitute a defective the product. It's a fact that if you build a boat with good quality resin, it's not going to blister. It doesn't even have to be epoxy or vinylester resin; isopthalic polyester resins have an excellent track record of not blistering

It can also be said with only slightly less certainty that blisters have rarely been shown to result in catastrophic damage to a hull. Certainly, it's true that severe blistering will degrade a hull over the very long term, meaning 30+ years, but that is most apt to occur on hulls that are already poorly engineered. Blisters are unsightly, disconcerting and cause a loss in speed as well as occasional loss in resale value. But beyond that, the need to repair is more a matter of esthetics than necessity. During a 35 year career, I've seen only three boats of which it could be said that blisters degraded the hull to the point of potential structural failure, and all three had other major contributing problems such as CSM comprising a major percentage of the laminate.

Blisters are more generally tolerated on older boats than newer, and for good reason. There's no justification for blisters on newer boats since it is widely known how to prevent them. It's my view that late model boats, say post 1992 or so, should be regarded as defective or built with substandard materials if the bottoms are blistered. If the client wants to buy a late model boat with blisters, he should be advised that this seriously affects resale value and that he should negotiate an adjustment in price if he feels the price does not reflect the condition, or that it hasn't been disclosed prior to survey.

There are numerous schemes promoted for blister repair. Many products and methods have failed, and because there is so little research to prove what works, I avoid getting involved with repair recommendations, and I suggest that you do the same. I point to the total disclaimers for all responsibility for use of the material printed directly on the labels of some of these products. If the manufacturer won't guarantee his product, I'm certainly not going to stick my neck out and recommend it. If companies like 3M and Interlux sell repair products, let them stick their necks out with recommended methods.

Sea Trial

The sea trial is usually the most grueling part of the survey because there's always so much to accomplish in so little time. For that reason it's important not to allow owners or brokers to limit the time you have available to complete the job. If forced into this situation, the surveyor is allowing others to control his work and he may end up overlooking things for which he may later have to foot the bill. Experienced surveyors know just how costly that "quick boat ride" can turn out to be.

The surveyor should also avoid being pressed into doing a sea trial first, before he has had an opportunity to become familiar with the vessel. Indicators or vital evidence of potential defects may show up during the other two parts of the survey that need to be evaluated during the sea trial. The sea trial should be done last because this is the time to check out what the net affect on the hull any other deficiencies may have.

Performing the sea trial is something that requires adequate time and preparation. Before starting, it's best to have everything opened up and ready to go. It's best to have a short list made in advance of what you need to check so you don't forget during this potentially hectic period. While the vessel is underway is not the time to be moving mattresses, pulling out drawers and opening up panels. This preparation work should be done beforehand. The surveyor cannot survey and operate the boat at the same time. That means he'll have to brief the operator on what he wants him to do.

The sea trial is the time when we want to evaluate the actual performance of the hull and internal structures. We've already reviewed most of the things to look for: We want to prove that the hull is sound in performance, not just appearance. The objective of the hull survey during the trial run is to put the hull under moderate stress. The ideal is to have 2-3' seas that will stress the hull sufficiently to show up any structural weaknesses. During the summer months, we often run into periods of total calm so that there's nothing to be done about it except running back and forth over your own wake. This procedure is not good enough but it's better than nothing. If the opposite extreme is encountered, heavy weather, it's best not to place yourself and the vessel at risk by insisting on an open water trial run. If at all possible, try to find an area in or around an inlet where some wave action will give at least a brief look at what is going on with the hull.

If there is no chance of subjecting the hull to any kind of stress, then it's wise to advise the client verbally and in the report, making it clear that the trial run was not conducted under any kind of stressful conditions. The surveyor needs to give the client the opportunity to decide for himself whether he wants to accept this, or try for another day.

Putting the vessel through a series of high speed turns is also helpful. High speed turning stresses a hull and can very easily show up structural weaknesses. A well built hull will not creak and groan badly in a hard turn; a poorly built hull usually will. Excessive noise in the forward section of the hull is usually a good indicator that the hull is twisting during a turn. If that's case, you've now been given a warning to look more closely than you otherwise might.

Probably the most important point to check is engine bed stringer deflection, for this can turn out to be a most costly problem. Measuring stringer deflection will give us a good indicator of overall hull strength. This is best accomplished during our ideal sea conditions, but even a soft swell or short chop can turn up interesting results. Since decks over the engine compartment are usually independent of the hull, it's usually safe to measure from stringer top to the underside of the deck. For this purpose, I use a folding wooden carpenter's rule. With just about any kind of boat, stringer deflection should not be more than 1/4" with the hull moving along through three foot seas. Any more than this the stringers are demonstrably weak and are likely to cause engine mount damage and alignment problems.

The remaining task is fairly simple and that is to generally check stringers, frames and bulkheads, checking how much, if any, bottom panel deflection is taking place. In well built boats there shouldn't be much. However, in a period when builders are constantly striving to make hulls lighter, when alarming amount of hull deflection are discovered, this needs to be carefully evaluated. Sometimes it's tough to arrive at a proper evaluation and further research may be needed.

I once was surveying a large, late model sport fisherman built by a very well known builder. The client was an avid fishermen and really wanted to put the boat through its paces and he was willing to wait for a day when we had some pretty good seas for a trial run. Once we got out in the Gulfstream and were tooling along at about 24 knots, I went forward, opened a hatch and popped down in the bilge. There was at least four feet of headroom down there and I could move around easily. I sat down on the bottom of the hull and was shocked that it felt like sitting on a magic carpet flying through the air, not a boat bottom riding over water. As I looked around there was visible panel deflection everywhere I looked.

Horrified and not knowing what to say to the client, I had the luxury of waiting until the next day to call the builder and speak to the head designer, with whom I was acquainted.

I told him my story and asked, "What the hell is going on?"

He laughed and said, "Yeah, I know."

"That's all you have to say?"

"Well, we designed it that way."

"Oh, really?" I didn't think he'd lie to me, but I wasn't sure that he was telling the truth, either. My objective was to get the load off my back and put it where it belonged.

"Sure we did. Why, was it breaking apart or something?"

"No," I said, "All that deflection of the bottom panels just scared the hell out of me, not to mention bruising my butt. I've got to tell the client something."

"I've seen it myself," he said. "We pushed our design parameters to the limits in our testing program and we know what it will take. Don't worry, we stand behind it and I promise you that it's not going to fall apart."

It was true, I knew, that this builder actually did do a lot of testing of their hulls, so at least I had reason to believe that he wasn't giving me the brush-off. Still, I didn't want any monkeys on my back.

"Can I tell my client that you said that . . . in writing?"

"Sure, why not?"

The long and short of it is that that boat went on to fish in tournaments all over the world and it never did suffer failure or fatigue. I could have made a bad mistake by condemning it, or by saying nothing about what I had observed. Instead, the problem was neatly solved by throwing it back on the builder who, I knew in any case, would stand behind it. But standing behind a failed product is not quite the same as catching it before it fails. Both myself and the client felt a lot more comfortable after consulting the builder. Things aren't always what they seem to be and we don't always have all the answers. Developing good contacts and performing a little research are not only part of the service we offer the client, but also constitute part of our never-ending learning process.

---

[1]The surveyor's experience and knowledge of a builder's reputation for quality, or lack thereof, is one of the surveyor's most useful tools. It alerts the surveyor to those occasions when he has to extend his efforts to determine the condition of a hull.

[2]See Chapter 10 DRIVE TRAIN for additional details.

Chapter 7

Stress Cracks & Surface Irregularities

Stress cracks are a commonly occurring phenomenon with reinforced plastic boats. A lot of boat owners get very upset when they see these cracks, sometimes needlessly, while at other times their fears are well founded. Clients will often ask about cracks and the surveyor will be expected to provide answers. This chapter is included not because stress cracks are unsightly and tend to upset people, but because they are often indicators of more serious, underlying problems.

After looking at many thousands of boats with stress cracks, I still have to say that evaluating the import of stress cracks, particularly in the bottom, is not always easy. There are often times when the surveyor can find no basis or cause for their existence, and thus it is left without an explanation to give. It will be useful to have an understanding of how and why these cracks commonly occur.

The primary reason why stress cracks appear in gel coat is because gel coat is brittle and the laminate to which it is bonded is less so. Gel coat is basically a resin to which a large amount of coloring pigment has been added, pigments that are oxides of metals like aluminum. Because reinforced plastic and gel coat are two very different materials they do expand and contract at the same rates when heating and cooling, nor do they have the same degree of elasticity and thus behave differently when flexing. We can add to this another factor, and that is the intended cured hardness. Gel coats that are harder than others are more durable, but they also have the down side of being more brittle and prone to cracking.

Gel coat cracking is the result of some kind of induced stress. This stress can come from improper design, or it can be the result of imposed stresses from within, without, or both. It can be the result of aging or faulty application such as excessive catalization or hardeners. By far, the most common reason for stress cracking is due to improper structure design. Even the finish on a flat panel will crack when bent too much. When it comes to large, flat panels, cracking usually results from excessive panel flexing or panting, such as on an unsupported hull side.

Cracking also occurs as a result of an engineering phenomenon called a stress riser. A stress riser occurs at point in a panel or hull skin where a normally somewhat flexible area is suddenly made rigid without a means of transferring the imposed stress gradually to the rest of the laminate. A good example is a strut attachment to the bottom without any kind of doubler. Another example would be a bottom stringer butting hard against the laminate with no fillet to distribute the load. Yet another is a railing stanchion attached to a deck laminate with no fillet or doubler beneath. The end result is that the amount of stress suddenly rises at a certain point and so stress cracks are likely to appear.

Stress Cracking on Bottoms

Stress Cracking on Bottoms is one of our biggest concerns, for here it may be a precursor of potential hull failure, so we want to do our best to try to assess the cause of any cracks that appear. Cracks most often appear at (1) the center of weak panels, (2) along the tight reverse curves of bottom strakes, (3) adjacent to bulkheads and, (4) paralleling stringers. Shown nearby are photos depicting each of these types of stress cracking, each of which is rather distinctive and easy to identify. However, we also need to be aware that there are no absolutes because laminates are not all the same and will behave differently. Obviously, a laminate

Fig. 7-1. Despite fouling and heavy paint build up, these stress cracks are highly visible right through the grime. Paint tends to make cracks more rather than less visible.

made of nearly all chopped strand mat is not going to behave the same as one made up of woven or stitched fabrics.

As the photos show, cracks tend to show up well on bottoms, particularly just as the paint starts to dry. One thing to be careful of is not to misidentify scrapes that can look like cracks, especially those scrapes caused by divers who clean bottoms with putty knives.

Weak Panel Flexing

Excessive panel (the unsupported area between frames) flexing is usually very distinctive; it's what is commonly called "oil canning," in which the weakness of the panel results in dimpling, like squeezing the bottom of an oil can. Most often this results in curvilinear cracking where the cracks more or less follow the perimeter of the dimpled or inset area. Most often the cracks appear in a semicircular arc that is rather large. In other cases the cracking may follow the perimeter of an area bordered by bulkheads, stringers or frames, resulting in a rectangular outline as shown in Fig. 7-2. In this extreme case of a boat that experienced massive bottom failure we have two distinct types of cracking showing. The panel area between frames is clearly outlined with cracks, plus there are several star burst patterns within this area. In this case, the bottom panel was flexing so bad that it was hitting the engine bell housing.

Serious panel flexing such as it would cause semicircular stress cracks is

Fig. 7-2. A good example of catestrophic panel failure in progress. This was the result of a too thin laminate.

Fig. 7-3. An open strake design caused these stress cracks. This bottom is beginning to look suspiciously weak with too much cracking for comfort.

always an indicator of serious structural weakness and must be addressed by the surveyor.

Hinge Effect and Hard Spots

In less severe cases flexing may only result in one or two cracks showing. Hinge effect is a term commonly used to denote a point where a panel is flexing off a bulkhead or stringer that has created a hard spot. Hard spots are stress risers that result from the transfer of stress from a stronger point to a weaker point without a transition zone of tapered laminate to gradually spread the load. Thus, the weak panel hinges off the reinforced panel and cracks.

Parallel Stress Cracking

Denoted by two or more cracks close together and extending for a considerable length, this type of cracking is usually associated with stringers, bottom strakes and bulkheads. One or two parallel cracks adjacent to a bulkhead is fairly common and generally does not indicate a serious weakness. But when the number of parallel cracks reaches three or more, it probably does.

Parallel cracking is often found on the inside radius of bottom strakes. The reason is usually a fault in the way the strakes are laid up. Usually the strake is left open on the inside where the vee shape of the strake can actually be seen. This causes the laminate to flex along the edges of the strake and in some cases it has lead to failure. We can judge by the severity and number of cracks appearing. Older and deeper cracks will look wider, may have breaks or chips showing along the crack edges, or fluids weeping out.

Figs. 7-4. This severe transverse cracking is caused by improper bulkhead installation. Failure is immanent.

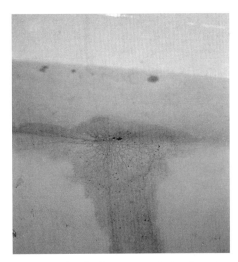

Fig. 7-5 Oil leaking out of this bottom strake foretells of a serious laminate problem.

Much the same can be said for cracks paralleling stringers. If they are few in number and do not appear wide and deep, then perhaps they are not threatening. A further thing we can to do is apply some pressure to the nearby laminate and try to see how weak it is. If we can move it manually by hand, then perhaps there is a serious problem.

Starburst Cracks

Star pattern cracks on the bottom indicate a small hard spot caused by something within, such as a support post for a deck resting on the bottom. Check the area on the interior for the cause. Usually does not require any further repair other than elimination of the hard spot.

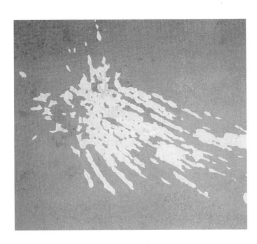

Fig. 7-6. The starburst pattern typically foretells of a hard spot on the interior. In this case the cracking is serious enough to indicate that the stress needs to be relieved to prevent laminate failure.

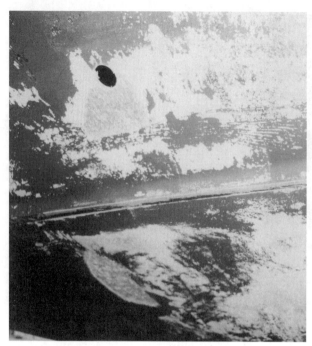

Fig. 7-7 In this case, severe panel flexing results in the outer skin breaking out and peeling away. Obviously, there are other laminate defects involved, which demonstrates my point that we never really know the quality of the laminate we're looking at. The sobering fact about this boat is that it was only two years old.

Gel Coat Break-Outs

Whenever gel coat begins to break away from stress cracks, as shown in Fig 7-4, this is a situation that points to a potential structural failure. In Fig. 7-7 the breakouts weren't small but involved big chunks of laminate peeling off.

Drawing Conclusions

While the cause of cracking may be easy to identify, judging the significance is usually quite another matter. Much has to do with the age of the boat and the severity of cracking. Certainly there are distinctions to be made between older boats and newer boats, so that cracking appearing on one will not carry the same weight as the other. Clearly, if you have some significant stress cracks showing up on a late model boat, these are going to progress over time and could very well signal a structural weakness. Conversely, an older boat has been subjected to numerous stress cycles over its life span, so that what we may be looking at is just age and fatigue. Once again, the question is whether that fatigue is life threatening. Is the hull sound or is it not?

In both cases we need to be concerned for different reasons. In the case of the newer boat, it is probably cracking due to a structural fault that may ultimately lead to a failure. With the older boat, fatigue may have so weakened a laminate that it is more prone to failure than we might otherwise have guessed.

Again, stress testing and observation during a sea trial may yield some clues.

To confuse the issue even further, stress cracks could be the result of a one-time incident, or may result from a situation that is ongoing. The surveyor's job is to try to find out. In an earlier chapter I stated that it was not the role of the pre-purchase surveyor to make an analysis of defects, but here we make a general exception to that rule by reason that this can be a very serious issue that needs some fast answers, and that it is often, though not always, within our ability to do so within a relatively short period of time. The photos shown in this chapter should help you in making these judgements.

There will always be occasions when we are uncertain as to the severity of the problem, in which case it is always better to err on the side of caution. Unlike physicians, we can't just order up a battery of tests. As often as not, how I arrive at my conclusions can involve some intangibles such as my knowledge of the builder and his track record on hull defects, as well as the level of quality and engineering of the vessel in question. If the builder has less than a sterling reputation, there's not much doubt about which side of the fence to come on.

Bottom Crazing

Shown nearby are several photos of boats where extensive crazing of the bottom gel coat has occurred. This does not occur often and I have seen only six such cases, all of them involving crazing covering nearly the entire bottom. All of the boats were at least 6 years old. In one case, it was so severe that the cracked gel coat was curling outward along the edges of the cracks and beginning to pop off.

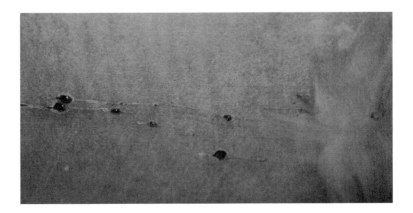

Fig 7-8. Ordinary parallel stress cracking caused by laminate hinging off of a stringer. Fluids and residue weeping out indicate water is migrating through the cracks and that they are more than just superficial.

What causes this is not known, though there are many theories. It appears to be similar to what happens with painted wood that absorbs water and swells; the wood expands but the paint doesn't and therefore the paint cracks because the surface to which it is attached expands. It is highly probable that that is what is occurring with these boats, since the phenomenon is always on the bottom and stops at the water line.

Cracking on Hull Sides

It seems to be a little understood principle, at least judging by what we see with so many boats, that when a boat slams off a wave, most of the energy sustained is transmitted from the bottom to the hull sides. Hence, one reason we see so much stress cracking on hull sides. This usually shows up in the forward half of the hull and usually just above the chine.

The reason why is very simple: The laminate thickness is carried at the same thickness from the chine up to the deck. The laminate below the chine is thicker than the laminate immediately above it. Rules of good design require that the chines be reinforced with a heavier laminate that tapers gradually up into the sides, detail work that is often neglected. And so cracks develop.

While I've never seen or heard of a failure occurring as a result of this, I have seen some very ugly and disturbing cracking on some boats. So what do you tell a client in such a situation? How about asking him if he really wants to buy into something like that? I point out that not only do they have to think about the potential for failure, but about what will happen when it comes time for him to resell the boat. That usually sets his thinking straight if he was previously inclined to buy it.

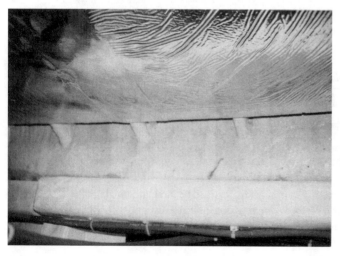

Fig. 7-9. This fuel tank foundation is sitting directly on the hull skin, so it's no surprise that the tank is leaking. Each of those support legs creates a hard spot which causes stress cracking an possible laminate failure. Also note the big step down in the stringer at left.

Large area panel cracking in the bows of sport fishermen is common. It usually results from inadequate framing, a problem of almost all boats, since builders rarely see fit to put any kind of framing on hull sides. When the bow is stuffed into a wave, serious panel deflection occurs and hence the cracking. In most cases I write it off as non structural. But it's best to check closely from the interior if at all possible.

Cracking on Decks and Superstructures

Cracking above the gunwale is what people see and get most agitated about. It is, of course, the least serious place for cracking to occur and with a few exceptions, is more often displeasing to the eye than being serious. Here are a few examples of when it can be serious:

- Cracks showing up at or near the center of decks, usually with no distinguishable pattern. Very often indicates a damaged deck core.

- Numerous and large cracks showing up in the amidships section around coamings and windshields, and in association with cracking around doors and bulkheads. Likely indicates the boat is bending lengthwise.

- Cracks appearing around raised bow hatch coamings. Likely indicates a weak deck or damaged core.

- Cracks appearing around base of bow pulpit and possibly deck flange. Stress damage to pulpit that needs to be repaired and reinforced.

- Excessive cracking around most of cockpit hatch corners. Indicates a poorly designed deck. Check it closely.

- Significant cracking in the lower portion of cabin and cockpit liners. Hull flexing may be stressing the liners, causing damage that could be serious to both liners and the hull. It can also be the result of liners that are improperly designed and/or supported.

- Excessive cracking along deck-to-hull join. Probable poorly designed deck flange for which repair is very costly or even impossible.

- Serious cracking around transom doors. Check for transom weakness and inadequate structural design.

- Random pattern cracking on deck around chair/seat mounts, consoles and other similar attachments. Will indicate either a weak laminate, or a core that is water saturated and deteriorating.

Fig. 7-10. Excessive cracking around this stanchion base suggests more than normal stress. In this case, a plywood core is competely wasted so that the laminate has been badly weakened.

Cracking that occurs around hardware mountings most often are associated with very hard gel coats. The screws cause the fracture. If the fractures don't emanate precisely from the fasteners, then most likely the hardware is stressing a weak laminate. Also, possible rotted deck core.

Surface Irregularities

Unusual surface irregularities are occasionally found that include alligatoring, a condition appearance that looks like wrinkles in the gel coat of no symmetrical pattern, print-through, post cure and gel coat voids.

Alligatoring

occurs as a result of over catalization. It results in high heat build up and rapid shrinking of the plastic causing a wrinkled appearance. The end result is an uneven surface texture that isn't supposed to be there. This is a harmless but unsightly cosmetic defect.

Print Through

This is another finish defect that although harmless, can be very unsightly. It is almost always found on darker pigmented surfaces and will be very prevalent in hotter climates. The worst cases are when insufficient mat is used against woven roving and this coarse weave fabric telegraphs its pattern through the gel coat. Initially, when the part is pulled out of the mold, this pattern doesn't yet show. It's usually not until long after the first owner has taken delivery that he first notices his hull sides looking like a piece of fabric. Most print through develops hand in hand with post cure, a condition in which "cured" resins continue to cure a bit more and shrink a bit when exposed to sunlight and heat. In severe cases, even the checkerboard pattern of core materials have telegraphed

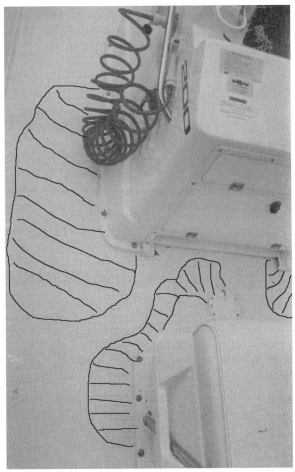

Fig. 7-11. Painstaking sounding turned up extesnsive deck core rot and delamination in this small boat. Console and seats were screwed to the cored deck. A flexing hull caused the screws to back out and letting water into the core. The moral of this story is how the deck problems are directly related to a weak hull.

through. While this is not known to cause any structural problems, the defect can be very unsightly.

Print through is also related to heat distortion problems that occur due to the fact that boat owners like to have black painted feature stripes and other dark colored paint work. Under direct sunlight, these dark surfaces can heat up so much that the plastic becomes unstable and shrinks. In worst cases, where a laminate is under stress, serious distortion can and does occur. Make it a point to examine all dark painted surfaces closely, particularly older boats.

In recent years, some of the better builders have been resolving the problem by using high heat distortion temperature resins in these areas that commonly get painted black, particularly larger sport fishermen where on later models the problem is now found much less often.

After having learned the hard way decades ago, builders are once again building dark colored hulls. Apparently they have forgotten all of the problems associated with heat and plastic. On two recent occasions I observed brand new boats with black hulls that had one or more large blisters on the hull sides. Several people erroneously thought these were water blisters, but they weren't. What happened to cause these blisters was a combination of high heat build up, followed by post cure shrinkage and gassing.

Excessive Gel Coat Thickness

Controlling the thickness of gel coat within the mold with a spray gun is not easy and so problems with too much or too little tend to show up in older boats. The application of too much or too little gel coat is common. Too thick gel coat is not normally a problem in the near term, but most always shows up over the long term as cracking or substantial chipping. This type of cracking can be random or in association with stress zones.

The opposite condition, too thin gel coat, is easy to identify. As it wears away, the underlying laminate becomes exposed.

Gel Coat Voids

These are simply bubbles or even somewhat larger areas where the skin-out mat does not make contact with the gel coat. It can be caused by either poor wet out, but it has also been theorized that it is caused by the release of gas during cure. One would suppose that if that were true, it would happen to most all boats, and since it doesn't, figure it's bad workmanship.

These voids usually don't begin to show up for several years or more. Much depends on their size, gel coat thickness and their location. The surface gel coat above a void will usually do one of two things. Either it gets stressed and punctured, in which case there is now a small crater showing on the surface, or it will result in small circular or semi-circular cracks showing. These round or nearly round cracks often mystify people as to their cause. They can be unsightly but are not harmful.

Mottling, Uneven Coloration

As boats age, it is very common to see the surface finish become blotchy, or to see distinct areas of differing color and color changes. This is caused by after-molding gel coat repairs, either as the result of damage, or repair work done by the builder as a result of mold release damage. This sort of thing is very prevalent on boats built in the Orient from poor quality molds, or smaller molded parts that are manually pieced together. No two applications of gel coat, even if from the same batch or can, will age the same; the color will change enough to become noticeable. It's a good idea to check to see if large area coloration changes are the result of damage repair.

Surface Porosity

Frankly, I don't know what causes the occasional case of gel coat porosity that I see. Most likely it is the result of a faulty spray-up application. Whatever it is, the condition doesn't seem to show up on new boats, but gradually develops and worsens over time as thousands of little pin holes erode and enlarge.

Chapter 8

Decks & Superstructure

Hull-to-Deck Joint

The hull-to-deck is one of the more critical, and often one of the weakest, joints involved in the construction of a fiberglass boat. It is the unifying structure that ties the other three sides of the hull together. Not only does it have to be strong enough to withstand the stresses imposed on it by the dynamics of the hull traveling at speed, but also to withstand the impacts and abuse it receives from hitting up against dock pilings. For the builder, attaching a deck to a hull is a time-consuming process that provides the motivation to perform the task as quickly and cheaply as possible.

Over the years, walking through boat yards, walking down the rows of boats, I've marveled at the percentage of all boats that have rub rails that are loose and starting to fall off. I always thought that it was just because the builder did a poor job of installing the rub rails, selecting poor materials and not fastening them right. Of course anything attached to a fiberglass laminate with screws doesn't have much holding power. Screws set into fiberglass shatter the laminate — particularly when the pilot holes are not exactly the right size — and make for a naturally weak joint.

It was not until I actually began my research of observing what happens to a hull when it is underway in a moderate sea that I began to realize that loose guard rails and weak hull/deck joints involved more than just fasteners. On smaller boats, the deck and rub rail are often installed all in one operation; on larger boats it's usually done in two operations. Bolting the deck to the hull is much better than screwing it, but then I began to notice that even some bolted deck joints came apart and so I wondered how this could be. Ultimately it was discovered that panting of the hull sides and bending of the hull longitudinally was usually responsible for the loose guard rails. But behind the loose guard

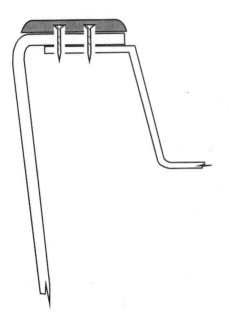

Fig. 8-1. Bulwarks style deck join. Stronger than most, it can leak after sustaining heavy impacts.

rails was a larger problem of a damaged hull/deck joint caused by panting hull sides. This accounts for why so many guard rail repairs fail: fastening a new rail onto a deck joint that is loose and continues to work inevitably results in the newly fastened rail to work loose as well, usually sooner rather than later.

Hull/deck joints have to be strong and the reason is this: Decks on fiberglass boats are like the roof on a house; without the roof, the walls are weak. On a boat, the deck ties the perimeter of the hull together. A very large part of the energy generated by the hull moving over the surface of water is transferred by the hull sides and the bulkheads up into the deck. Thus, if the joint is not strong, it will fail. And fail they do, by the thousands. On screwed-together hull/deck joints, the action of the hull side moving upwards causes the hull flange to shear against the deck flange. Being naturally weak, the stress is on the screw holes and the threads of the screws begins to grind into and shatter the laminate. Continued stress eventually results in the screw holes becoming enlarged and the fasteners then go loose. In a progression of fastener failures, the deck joint continues to weaken and the condition worsens to the point where rails start loosening and falling off. Refastening the rail with new fasteners into new holes is only a temporary fix that will not last long because by now the whole deck is somewhat loose and the new fasteners will quickly lose their purchase.

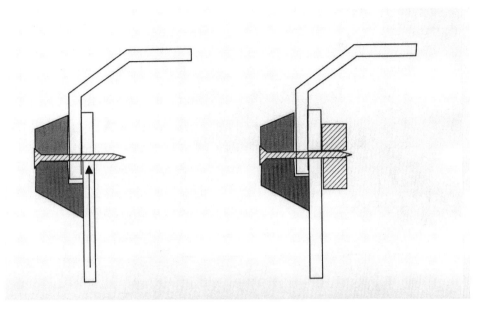

Fig 8-2. Bad and better: The common deck flange lap joint, with and without backup strip. Upward forces in the hull sides cause the side panel to shear against the screw, resulting in elongated screw holes. The backup strip bonded in place helps to distribute the load and reduce fastener failure but still relies on a single fastener.

Methods of Attachment

There are at least four main methods for attaching decks to hulls: simple screws, bolts, screws or bolts through a backup strip of wood or aluminum, and screws and bolts with glass bonding over the inside of the joint. Lesser quality builders resort to just screwing the deck on; the better builders will screw or bolt through a backing strip of wood or aluminum and then glass the whole thing over. The later method results in a joint that is sufficiently strong and rarely fails, even after sustaining heavy impacts. Glassing on the inside not only adds strength and retards working, but also serves to prevent the inevitable leaks that occur around screw holes or when a joint becomes loose. In fact, water leakage into the interior around the deck joint is one of the prime indicators that all is not well and is a signal to look closer.

To make a good check of the hull/deck joint, first go to the rope locker where the inside of the joint is usually easily visible. Once it is determined how it is attached, then if leaks are found or the guard rails are falling off or loosening, you'll know why. If they are, one can remove a line of screws sufficient to move the rail out of the way in order to get a peek at the joint. We want to know if the screw holes are elongated which, if they are, is evidence that the

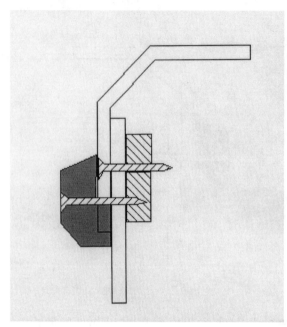

Fig . 8-3. Better and Best. At left, deck is screwed on independently with a doubler strip behind. At right facing page, the bonded joint ties hull and deck together with a heavy layer of glasss that makes the joint watertight.

hull is working and may be at the source of the problem.

Hull lap joints are often poorly fitted, particularly on small boats where the builder may cut every possible corner and performs the mechanical fastening of the deck at the same time he is installing the rub rail. This is the worst possible joint of all. Obviously, when done this way, the installer cannot see the joint because he is placing the rail over it and drilling pilot holes and installing screws all at the same time. This procedure often causes lines of screws to either completely miss the lap joint, or ends up placing the screws on the very edge of the lap. This is the primary method used on boats under thirty feet and accounts for most of the major hull/deck/rail failures.

Aluminum rivets have been used for a long time to fasten hulls to decks, primarily in small boats. This is a totally unacceptable method that is doomed to failure. It is the hallmark of a grossly inferior product (especially in seawater) and the client should be advised accordingly.

Weak Hull Sides

There has been a trend in the last decade or so to reduce costs by eliminating the labor involved in creating frames of any kind in hull sides. This has resulted in a profusion of boats and yachts with completely unsupported and notoriously weak hull sides. All one has to do is bang on the side of the hull with a closed fist to locate them. When the whole hull side shudders under the impact of your hand, imagine what it does when the hull slams down off a wave.

When we find conditions like this, as we often will, what we have witnessed is a serious structural weakness that may create consequences that go far beyond just the deck joint.

Tens of thousands of boats have toe rails with extensive and serious stress cracking caused by the weakness of the deck joint and the inability to withstand impacts against pilings that they should be able to withstand. Often surveyors simply attribute this to piling damage when the real cause is structural weakness. Moreover, weak deck joints usually translate into a condition of general weakness of the superstructure and accounts for so many of the leaking windows

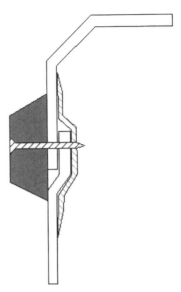

Fig. 8-4.

and hatches that we find. If a deck structure is not reasonably rigid, all that movement and flexing causes joints to open up and result in leakage. Once this happens, it becomes a chronic problem that cannot be solved. In about 25% of all my surveys the client is advised of structural inadequacy of the hull/deck joint.

Leaking port holes is another one of the symptoms of panting hull sides. When hull sides flex, the seals around flanges loosen and then leak. Leaks around hatches and hardware can also be a symptom of structural weakness if the deck itself is weak. Further, when a designer attempts to achieve large, open interior spaces, he usually does this by eliminating bulkheads. Today there are legions of express cruisers with cavernous interiors that utterly lack adequate deck support. Without the support of these bulkheads from below, decks are so poorly supported that they sag, or flutter during slamming. When the hull slams off a wave, the whole deck itself may shudder, particularly when it is supporting the weight of the superstructure above. Considering these factors, we can now understand why delaminated decks and chronic leakage are so often a problem. More often than not, leaking windows are not the result of poor quality windows or installation, but rather the weak structure to which they're attached.

Fig. 8-5. This situation should speak for itself. The deck on a 36 footer simply screwed together. 18 months old, the interior is already almost ruined from massive leaks.

Decks

The survey of a two year-old, half-million-dollar 43 foot sport fisherman recently reminded me once again of why it is necessary to sound out decks thoroughly. After sounding out the foam cored deck, nearly a dozen areas of significant delamination were found, including extensive delamination around the fore deck hatch. The hatch was an aluminum frame screwed directly to the deck. The disbonding here was most likely initiated by the upward pull of the jigsaw teeth when the hatch opening was cut (the opening was not created in the mold, as it should have been), and later progressed into massive disbonding because there was no support from below. The deck was weak and would sag when walked on.

Builders of wood boats knew that they had to frame out a hatch to keep the deck from sagging, much the same way a window in a house is framed. Many fiberglass boat builders don't seem to recognize this. If they just cut a hole in a cored deck and screw on a hatch frame, the deck will sag, and the hatch frame will eventually leak and water will get into the core. Proper construction requires a non-cored fillet be fabricated around the hatch perimeter so that the fasteners will set into a solid laminate or a lumber core. This occurs mainly on mid to large size yachts, and particularly sport fishermen, where the superstructure has a fairly high profile, but can also occur in low profile boats such as express cruisers where long windows have no support posts. I'm constantly amazed at the number of yachts I find on which the housetop is supported only by the aluminum window frames. Imagine this! A flying bridge supported only by the rear bulkhead and the cabin window frames. Yet we see this all the time. It is the inability of window glass and frames to support the weight above that results in cracked salon windows and leakage. Again, there's no remedy for it because it's a design problem that can't be corrected short of costly alterations.

The surveyor should pay particular attention to motor yachts that have large bridge decks that are extensively equipped with everything from galley appliances to hot tubs, tenders, jet skis and a Rolls Royce. The fundamental question has to be: Was the deck designed to carry the weight? In many cases it was not and this can be the fault of the builder or an owner who failed to get professional advice before he made significant changes such as adding a davit and a Boston Whaler without regard to whether the structure could support it. This first sign of trouble is usually leakage, but it's always a good idea to look around below and determine how much support the upper deck has. If there's nothing but windows all around and no pillars or bulkheads, there could be a problem. Another unintended consequence of adding too much weight above is increasing the center of gravity and reducing stability. I've seen this happen fairly often and it's something to be on the alert for.

While I'm not suggesting that the surveyor should, as a routine part of his survey, evaluate stability factors, he does have a responsibility to advise the client if the vessel appears patently unstable. One way to make a quick assessment is to note the beam to height ratio, or the beam to length ratio. If a bridge deck motor yacht has a particularly high aspect ratio such as 1.5 times beam, it's a good idea to pay attention to how the vessel handles in a seaway.

Bear in mind that a lot of large motor yachts are being designed with the maximum beam of 18' so that they can be hauled in a standard travel lift. A 35' cruiser with a 12' beam has a beam to length ratio of 35% but a 72 footer with an 18' beam has only a 25% ratio. Give that same 72 footer a particularly high aspect ratio, add on a bridge deck equipped like a hotel pool deck complete with tenders, hot tubs and all the other goodies, chances are that you've got a stability problem. The 72 and 80 foot Hatteras motor yachts, both of which have 18' beams, are two good examples of boats that are can be tender due to narrow beams. Moreover, their very spacious upper decks invite the addition of tons of additions and equipment which can make these yachts rather unpleasant at sea.

Builders of yachts this size are usually not so dumb as to ignore performing their basic stability calculations so that they know just how far they can go with adding equipment high up. It is usually the owner that adds the extra weight that pushes it past the limits. While the surveyor may not wish to raise this issue

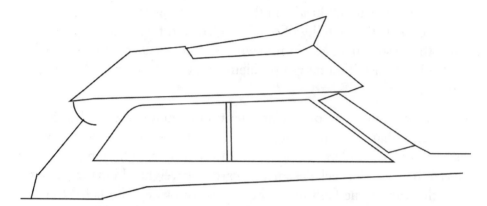

Fig 8-6. Flying bridge sedans typically have only the window frames at the forward end for support. This often means that the window glass is carrying the load and accounts for why windows in this style boat are so often cracked. When these boats have acute window leakage problems, look for a lack of support for the bridge deck.

in a written report, at the very least he should discuss the situation with the client.

Many small to midsize boats have weak housetops. This usually doesn't cause much of a problem unless the flexing is causing disturbance in way of attachments such as bridge pedestal seat bases, window and hatch frames. Excessive flexing can cause screws to loosen and cause leakage, as well as flexing around hatches. Check the interior for water stains on the headliner and also whether water is being channeled and leaking out at other odd locations. Headliners will occasionally channel the water and leak it out in the strangest places. Rust and corrosion around overhead lights is a strong indicator of possible leakage.

Another serious effect of weak housetops is that it may cause disturbance of the cockpit (on express cruisers) or pilothouse windshield attachment. Not only can it cause leaks into the windshield area, but since windshields are usually attached from below, it can also cause leaks into the interior. Numerous express cruisers suffer from this condition where not only does water leak into the interior but also finds its way into the helm instrument panel.

The simple way to test for weak decks is put them to the test by bouncing on them. A well constructed deck or housetop shouldn't have any give at all. When I find evidence of substantial leakage, but I'm not sure how bad it is, if the sea trial doesn't produce spray that shows up the leaks, the old water hose test usually produces the answer.

Core Materials

Most superstructures and decks utilize some kind of core material that can range from foam, balsa, plywood to plastic honeycomb such as NidaCore. On more carefully crafted boats, plywood blanks are often installed as doublers within the laminate for cleats and anchor windlass foundations.

Go-fast boats need to have very strong decks because their long snouts usually make up a major structural element of the hull. Several builders that I'm familiar with perform a painstaking process of cutting numerous blocks of plywood and fit them together to form a rigid backbone of the deck.

On sport fishermen, the cockpit gunwales are sometimes cored with ply-

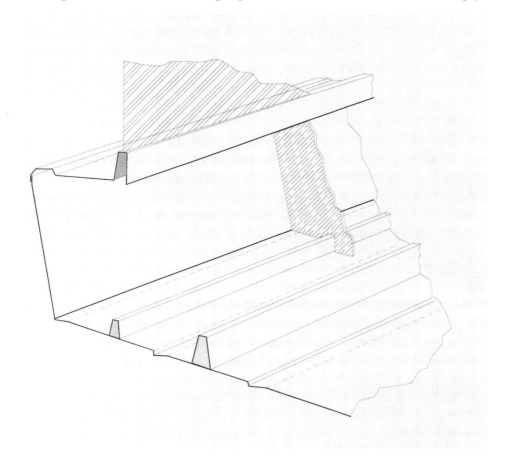

Fig 8-7. This drawing illustrates how unsupported side decks can cause severe leakage of house side windows. Lacking support from below, the deck sags and pulls the window frame seams open. This is why attempts to fix side window leaks usually fail.

wood for extra strength. Be wary of unsealed cut-outs for things like rod holders and filler and hawse pipes.

An interesting feature of plywood is that it usually causes a disturbing crackling sound when the deck is walked on. This should not be immediately taken to mean that there are delamination problems, for this is a regular feature of plywood cores. Instead, the deck should be sounded out if delamination is suspected. However, resins bond very strongly to plywood and delaminations are unlikely. Normally, shoddy workmanship results in incomplete bonding rather than delamination.

Whether balsa or foam, cores utilized in superstructures have the distinction of being subject to print-through, especially when areas are painted dark colors which absorb heat. The cause of this is post-cure shrinking of the plastic. These surfaces can heat up to nearly 200 degrees under the summer sun. This accounts for the ungainly checkerboard pattern that is nearly always present when house sides, and particularly the sloping forward house faces, are painted black as is the current fashion. There is virtually nothing that can be done to prevent this short of not painting it black in the first place.

Even attempts at refairing usually fail to achieve the desired results because high temperatures will continue to affect the stability of the material. Expansion and contraction due to heating and cooling can also result in buckling of unusually thin outer laminates and may result in cracking. Incomplete bonding due to poor craftsmanship is commonplace and can produce various surface irregularities such as waviness or even the appearance of large blisters. These irregularities can show up on hot days and disappear on cool days due to expansion and contraction.

Larger motor yachts frequently have major alterations to the extent that the surveyor should be wary of them and devote closer attention to them. Such modifications are often done on low budgets and involve inferior materials and workmanship, sometimes to an appalling degree.

Custom boats and foreign imports, particularly from the orient, are also subjects for poor workmanship and detailing along house sides and bridge coamings. Some do not have molded superstructures, but have structures that are assembled in pieces that are bonded together, faired over, and then sprayed with gel coat.

Making it a point to sight along the plane of all surfaces will usually expose these irregularities and often identify the source of the problem, be it irregularities or disbonding. Long wrinkles send up a red warning flare, for wrinkling may be evidence of structural instability. If wrinkles are appearing, it likely means that some degree of bending or twisting is going on and the cause of this should be further investigated. Yachts that have had additions and alterations deserve special attention as these usually involve gobs of fairing material.

Bridge and house extensions offer another potential avenue where workmanship may not be what it should be. Sometimes underlying structures were never intended to support additional weights or stresses so that the addition of the new weight causes a failure of the original structure. Anyone who has spent much time around boat yards knows that putty has become the all-time favorite material for covering up problems or avoiding doing the job right to begin with. Rather than providing a proper lamination, it's quite common for workers to simply apply an inch or two of bond-o to save time. Most of these materials are not intended to be used this way. When applied beyond a certain thickness, the material becomes unstable and produce all sorts of strange results.

Bubbling and blistering in these areas usually means that a cheap, polyester fairing was used, and that it has since absorbed water. The condition cannot be resolved short of eliminating the offending material completely.

When extensive modifications are encountered, splices into existing cores should be checked closely to ensure that there is sufficient overlap to make for a strong join. Joints filled with a lot putty and fillers are often structurally weak and dimensionally unsound and exhibit stress cracking or age shrinking of the filler. The danger here is that if the new owner attempts to repair it and finds that the core is saturated with water, he may ask the surveyor to assist with cost should he fail to give warning. All areas of cracking on the superstructure and decks should be treated seriously with cored laminates.

Check flying bridge decks and house tops by looking at the outer perimeter, along the aft edge and especially side edges, perhaps up under the window overhang. Since the deck is crowned, this is where water will migrate and will often show up as constant weeping or even outright dripping. Mold, moss and weep stains usually reveal this condition, and so will moldings that are unusually corroded. The same holds true for extended deck house tops. I've even found ferns growing out of the edges of bridge decks. Have you ever wondered why aluminum enclosure slide tracks on the underside of the deck often waste completely away? This is because they're being fed a constant source of water from a saturated core through the screw holes on the underside.

Older boats often have numerous holes showing on decks, house sides and tops, holes that are either not filled or hastily filled with caulking. Any hole into a cored laminate is cause for suspicion of water entry into the core, particularly when they appear in low lying areas that may trap water. The same holds for equipment, especially load bearing equipment, attached to cored structures, particularly decks. Be especially wary of tender cradles, life rafts, deck boxes and the like. If this equipment is screwed or bolted through the core, without benefit of fillets, there is a good possibility that it could be leaking water into the core.

The odd thing about saturated cores is that the water will seek a place where it can leak out usually at a screw hole somewhere on the underside far from the source of ingress. If the underside of the core can be seen, water saturation usually results in darkening of the core so that it becomes obvious. If the deck is crowned, by all means check around the underside perimeter because this is where the water will end up. It is easy to mistake water stains running down the inside of a hull side ceiling as a leaking deck joint when it may be water leaking from the deck core. Unfortunately, the undersides of decks are often completely obscured by headliners so that nothing can be seen. But unusual water spotting of the headliner may signal the problem. Or it may not. The best way to keep one's feet out of hot water is to recommend dropping a section of headliner and drilling some pilot holes to see if water runs out. This doesn't necessarily mean that the surveyor should do this, just make the recommendation to cover yourself.

Drainage

Unless a designer considers water drainage from the decks at the outset of the design process, yachts can end up with chronic drainage problems. It's easy for designers and builders to forget that a boat crashing through heavy seas can take hundreds of gallons of water over the bow all at once, or be subjected to torrential rainfalls. Both occurrences can overwhelm a poorly considered drainage system.

A common problem stems from cockpit yachts on which the water draining from the foredeck, travels down the side decks and dumps into the cockpit, causing all sorts of damage and problems. The side decks should have a breakwater and adequate scuppering.

Another consideration has to be that yachts do not always sit on their designed waterline. It occasionally happens that a boat is hauled and blocked with the bow in a slightly down position, thus causing water to run forward, a situation that a designer is unlikely to consider. But good designers do consider these things.

The side decks of motor yachts need to have a sufficient number of scuppers so that water will be drained off no matter how the vessel is trimmed. Otherwise, standing water is likely to find its way in through deck fastenings which are very difficult to keep completely water tight because of the stress to which they are constantly subjected. Good scuppers must be necessarily large so that leaves and debris do not easily clog them up. All too often, scuppers are so small that it only takes a leaf or two or a piece of clear plastic to clog it up. Motor yachts are also prone to having poor drainage on the raised aft deck where, if not correctly designed, water is likely to leak into the aft quarters. It's quite common to find the deck drain scupper immediately adjacent to the mooring cleat and it doesn't take an engineer to figure out what is likely to happen here. The stress on the cleat will constantly break the caulking seal of the scupper. The aft quarters of motor yachts with aft deck scuppers should be checked for leakage from the interior overhead. Water stained paneling, headliners or loose and peeling wall coverings are usually a tip-off to leaks.

Flying bridges often make for a great water catchment system capable of containing hundreds of gallons of water that has to be safely channeled away. A well designed yacht will have a deep and wide gutter around the perimeter. Lacking this, serious problems can occur when water finds its way into the

Fig 8-8. Bow pulpits can create a tremendous lever arm and stress on the hull/deck joint. As a result of plunging into a wave, this pulpit has not only broken the deck joint loose, but fractured it as well.

hollow area of the bridge coamings since bridge decks are usually cored. Frequently we find that various electronic equipment has been mounted either within the coaming or under bridge deck seating, fastened with screws driven directly into the deck laminate. Installers seem to believe that water will never get into this area and so they don't use any caulking. Even worse, installers or the builder may drill holes directly through the house top to run cables. Sometimes there are pre-designed conduit holes which lack cofferdams so that when the area fills up with water, it runs down through these openings.

It should be born in mind that, unless the inside of the coamings have good-sized drains, they can easily be plugged up and cause very large amounts of water to accumulate and then run down the openings. The bridge deck drainage arrangement should be inspected for these problems. If the builder has considered drainage at all, the method of drainage should be easy to spot. The large cavity within the forward coaming is usually accessible. The surveyor needs to crawl inside and inspect the interior for signs of standing water in the outboard corners. Sometimes high water lines are apparent indicating a standing water problem. Just because the wire conduits are on the high side of the crown doesn't mean that the compartment can't fill up or that the boat won't roll, causing water to surge across the deck. All conduits should be fitted with a cofferdam to at least contain and prevent limited amounts of water on the decks from going down the hole.

An illustration of just how serious this can be involved a 55 foot motor yacht owned by a Canadian and kept in Florida. He used up all the fuel in his aft tanks and left the boat for months trimmed down by the bow, unaware that the average rainfall is more than 60". All this water was being trapped on the bridge deck, flooding down not only through the holes under the bridge coaming, but also through the deck hatch down into the pilot house. This destroyed the entire interior of the yacht and the resulting damage was assessed at over $120,000.00. This condition could easily have been diagnosed during a survey because the bridge deck was totally flat and there were no cofferdams around the wire conduits through the deck, or around a deck hatch.

Towers

Towers of all types need careful inspection. It is a fairly common occurrence that towers become damaged by vessel pounding. As a hull slams down into a trough, the tendency of the tower is to whip forward. This sets up some heavy stresses in the tower that can crack welds and bend tower legs. Moreover, after the recent spate of hurricanes, more and more sport fishermen are being found with damage that heretofore was not discovered or repaired.

Sight the tower legs to make sure that they're straight. It's also a good idea to stand back and check the tower to make sure that it is not visually out of kilter. I've found several that were off by as much as six inches. Then check over the welds for cracks. Towers and outriggers should also have good lightning grounds, but more often than not, they don't.

Tower legs need a strong foundation. If the builder hasn't provided for this, there could be a problem. Check extra carefully around the tower leg bases for dimples, distortions, and cracks, as well as the possibility of deterioration of a plywood core foundation.

Tenders, Pulpits and Davits

Bow pulpits can create tremendous leverage on the deck and the hull joint, either by striking a dock piling or plunging down into a wave where the upward force of the wave can literally tear the pulpit off or lift the deck. When hitting a wave, it acts just like an old fashioned beer can opener. Both the hull and the deck flange in way of the pulpit need to have extra heavy laminate and should be bolted and bonded. The presence of damage is most easily determined, if it does not appear on the exterior, from within the rope locker where the fasteners or tabbing is visible. Try bouncing on the end of the pulpit to see if it is lifting the deck or if the bolts are loose.

Boat davits may be add-ons, provision for which was not anticipated by the

Fig. 8-9. This owner, without considering the engineering problems, simply added a cradle for his inflatable onto a swim platform. Neither the platform nor the boat transom were designed to carry this kind of weight on a seven foot lever arm. The brackets are punching through the transom.

builder, nor adequately designed by the installer. Boat davits deserve careful evaluation since there have been several fatalities involving davit and equipment failures that I know of. Davits should never be mounted directly on a deck or house top but rather have a foundation either on a structural bulkhead or on a hull member.

Most of the stress on a davit is leverage and for that reason the foundation needs to be strong. A davit posted through a fore deck or aft deck housetop works to tear at the deck surface and may disjoint the supporting structures, particularly in the case of a house top mounting where the upper deck is mainly support by window frames. Both the weight of the tender or the leverage of the davit can end up weakening the entire house structure causing damage or leakage.

Most of the big name davit builders know how to make good installations so substandard installations are fairly rare on late model boats. Beware of oddball davits that look like bolt-ons. It's not uncommon to find jury-rigged contraptions designed by amateurs. Davits are fairly dangerous devices that generate frequent accidents. I do not recommend that the surveyor should test them by lifting the tender unless you get the captain or owner to do it. If not, don't forget to state in your report that the davit was not tested.

A variety of transom dinghy mounting contraptions have appeared on the market lately which are essentially bolt-ons. These, can create a lot of leverage on transoms and decks so the manner of mounting deserves some attention. Some of these things are intended to rest entirely on a swim platform that may not have been designed to carry the weight, particularly when someone tries to lift a dinghy full of water. Look for platform bolts starting to pull through the transom or otherwise causing distortion.

Be especially wary of those huge bolt on hydraulic tender platforms. Some of these things are up to six feet wide and create a six foot lever arm on the transom. Few boats are originally designed to carry this kind of load, and reinforcements for the installation often fall very short.

These devices are also known to cause serious trim and performance problems by placing heavy weights far aft of the hull.

Chapter 9

Cockpits

It might seem odd that a whole chapter has been devoted to cockpit design, and you might even be wondering why it has been included at all. The reason is simple: faulty cockpit design is the leading cause of small boat sinkings, particularly outboard and stern drive boats, and to a lesser extent, smaller inboards and sport fishermen. This chapter will review some of the most commonly found design defects, how to locate them, as well as offering some solutions on how to deal with them.

Every year thousands of small boats sink, usually at their docks, with no one aboard and no one witnessing the event. In most cases the reason why it happens is the result of bilge pump or battery failure. Indeed, bilge pump and battery failures invariably figure in to scheme of events, but investigators often don't go far enough to find out the whole reason these components failed.

That so many small boats suffer from unseaworthy cockpit design is simply the result of cockpit scuppers that allows water to back-flow onto the deck and then find its way into the bilge via leaking hatches or other openings. Designers could easily create more seaworthy designs by giving the vessel sufficient freeboard so that the decks would not have to be placed at, or near the water line. But the tendency is to create boats with low freeboard mainly for stylistic considerations, and it is this low freeboard that forces the designers to set the decks dangerously low down in the hull.

Of course, there would be no sinking hazard were it not for the desire to create "self-bailing" cockpits. Unfortunately, what many boats end up with are "self-sinking" cockpits that render the vessel unseaworthy. Larger sport fishermen (40 feet and over) rarely have faulty cockpit designs because as vessels get larger the freeboard is of sufficient height that decks can be placed well above the water line and scuppers don't threaten to sink them.

For safety purposes, in sport fishermen and runabouts, optimal gunwale height is about 24 inches. At this height, the top of the gunwale falls just above the knee of a six foot person and affords a degree of leg leverage against the gunwale to keep people from falling overboard. Design-wise, this is an important consideration. Cockpits lower than this do not provide such leg leverage and make it easy for people to fall overboard.

The concept of the self-bailing cockpit is to permit large amounts of water entering the cockpit to drain out through cockpit scuppers, draining the water overboard rather than into the bilge. The original concept was adapted from freeing ports on the decks of ships and sailing vessels and applied to the sport fishing yacht. Backing down on a fish, these boats can take large amounts of water over the stern which needs to be drained off fast. As time went on, the idea worked its way into smaller and smaller boats, resulting in the situation today in which we routinely find 24 foot runabouts with the self-bailing cockpits that have decks located dangerously close to the water line. Many, if not most, of these boats really have no need for cockpit scuppers as they are not intended as sport fishermen.

A scupper is nothing more than a hole in the hull intended to let the water out. But it seems that many builders tend to forget that it's a two-way street: Water can flow in just as well as it can flow out. Moreover, all too often it seems that the deck and scuppers are designed without regard to changes in trim or weight loads. Some boats that float okay when empty, end up with the decks awash when loaded up with people and gear.

Self-bailing cockpits would not be a problem were cockpit decks made fully water tight. Few really are because it is usually necessary that decks be fitted with hatches to provide access to bilge pumps, steering gear and the like. Any opening that is not water tight is a potential source of water ingress into the hull. In addition to hatches, many boats have a large, removable deck section above the fuel tank. Although it may be caulked, keeping a such large hatch section water tight is difficult, at best.

Plastic Hatches

It is ironic that most boats have bow deck hatches that are of superior watertight integrity than the ones used in cockpit decks that are known to go awash, thereby allowing large amounts of water to enter the hull. One of the primary culprits that destroy the water tight integrity of a cockpit deck is the rectangular plastic deck hatch that is used in most all small boats. While these

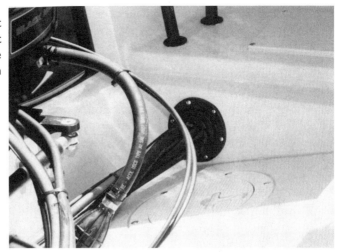

Fig. 9-1. A motor well that should be water tight but isn't due to the control cable pass through located within the well.

hatches may appear to be water tight, actual testing shows that they usually are not. Fitted with o-ring type gaskets, for these hatches to be water tight requires a precision fit between hatch cover and hatch frame. Under ideal installation circumstances that close fit can be achieved. In actual usage, cockpit decks are rarely completely rigid, but usually flex quite a bit. Because the hatch frame is a weak plastic molding, whatever flexing is experienced by the deck is also re-flected in the frame that is attached to the deck. This causes a failure of the o-ring to seal and allows water to drain into the bilge.

Many of the hatches that I have removed from cockpit decks show that the hatch cover o-rings will not make a tight seal under any conditions, even if perfectly installed. One reason for this is that the o-rings tend to get stretched and flattened out around the hatch cover corners so that there is virtually no contact at all between o-ring and frame, thus leaving a large gap through which water can enter (See fig. 9-2). Another factor that affects the sealing capability of the o-ring is whether the hatch frame is distorted at the time it is installed. Since the hatch frame is flimsy, the installer has only to pull it out of shape a few millimeters while making the installation to destroy any chance of it sealing.

It is not rain water leaking through these hatch covers that we're primarily concerned about. The real problem is when the deck is so low that water backs up through the scuppers and provides for a continual source of leakage into the hull. Fig. 9-4 shows such a hatch installed immediately adjacent to a deck scup-per. Because the deck was only two inches above the water line, it was only a question of time before this boat sank. In fact, it sank twice because no one understood why it had sunk the first time. Everyone involved thought that the gasketed hatch covers were water tight. Actual testing revealed that, when the deck was flooded with water, they leaked at rates up to 35 gallons per hour.

On the other hand, the smaller round hatches or ports have been found to be much less prone to distortion, yet both round and rectangular hatches are both subject to damage and abrasions to the o-rings caused by the introduction of sand and debris into the gap between hatch cover and frame. When decks get hosed down, this gap is a natural collection point for dirt to accumulate. When the hatch gets removed and reinserted, the dirt that has accumulated abrades and damages the o-ring.

The following is a check list for inspecting boats with plastic deck hatches:

- Examine the o-ring to see if it's standing proud of the vertical surface of the cover. It is probably not making a seal if it is not.

- Open all hatches and ports and check for damage to o-rings.

- Check hatch opening for evidence of leakage in the form of water or drip tails along the underside of the frame and below the hatch opening.

- Flood the deck with water, then open hatches and check for signs of leakage.

- Discoloration marks left by the o-ring on the hatch frame will often tell whether the o-ring is making good contact with the frame. If the o-ring imprint occasionally disappears from the side of the hatch frame, it's probably leaking.

- Check deck for excessive flexing by bouncing your weight on it. Check to see that all removable deck sections are thoroughly caulked and that there are no cracks or gaps in caulking.

- All openings in the cockpit liner or motor well should be at least 12" above the water line or any point where water may accumulate.

Fig. 9-2 . It's obvious that this hatch o-ring does not even touch the sides of the frame in some places.

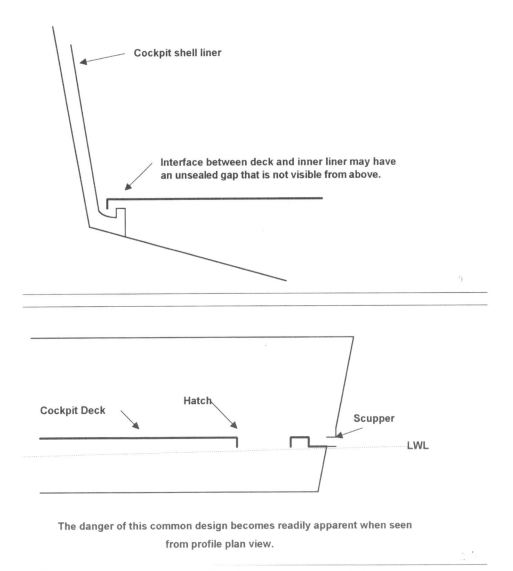

Fig. 9-3. Sectional views of outboard boat cockpit reveals how design errors can cause sinnking.

It is a common misconception that any sort of flapper or floating ball stopper or check valve will prevent water from back flowing into the cockpit. A deck supper is a another natural accumulation point for dirt, leaves and debris, and even though the stopper or flapper may nominally seal the scupper, over time an accumulation of dirt or debris will prevent that seal. For that reason, flappers and ball stops should never be relied upon. Their real purpose is to prevent large amounts of water from flooding the cockpit when backing down, not to keep the boat afloat. When a deck is too low, sufficient amounts of water will seep by these devices and flood the deck.

Judging when deck scuppers are situated too close to the water line is not an easy proposition, but there are number of things that the surveyor should do to determine whether the boat is seaworthy.

ABYC standard H-4 (5/19/94) provides us with a well-defined guideline as to what constitutes acceptable cockpit deck height. Unfortunately, this standard was not even scheduled to go into effect until the summer of 1996. It reads as follows:

> *H4.4.7 The minimum height of the cockpit deck (sole) above the waterline, with the boat in static floating position, in centimeters shall not be less than 1.83 times the length of the boat in meters (0.02 times the overall length of the boat in feet) but not less than eight inches (20cm). EXCEPTION: Boats with watertight cockpits. NOTE: This standard is recommended for compliance by July 1, 1996."*

Application of this standard leads to the inevitable consideration of what constitutes a watertight deck. The preceding discussion addressed the matter of determining whether a cockpit deck is truly watertight. Is a deck that is fitted with plastic hatches water tight? Based on my investigations, the answer is no, they are not. Using the ABYC standard for a 24' boat with a non-watertight deck, the minimum deck height would be 5.75". Very few 24' boats have cockpit decks this high, which brings our focus back to the matter of hatches and whether they are truly watertight. We may find ourselves faced with a situation in which a builder intended for the cockpit to be watertight, but the boat has a deck only two inches above the waterline and used hatches that are supposed to be watertight, but are not. What do we do? Here we have a situation in which the boat is danger of sinking, and that assessment is backed up by non-compliance with the ABYC standard, late though it may be. Since we cannot do anything about the height of the deck, there are only two reasonable options. First, we could make a recommendation to install hatches that are watertight, but that would be expensive. Second, we could recommend closing up the scuppers, but that's not a good idea with a fishing boat. A more reasonable option would be to recommend to the buyer that the hatches or ports be kept sealed with silicone sealer. He may not do that, but at least you've got yourself covered by addressing a hazard.

When we look at a boat in terms of freeboard, we normally make that assessment by the distance from the waterline to the top of the gunwale. If a boat has hull scuppers, that is an erroneous judgment. The *effective freeboard* is the height of the cockpit scuppers above load water line (LWL). One way to determine whether there is adequate effective freeboard is to simply have several persons stand in the cockpit at the stern and measure the change in trim. A change in trim is a change in hull immersion on the fore and aft plane. Transverse trim is called *list*. The moment, or addition or shift in weight, to change the trim one inch is the number of pounds required to raise one end and depress the other 1/2". This is because the net change is the combination of change at each end. A one inch change in trim thus is the product of a half-inch at each end.

Since most boats will have the fuel tanks located aft of midships, it's important to take note of the fuel capacity and amount of fuel on board. A 150 gallon tank of fuel will weigh approximately 1000 lbs. A half load of fuel would therefore mean that the vessel is 500 lbs. short of its full load.

Outboard boats, and particularly those with engines mounted on so-called brackets, are particularly vulnerable. Outboards and stern drive boats have a center of gravity substantially aft of midships and a normal state of trim down by the stern. What makes these boats vulnerable is not only the trim down by the stern, but also by the fact that any water accumulations in the hull will also accumulate aft. Calculations show that one inch of rain falling in the cockpit of

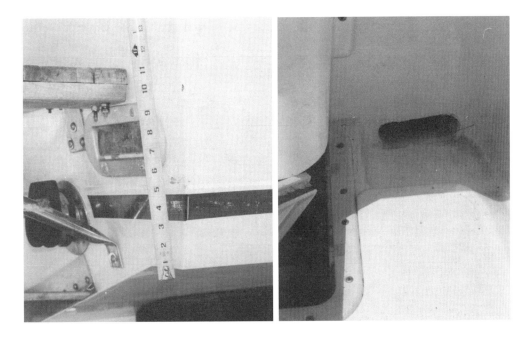

Fig. 9-4 . Outside and inside views of badly designed scupper/deck arrangement. Note that scupper is only a few inches away from a leaky hatch.

a typical 24' open boat translates to a quantity of about 90 gallons of water weighing over 700 pounds. When all that water runs aft, it's usually enough to sink any boat with a self-draining cockpit. This is not to suggest that one inch of rain will sink a boat, but to show by comparison that 90 gallons of water is not that much and can easily be accumulated in a short period of time.

Estimating Changes in Trim

When a surveyor encounters a boat with cockpit deck that is dangerously close to the water line, it is important to determine what the effects of a change in trim will be. Say, for example, he encounters a boat such as the ones shown in Fig. 9-4. Further assume that the deck is 2" above the water line and the 150 gallon fuel tank appears to be about 1/3 full. Making an exact calculation of the moment to change trim is a bit too cumbersome, but there is a simple method the surveyor can use to determine what the effect of a full tank will be. That is to mark the water line on the transom at the center. Now get out of the boat and observe what the effect of your own weight was at the time you made the mark. Assuming that your weight is 175 lbs. and the boat sank three quarters of an inch at the stern, the weight to change the trim one full inch (meaning a 1/2" at each end) would be 233 lbs. (175 lbs./ 3/4") If the fuel tank holds 150 gallons and is 1/3 full, with fuel weighing about 7 lbs. per gallon, the tank could hold another 100 gallons or 700 lbs. of fuel. Divided by our moment to change trim of 233 lbs., theoretically, a full load of fuel would cause the vessel to settle down another 1-1/2 inches assuming that the tank is somewhere aft of amidships.. Of course the placement of the tank will have a lot to do with exactly

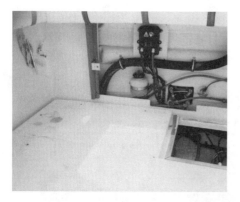 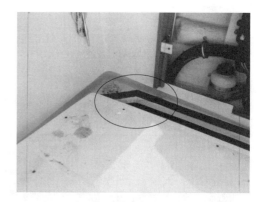

Fig.9- 5. This boat has a hidden scupper and a hidden problem. These photos were taken with the boat afloat. At right, the deck has been partly removed, revealing water backing up through the scupper and pouring over the deck opening. In this case, the deck gasket did not do its job of completely sealing the deck, causing the boat to sink.

how much; the farther forward of the transom it is, the less the effect will be. Adjusting for other factors such as bilge water and other equipment that may be loaded aboard at a later date, this simple calculation at least gives us a reasonable basis for estimating the potential change in trim and how it may affect seaworthiness. The above calculation is particularly useful for outboard or stern drive boats where bilge water will always run aft. It gives us a very good handle on how far the stern is likely to sink with the addition of weight.

Pounds per Inch Immersion

The effect of load on our example can be demonstrated by calculating pounds per inch immersion. This is the amount of weight required to sink a boat an addition one inch assuming the weight is placed in the center of buoyancy. To calculate PPII, measure the surface area of the water plane. Do this by dividing the hull up into a rectangle and a triangle (to represent bow section) as

$$\text{Pounds per inch Immersion} = \frac{\text{area water plane x 64*}}{12}$$

* Use 62.5 lbs. for fresh water

A typical 24' runabout has a moment to increase immersion one inch (PPII) of about 700 lbs. assuming that the additional weight is placed at the center of buoyancy. The center of buoyancy will typically be located about 8-10' forward of the transom, taking into account the vee shape of the water plane. In most cases, the fuel tank will be found to be located at that point, and therefore the net change between full and empty fuel tank will be about one inch or so. However, the moment to change trim will increase directly in proportion to how far aft of this point a tank may be located, somewhere between one and three inches.

Four people on board and a load fishing gear, loaded coolers and the like will have a similar effect. Therefore, our typical 24 footer can easily undergo a routine change in trim of three inches, more than enough to cause problems for a boat with a leaky deck.

Ultimately, the surveyor is faced with a question of seaworthiness. If a deck will go awash when the vessel is heavily loaded, clearly it is not seaworthy. This leads to the question of whether it is really necessary that a cockpit be self-bailing. For boats with decks close to the water line, and decks which are impossible to make reasonably water tight, the only solution is to close off the scuppers and make sure that the boat has a good bilge pumping system and adequate battery power to handle heavy accumulations of rain. For boats with leaky deck hatches and other openings, replacing the hatches with well-caulked or gasketed, screwed-down hatch covers is a more sensible option. And although screwed down hatch covers make bilge access a little more difficult, the use of a screw gun can usually open up the hatch in less than a minute. Moreover, making the hatch cover of clear Lexan can allow one to instantly check the bilges for high water.

Are Scuppers Necessary?

Cockpit scuppers are only beneficial if the level of the cockpit deck meets the new ABYC standard. Otherwise, they are clearly a hazard. However, in saying that, for open boats it then becomes vitally important the vessel be fitted with adequate bilge pumping capacity and battery power to meet the needs of discharging the rain water that will end up in the bilge. A deck cover, of course, solves most of this problem. Baring that, since we know that 1" of rain at most will accumulate 90 gallons of water in a 24' hull, we can extrapolate from that a 10" rainfall would put 900 gallons of water in the boat. A pump with a 1500 GHP capacity[1] connected to a 90 A.H. battery should clearly be more than adequate to handle this with a substantial margin of error. With a dual pump and battery system, the potential for system failure is even further reduced to the point where only the failure to maintain the system poses a serious threat.

When the height of the deck is marginal or questionable, prudence dictates that the surveyor should recommend closing up the scuppers and placing reliance on the pumping system.

Motor Wells

Make no mistake about it: There are tens of thousands of outboard boats whose motor well design is patently unsafe. Most of these will never be seen by a surveyor since small boats are rarely surveyed. Most outboard boats are stored on trailers or in storage racks, but many others are docked afloat. Others are used on inland lakes and rivers, yet significant numbers are used in the open ocean, often venturing far from shore. Fortunately, more an more outboard boats are being surveyed in recent years simply because outboard power is being used on increasingly larger vessels, or vessels of greater value.

Most outboards have cut down transoms to facilitate mounting of the motors. The function of the motor well is to make up for this loss in freeboard at the transom. For some reason, many builders simply don't think that this is necessary and eliminate the motor well altogether. Some do it so that the boat can serve as a more convenient swimming or scuba diving platform. Others adhere to the idea but corrupt the principle by various design mistakes.   But a motor well has only one purpose: to keep water out of the boat.

One popular builder used no motor well at all but placed a fold-down teak gate or door across the back of the boat which gives the appearance of a well. He might as well save the cost of teak and labor since this arrangement served no useful purpose whatever. Others use a scaled down version of a motor well that is equally useless. Again, we're mindful that if a cockpit deck is truly water-tight, the necessity of a motor well is diminished. But we also know that very few boat decks are truly watertight, and most others leak like a sieve.

For our purposes, unless a deck is watertight, seaworthy design dictates that a motor well should be fully capable of keeping water out of a boat hull, much the same way a full-height transom would. If you've ever gone fishing in an outboard boat while anchored in a seaway, then you know how much water can pour over a cut down transom as the boat pitches and rolls. Leaky decks combined with weak batteries or faulty bilge pumps can easily lead to disaster, and occasionally does.

Many boats have motor wells that are properly designed but whose pur-pose has been sabotaged. If the motor well is full of holes, the purpose of the well has been defeated. It's truly astonishing how many builders, dealers and riggers are completely ignorant of this, and who take a perfectly seaworthy hull and violate its water tight integrity by making a lot holes in the motor well (See fig. 9-1). The primary offender are the holes in the side of the motor well for the steering and control cables, electrical and fuel lines. These openings are routinely placed at the bottom of the well where water sloshing over the tran-som will enter the hull through these openings. The ABYC standard specifies that openings for controls should be fitted with rubber boots. Many people apparently conclude that adding a rubber boot around the cables will keep the water out. It doesn't. Boots may reduce the size of the opening, but not elimi-nate it.

The solution for this is that the cable opening should be located as high up in the well as practical. The ideal placement, considering the needs of the control cables, is that the bottom of the cable hole should be two inches above the lowest point of the transom. With this placement, even if the well fills up with water, it will not drain into the hull. That the shape of the well causes too sharp of bend in the cables if the openings are located elsewhere is not an excuse for creating a hazard that will sink the boat, although it is one that is often heard. That's not the surveyor's problem but the builder's or the owner's if he declines to correct it.

Most outboards, when docked, will experience constant water sloshing over the transom, particularly in bad weather conditions, or where they are subject to the wakes of passing vessels. To prevent the boat from eventually sinking, the bottom half of the well must be water tight without exception. We should remember that just because there are drain holes intended to let water drain back out of the motor well, that does not mean that those drains won't some day get stopped up with leaves or other debris. The assumption that something won't happen is precisely what causes so many boats to sink. Good design dictates that the unexpected be anticipated.

Many builders install plastic inspection ports in the bottom of wells, either the press-fit or screw in type discussed earlier. In considering whether such ports are really water tight, we need only ask ourselves whether we'd risk installing one of these things in the bottom of the hull. Obviously, no one is that foolish. Then why is it any less risky to install a port at the bottom of motor well or in a self-bailing deck situated close to the water line? Only because the risk of placing it at the bottom of a motor well is less obvious to the uninitiated. Only when the boat is subject to adverse conditions does the danger become apparent.

Ideally, motor wells should have no openings in the area where water would accumulate if the drainage holes were blocked. This means up to the level of the transom. But it is often necessary to provide access to a bilge pump or other equipment below decks. Press-fit cover ports are absolutely unacceptable. The screw-down type with an o-ring under the top lip will perform much better. The easiest, but least permanent, solution for ports installed in the bottom of a motor well is to advise the client to seal the port cover with silicone sealer. This is done by applying a bead of silicone on the lip, and then screwing the lid in place. The drawback is that this needs to be redone each time the port is opened.

Design Trends

Boat design trends in recent years has been rather free-wheeling and often flies in the face of common sense, yet alone reasonable design standards. The boat without a transom is a rather typical example. A boat without a transom might be a seaworthy design for inland lakes and rivers, but one really has to wonder what a designer was thinking of in creating an open-ended forty-footer that is very likely to be used in the open ocean. One has to wonder whether the designer or builder of such creations has ever been at sea when the weather turned ugly. Have they ever had the experience of having water in the fuel and loosing both engines while at sea? Do they know what it's like to be adrift in 5-6 foot seas without power? Have they ever had the experience in taking a wave over the stern of a boat that *does* have a transom, yet alone one that doesn't?

Surveyors who wish to avoid serious lawsuits should be on the lookout for such patently unsafe designs. The open stern design made a brief appearance in both outboard boats and larger cruisers in the early 90's. Then this practice suddenly stopped. Recent years has seen the proliferation of the platform extension design for the vast majority of outboards. The beauty of this design is that when done right it completely eliminates most of the hazards discussed so far. This design eliminates the old fashioned motor well and cut down transom and replaces it with a cut down hull extension that is sort of like cross between a bolt-on bracket and a swim platform and serves the purposes of both. The transom is then moved forward and usually has a door in it to access the platform extension area.

However, some designers have even managed to screw up this design by placing shallow wells in the platform along with openings for the cables and once again, access ports. Most that I have seen are designed right, but we still have to be on the lookout for mistakes.

Older outboard boats, with their engines hung off the stern, can be highly vulnerable to taking on water and going down suddenly. There are still thousands of these boats around and the surveyor will continue to run across them for many years to come. In one recent accident, a boat owner was anchored in the ocean near the shoreline fishing. His dog was becoming a nuisance and so he locked the dog in the cuddy cabin. In his statement to the insurance surveyor he said that the boat took a wave over the stern from the wake of a large yacht going by. His boat went down so fast that he and his wife didn't even have time to rescue his dog from the cabin. In another instance, two guys were out snapper fishing at night. They said one minute they were standing near the stern casting, then next minute they were swimming, stating the boat went out from under them in less than 60 seconds. There was so little floatation in the stern, combined with the engine aft, and so many sources of leakage in the deck and motor well, they didn't have a chance of even noticing what was happening. It happened so fast that they didn't even have a chance to pull life jackets out of readily reachable cockpit side pockets.

In a time when boating is considered to be a recreational sport that requires little or no knowledge or training in seamanship, the surveyor should be mindful that he stands in the middle between bad design and the ignorance of the boat owner. Heading out in the open ocean in a small boat with the wife and children is serious business that is often treated with casual disregard for the hazards. When faced with the spectre of designs such as the boat with no transom, the surveyor would do well to remember that the boat owner may be completely ignorant of the hazard. A common assumption among boat owners is that since the builder built it that way, it must be OK. Surveyors know better. Or at least they should. Of course when the surveyor states the nature of the problem in his report, this is either going to kill the sale or guarantee that the client can't get insurance.

Ultimately, the surveyor has to decide for himself whether he wants to run the risk of ignoring the problem, or endure the momentary wailing and gnashing of teeth that is guaranteed to follow from client, seller, broker, dealer, manufacturer or all of them together. But compare this momentary discomfort with the potential for the permanent anguish that could result should the vessel go down and cost someone's life.

Sport Fishermen

Sport fishermen over forty feet are rarely subject to faulty cockpit designs simply by virtue of their size. Great advances in mold tooling in recent years has changed all that. It is true that tooling know-how has lead to more free-wheeling design ideas, some of which can be rather ill-conceived to say the least. But by and large the cockpit of larger sport fishermen are safer today than they were in the past.

Transom or "tuna" doors pose little threat to seaworthiness so long as (1) the cockpit is sufficiently high, or (2) if the deck is low, the door is adequately gasketed. In recent years I've found increasing numbers of 35-42' sport fishermen that have transom doors with large gaps in the jambs, low decks and a hatch cover immediately inside the door. When this situation was pointed out to one owner he said, "Yes, but the hatch has a gutter with drains around it." The drain consisted of a 1/2" diameter hole that was already plugged up with debris on his less than one-year-old boat. The deck was 8" above the waterline (the ABYC standard would have required 9") but wave action was continuously slopping water through the gaps in the door. Docked at a poorly protected marina, this vessel was a prime candidate for sinking.

Deck Wells

Many if not most late model sport fishermen have fiberglass boxes designed to fit into hatch openings that can pose additional hazards. These boxes have to occasionally be removed to inspect and service equipment under the deck. Foremost among these is the fishbox or bait well that is fitted with drain or water circulation plumbing. The beginning surveyor will soon discover for himself what a problem these things can be. The danger here is that because these wells are removable, and when they are removed, the plumbing and fittings can get damaged in the process. Numerous instances have occurred where the hoses came off the connection to the bottom of the well, or the through hull fitting, and then sank the boat because no one noticed what happened. In other cases plastic fittings have fractured, again allowing the drain hose to drop down, and again sinking the boat.

It is imprudent to rig a bait well into a hatch box since the potential for an accident is ever-present. The same goes with drained fish or storage boxes. The drains in these boxes are a convenience, not a necessity; they're not worth the risk of sinking the boat. Sometimes these drains, particularly for bait wells, will go directly to an underwater fitting. This should never be permitted because of the potential for disaster. In other instances, the drain is to an outlet above the water line, if only an inch or so. It's prudent to recommend that these be capped off. At the very least, the drain line should be fitted with a check valve.

One way to deal with these issues is to place a cautionary note in the report.

[1] Because of static head pressure and other restrictions, divide rated pump capacity in half to estimate real world performance.

Chapter 10

Drive Train

Drive train is a term that I borrowed from the automotive industry because no marine term exists to describe the complete drive system in powerboats. While the term "running gear" is often used to describe the shaft, propeller and strut, the components of the complete drive train consist of the engines, struts, engine mounts, transmission, shaft, stuffing boxes, struts and, of course, the propellers. Before we can properly survey a drive system, we first have to have a solid understand of the basic mechanics and the stresses to which the system is subjected. In this chapter, we'll cover the basics and deal with some of these issues.

Perhaps one of the primary reasons that we find so many problems occurring with drive systems results from failure of designers and builders to think in terms of the entire drive system. The drive trains in inboard powered boats, unlike those of outboards or stern drives, can span considerable distances. The span of the system runs from the front of the engine to the tip of the propeller shaft. In large yachts such as those built by Broward Marine, where engine rooms are actually forward of amidships, the length of the drive train is often over forty feet long. A rule of thumb is that the alignment of the drive system becomes increasingly critical in direct proportion to its overall length. Unusually short drive trains can tolerate substantial degrees of misalignment while unusually long drive trains can tolerate very little. The reason for this should be obvious: the degree angle of misalignment off center is magnified in direct proportion to the length.

A general rule of good system design is that the drive train should never be made totally rigid unless the hull is also totally rigid. Most production built, fiberglass hulls are not rigid and are subject to considerable flexing. While one rarely notices this, and it normally doesn't cause any obvious damage, many hulls will flex as much as 1" out of central axis alignment.[1] If you have trouble believing this, try stringing a guy wire for a long distance anywhere between two points on the interior and watch how it alternately slackens and tightens while underway. Only steel and aluminum yachts have a substantial degree of rigidity. However, while fiberglass hulls tend to be flexible, the foundation for the drive train must be quite rigid. Since engines are mounted on stringers, this means that the stringer system must have sufficient strength to maintain stability from engine to propeller. If it doesn't, bending and twisting of the hull as it travels at speed over rough water will throw the system out of alignment and cause accelerated wear and possible damage to system components.

Fortunately, most fiberglass boats tend to twist about their transverse, midship axis with the bow half going one way and the stern half the other. This type of twisting generally has little effect on the alignment of the drive system. The most destructive type of structural inadequacy on fiberglass boats comes from stringers that don't have adequate strength. Either that, or in combination with inadequate bulkheading or transverse framing, hull flexing between the stringers, allowing one stringer to ride higher than another, can throw the system severely out of alignment. Boats with weak structural systems are fairly common and are one of the sources of chronic transmission and alignment problems. Numerous cases have been documented where stringers were so weak that shafts have bent and transmission casings and bell housings have fractured from the resulting stress.

The drive train is anchored to the hull at three primary points: engine mounts, struts and stuffing box (See fig. 5-4 in chapter 5). Engine mounts don't merely hold the engine in place, but carry the full thrust load of the propeller. For that reason, not only the mount, but the structural member to which it is anchored, must be adequately designed to carry this load. Hard mounts are commonly used in steel and aluminum vessels but rarely in fiberglass yachts. Hard mounts are undesirable because, without sound dampening, engine vibrations are transmitted directly to the hull. But even more importantly, with fiberglass yachts, whose hulls we know are not completely rigid, to have the drive train solidly anchored at all points is a recipe for trouble. This means that with flexible mounts on the engine and rubber cutlass bearings in the struts, most yachts have drive trains that are somewhat self-aligning. When hulls bend and twist slightly, the flexibility in the mountings and bearings allows the shaft to self-center somewhat.

There's probably no better way to check the strength of the stringer system than by running a vessel at speed in some moderate seas. Any weakness in the stringers is bound to show up when a hull pounds. Stringer deflection can be measured at midpoint between bulkheads by setting a folding rule on the top of the stringer and measuring up to a deck beam. Since decks are usually independent of hull bottoms, any deflection of the stringers should show up here. If you decide to make this part of your normal survey routine, you're likely to be surprised at the amount of deflection you find even in well built hulls.

How much is too much? Experience shows that flexing from 1/4" to 3/8" in vertical measurement generally does not cause much of a problem with boats under forty feet. For larger boats, this amount is likely to be disastrous. Half-inch is borderline and more than that this is going to throw the system seriously out of line and be likely to cause damage. The first sign of trouble will usually show up in the engine mounts breaking down, system bolts loosening, excessive cutlass bearing wear, and chronic stuffing box leakage.

Engine Mounts

Well designed engine mounts serve the dual purpose of holding the engine in place, reducing noise transmission into the hull, and at the same time permitting a limited amount of engine movement sufficient to keeping the engine and shaft aligned. Remember that most systems are self-centering except for rigidly mounted engines. Obviously, when engine mounts are not of sufficient strength, or are too soft, they will permit excessive engine movement that, in itself, will cause misalignment.

Gasoline engines rarely have engine mount problems, but for diesel engines it's another matter altogether.

It is very common for diesel engines of 400 HP or less to be fitted with inexpensive mounts that will permit excessive engine movement, either transversely or longitudinally. Typically, such mounts consist of a rubber isolator set in an aluminum casting with a single vertical engine mounting stud as shown in Fig. 10-2 upper right. This type of design permits full, 360° movement. These mounts generally work well when properly matched to engine power and in-

Fig. 10-1. Experienced designers know that mounts alone aren't enough to stabilize engines in high performance boats, especially when stringers are extra tall. Here, the designer has added a massive stabilizer bar between the engine foundations. A web frame at this point will accomplish the same purpose.

stalled correctly. However, the long length of the mounting stud provides an opportunity for the designer or installer to forego precise placement of the engine and use the long studs to make up for any error or excessive tolerance in engine placement. In other words, engines often end up being mounted high up on the studs so that the engine ends up essentially mounted on "stilts." When this happens, an excessive lever arm is created so that the thrust of the propeller causes the engine to move forward (or aft in reverse).

With this type of mount, the surveyor should check to see how high the engine is mounted on the stud. The higher it's mounted, the more leverage will be applied to the rubber. When it is near the top, this is a signal that a back down test should be carefully conducted to determine how much movement is permitted. It should also be born in mind that the engine is not only moving fore and aft, but is actually traversing through an arc, involving vertical movement as well. Further, that engine torque lifts on one side and compresses mounts on the other.

The engine center of gravity in relation to the engine mounts also has an effect. An engine that is slung low with a good portion of the engine hanging between the mounts will be much more stable than an engine sitting high above the mounts. A Caterpillar 3208 engine has a very low profile, while a Detroit 6V92, 6-71 and Cat 3176 have very high profiles. The rubber isolated

Fig.10-2. The many different styles of engine mounts. Above left, MAN mount: lower left, Ace mount: above right, Bushings, Inc. mount.

stud type mount (Fig. 10-2) is a poor choice for high profile engines. This type mount will usually work reasonably well for the Caterpillar, but is inadequate for the Detroit, even when horsepower ratings are the same.

Engine "shuddering" is a phenomenon in which the engine "shudders" or shakes when a high speed vessel begins pounding in a seaway. Shuddering most often occurs with high profile engines where the engine center of gravity is well above the mounts. The surveyor should be on the lookout for this condition during the sea trial. Engine movement should be as close to zero as possible. The style of mount shown in Fig. 10-2, lower left is more suitable for use with high performance diesels, especially for high profile engines. This type of mount is much more stable both longitudinally and transversely than Bushings, Inc. or MAN mounts. The mounting stud is attached to a wider and much longer base which does not permit much rocking action. It makes one wonder why bother to align couplings to 0.003" when engines are moving 0.250" or more?

From experience we know that smaller diesel engines are more prone to being poorly mounted than their larger counterparts. The surveyor should keep in mind that when an engine is not stable, that is actually visibly moving, it is subject to severe stress on the transmission that can cause damage to the bearings and output shafts. The rear engine mounts carry the major part of the

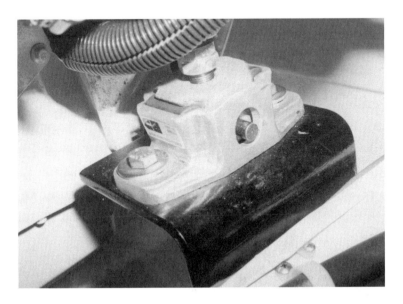

Fig.10-3. New style Caterpillar mount (1999). Note how precarious this installation is with the mount bolted onto a very small angle bracket that has insufficient mounting surface and will eventually work loose.

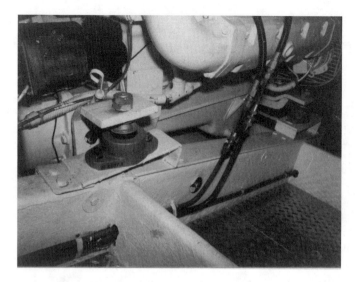

Fig.10-4. These mounts are improperly set on an angle which caused the engine to settle aftward and throw the couplings out of alignment. The mounting surface should be level so that the rubber part of the mount does not become overly stressed. The MAN mount shown in Fig. 10-2 is also set on an angle. That mount was broken because of that improper mounting.

thrust load and, for that reason, it is most important that the rear mounts be sufficiently strong and in good condition. Otherwise, the entire drive train will be subject to movement.

Struts

While engine mounts anchor the forward end of the drive train, the propeller shaft struts anchor the aft end. The function of a strut (referring here primarily to the main strut) is to stabilize the propeller shaft that is driving a

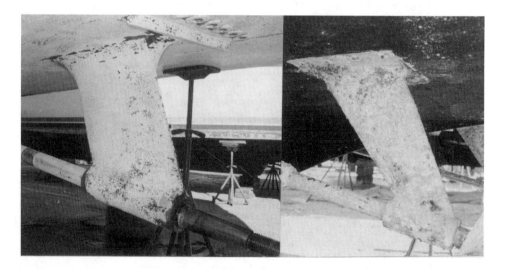

Fig. 10-5. Note the huge difference in the size of these two struts though both are on forty footers. The one on the right is so flimsy that it vibrates and causes the bolts to go loose.

spinning propeller. The struts are not intended, nor should they carry any of the thrust load. The prop hub should not be in contact with the strut, and there should be a sizable gap between propeller hub and strut bore face, typically calculated at 15% of propeller hub length, so that the propeller hub stands no chance of coming in contact with the strut. High speed vessels, when they are thrown into a hard turn, can generate very heavy loads on the strut and the hull. If both are not sufficiently strong, movement, misalignment and possible failure can occur.

Improperly designed struts and strut-to-hull mounting structures are very common and occur for a variety of reasons. In years past, poorly designed, weak struts were more of a problem than they are today, though the problem still persists. First, we need to realize that for a strut to be effective, it needs to be absolutely stable relative to the hull structure. And if the hull structure, usually meaning the bottom panel, is not stable, neither will the strut be. The following is a list of the most common strut mounting defects:

- Strut base is too narrow

- Strut arm too long relative to base

- Strut arm too narrow through cross section

- Flexing of hull panel to which strut is mounted

- Inadequate doubler of fillet under strut base

- Use of wrong type or size of bolts for mounting

- Inadequate hull framing throughout aft section

Strut bases where the width is less than 50% of the length of the strut arm don't provide sufficient mounting surface to resist propeller torque and other stresses (see fig 10-8). The strut arm acts as a lever so that the wider the base, the more stable it will be. The smaller the strut base foot print, the more load is applied to a smaller surface area of the hull. Since the strut load is transferred to the hull, it is imperative that the hull structure be sufficiently strong. If it is not, bending and distortion of the hull skin will occur. Not only does this allow the shaft to go out of alignment, but also poses a threat of hull failure.

We occasionally see strut arms that are very thin in cross-section or narrow in width. Struts like these can easily be bent from propeller load or hitting floating or submerged objects. The surveyor does not have to be a structural engineer to know when a strut is too weak. If it looks to be too small, it probably is. Compare the struts shown in the photos shown in Fig 10-5. The strut

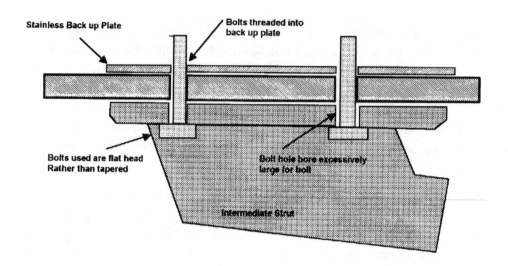

Fig. 10-6. Anatomy of an improper strut installation.

arm base at left is less than half the one at right and allows so much wobble that the base constantly loosens and results in excessive bearing wear and galling of the shaft.

Strong, well designed struts can't do their job of stabilizing the shaft unless they are attached to an equally strong hull structure. With increasing frequency, we are finding in late model boats struts that are bolted directly to the hull with no back up whatever, often without even good-sized washers under the strut bolt nuts. There have been cases where boats have grounded from the tide going out, resulting in the struts being pushed up through the bottom. This should not happen, and only does so due to poor design. Unless a hull is of

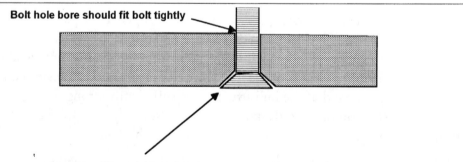

Fig. 10-7. The proper method of installing strut bolts.

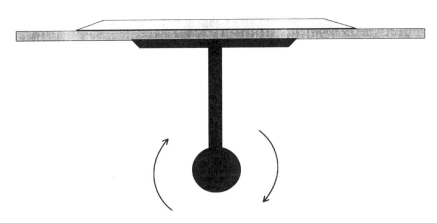

Fig. 10-8.

extraordinary thickness, it is necessary that a fillet or buildup of extra layers of laminate be added in way of strut mounts. Merely adding a hard-edged doubler to a very thin hull skin is often a prescription for disaster. Figure 10-8 shows the correct relationship of the strut to internal doubler or fillet. The fillet needs to be about 50% wider than the strut base in order to properly distribute the load. A doubler or fillet the width of the strut base is of no value whatever. Remember that the torque created by the rotation of the propeller is amplified by the lever created by the strut arm. Lacking adequate back up and base width, the strut will begin to weaken the laminate and may ultimately fail.

Figure 10-9 is an example of what can happen when a builder attempts to short cut the strut installation. Using only two brass strips as back ups for the bolts, and no doubler or fillet at all, the hull shown in figure 10-9 fractured.

Strut Bolts

Another critical part of the strut installation are the strut bolts. True strut bolts are specially designed bolts which have two distinct characteristics. First, it has a steep bevel under the bolt head. Bolt heads which have a shallow bevel angle are weak and prone to breaking off below the head. Second, the threads on a strut bolt do not run the full length of the shaft. The reason for this is that the bolt can be fully bedded and sealed, so that the threads don't channel water into the bolt hole. The problem here is not merely the potential for leakage, but rather that this condition creates a potential for crevice corrosion to attack the bolts as shown in Fig. 10-13.

The bevel for the strut base countersink and the bevel for the bolt head need to be precisely matched. So, too, does the bolt hole need to be closely

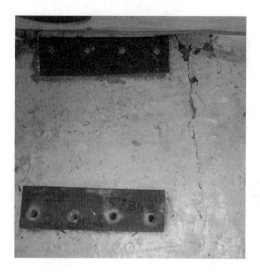 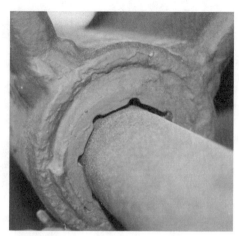

Figs. 10-9, 10-10. Left, the result of failure to reinforce hull laminate in way of struts. Right, shaft badly misaligned with strut.

matched to the diameter of the bolt. All too often they are not, and when this happens the strut can move, eventually allowing the bolt holes to elongate which can result in leakage and even bolt failure. Another fault that is commonly found is the use of the wrong type of nuts backing up the bolts. Shake-proof or nylon insert type nuts should never be used for several reasons. The first is that due to a limited number of metal threads, these nuts are weak and prone to cracking. Moreover, the nylon inserts are electrically incompatible with stainless and tend to cause rapid corrosion. The preferred nuts are double-nutted standard stainless steel with properly sized flat washers underneath.

Shafting

One of the most important parts of the propeller shaft is the manner in which the prop is fitted to the taper and the manner in which the shaft is fitted to the coupling. During the course of survey, there's not much a surveyor can do to check these points short of rocking the propeller on the shaft to see if the bore of the prop is seating solidly on the shaft taper. There should be no gaps appearing at either the front or rear of the bore. If it's loose or rocking, there may be damage to the key or key way.

With shafting lengths exceeding twenty feet, trueness becomes increasingly critical in direct proportion to the length. This occurs because any degree of error is multiplied as a function of length. That's why small, short shafts can tolerate much greater degrees of intolerance than larger or longer shafts. Shafts can be either physically bent or distorted (not permanently bent) by flexing in a hull. A rotating shaft that is bent to some degree will develop a natural tendency to straighten itself. But no matter how well stayed a shaft is, a bent shaft is whipping at some point along its length. A shaft that is stayed with strong main and intermediate struts, for example, will transfer that whipping action to the inboard end, and it is for this reason that bent shafts are so easily detectable at the engine end on any installation involving flexible engine mounts. A shaft that has a bend of just a degree or two, is usually sufficiently out of round that it will work the engine on its mounts. This is also one of the primary reasons why engine mounts become damaged. The same holds true for a badly bent propeller that can so unbalance the drive train that the engine mounts are strained.

Fig. 10-12. The clean area on this shaft indicates that the shaft is loose and sliding in coupling.

This is why surveying the engine mounting system, coupling and shafting inboard of the stuffing box during a sea trial is such a critical part of the survey. Whenever there is a problem or damage, it is most likely to show up at this point. Nor does the surveyor need sophisticated measuring instruments: all significant misalignment in the drive train is visible to the naked eye with the vessel running along at idle speed. It should also be remembered that bent or misaligned shafts have a tendency for self-centering at high speeds. It is not uncommon to see severe whipping in a shaft

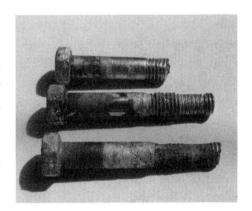

Fig. 10-13. Stainless hex head bolts used as strut bolts with aircraft nuts. Note how threads are wasted and bolts fractured at threads.

at 1,000 RPM that completely disappears at 2,000 RPM. 600-800 RPM is the ideal speed for checking.

I have often observed surveyors dial indicating shafts in place with the vessel hauled out, and would caution that this practice is useful only for determining whether a shaft is bent aft of the main strut. Most boats change shape when they are hauled out, so that there is a good chance that straight shafts are thrown out of alignment when the vessel is hauled. The surveyor runs the risk of diagnosing a bent shaft when, in fact, the shaft will recenter itself once the vessel is launched. The trueness of propeller shafting "in place" is not measurable in thousandths of an inch because of this hull-induced bending. There is also the likelihood that when the shaft is rotated (usually by pulling on the propeller blades, you'll move the shaft in the rubber bearings, thereby gaining a false reading. Checking for trueness tolerance can only be accomplished with the shaft removed and on a zeroed-out roller bed.

The following comments generally apply to shafts of 2" diameter or less and engines of 600 HP or less. In our view, shaft runout tolerances are not quantifiable if only because of the myriad differences in systems and factors involved. With any system with flexible engine mounts, shaft runout should never be so acute that it causes visible movement of the gearbox. Another indicator is whipping visible in the stuffing box collar. It is very common to see considerable whipping of the stuffing box between a very narrow speed range, say 600 to 800 RPM, and then to observe that it completely disappears at all other speeds. This usually occurs as a result of an imbalance in the drive train typically caused by a propeller that is either bent or out of balance. In fact, by the time a propeller has been reconditioned several times, it is substantially out of balance, keeping in mind that "reconditioning" does not normally involve dynamic balancing. It is a phenomenon similar to many automobiles that develop a vibration at one speed only. Boat owners and the industry generally accept this degree of intolerance without complaint. The critical factor is whether the degree of runout and vibration becomes destructive and it is up to the surveyor to make this call. The assessment of vibration levels in a drive train will be further discussed in detail in the Sea Trial chapter.

How well the surveyor is able to check all the various points discussed in this chapter will vary widely from boat to boat. The point to keep in mind is that the surveyor should sufficiently evaluate it to at least satisfy himself that the system is sufficiently well designed to ensure trouble-free operation of the vessel.

Packing Glands

Also known as stuffing boxes, these devices create a seal between the shaft and the hull. The standard flax gland has been in use for well over 100 years and is very effective so long as the packing is installed correctly, the engine/ shaft alignment remains stable, and the packing is replaced periodically. The part that makes the seal is a braided material impregnated with what is basically wax. The draw backs to this type are many. The packing wears over time and will start leaking, at which point it can be retightened. Unfortunately, overtightening will cause friction that will melt the wax in the packing, at which point it will start to leak again. Moreover, the flax packing gland is unforgiving of bent shafts and engine misalignment. When either of these two conditions exit, the gland will leak, and that leakage is usually intermittent, depending on the point where the shaft stops rotating. In other words, it may leak one day and not the next.

Another major complaint is that stuffing boxes often get stuffed back into places that make working on them next to impossible. Hence the yearning for something better, some kind of "maintenance free" gizmo that will last forever with no effort.

There are two very important points about the flax gland that should not be overlooked. They should always have splash guards fitted over them to prevent the rotating shaft from throwing spray around the engine room, without which very serious and costly damage can occur. Secondly, the hose clamps connecting the hose sleeve should never be allowed to become corroded. If the hose lets loose, this can allow a huge amount of water in that will probably sink the boat.

Fig. 10-14. Lip seal type glands for rudder at left, shaft at right.

Recently there have been a plethora of new types of glands introduced on the market, commonly called "dripless" type. These break down into to other basic types: mechanical seals and nitrile lip seals. Mechanical seals utilize two facing plates or rings attaching to the shaft that are held together by spring tension applied by a variety of means. This is all covered over by a rubber boot that completes the seal. Like the other types, they do have a water injection port, but are not heavily dependent on cooling water as the others are. The water contained within the bellows alone is enough to keep it cool. This type is usually distinguishable by having either a full blown bellows or something similar to a bellows. The advantage of this type is that it is somewhat tolerant of shaft movement, is not prone to overheating. They will not tolerate excessive engine movement and will leak under conditions of heavy vibration.

The nitrile lip seal gland uses a floating collar around the shaft which has one or two internal lips, sort of like external o-rings, that make the seal. This type is dependent on cooling water, as well as being less tolerant of system misalignment. Yet another type of lip seal uses oil as a lubricant and is distinguishable by the nearby reservoir. Lip seals are cheaper than all other types, and the primary problem with these results from faulty installation. This happens when the lip seal end is slid on over the shaft from the inside end, causing the lips to face in the wrong direction which results in leakage. To get them on properly, the shaft has to be beveled on the end before installation.

With so many different types and brands now in use, I can't begin to evaluate most of them. I've seen very few of them leaking. The Tides and Strong Seals are two well known names that are mostly only found on high end boats because of the cost. I have found both of these types to become damaged as a result of shaft bending.

---

[1] If the hull stringers are quite strong in the aft section, a hull can still twist without substantially affecting the drive train alignment because hulls tend to twist about their central, transverse axis. If all of the drive train is aft, then it most likely will not be materially affected.

Chapter 11

Gas Engines

The survey of diesel propulsion engines is a specialty that should be considered separate from the general hull survey. To perform a thorough survey of a pair of fair-sized diesel engines takes a considerable amount of time. In most of the larger yachting centers of the U.S., diesel engine surveys are performed by diesel survey specialists, and unless the surveyor is one himself, and has all the necessary diagnostic equipment, he would be wise to leave it to a specialist.

In smaller boating regions, finding a someone competent to perform diesel engine surveys can be a problem. So too, is using mechanics from engine dealers who have an obvious conflict of interest. This, however, is not the major problem with dealers, which often is that the people they send out are mechanics, not surveyors. Further, I have run into the problem that most dealer mechanics are experienced with highway vehicle engines and not salt water marine engines. There were many times when I have seen my client pay a very hefty sum for a machinery survey, only to receive a less than satisfactory survey, often times at truly incompetent levels. I've had mechanics show up with nothing but a flashlight, no tools, no gauges, no test instruments and not even a piece of paper to take notes on.

The opposite extreme is the professional marine engine surveyor who shows up with three or more cases of equipment and probably knows more about the history of the engine than the people who build it.

There will be times when a client will want the surveyor to perform something less than a full engine survey, and this is okay so long as the surveyor has a solid working knowledge of the subject engines. This I call a visual inspection and performance test. It will essentially cover many of the aspects discussed below. Unfortunately, doing this creates the risk that the client will place an over reliance on this limited effort. Therefore, I go to considerable lengths to

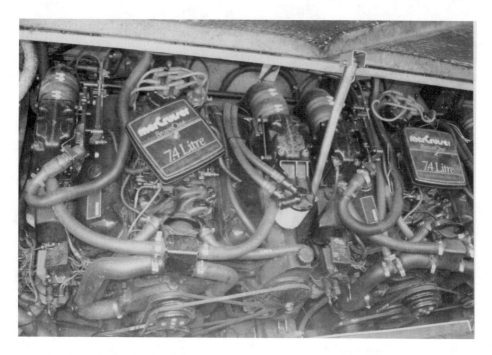

Fig. 11-1. This is the kind of thing a surveyor hopes he rarely has to confront. It's impossible to do a compression test on these engines. An installation like this poses a nightmare to maintain. Nothing under, beside or behind the engines can be seen or reached.

impress upon him the fact that what I can do is *limited*, that I am not utilizing a full suite of diagnostic instruments. Obviously, when one does this, the written report needs to stress these points as well.

I will not take numerous temperature readings with the infrared pyrometer because the interpretation of diesel temperatures can be quite different than for a gas engine. Moreover, I do not want my report to suggest that this has been a diagnostic analysis when it hasn't been. I want it to be clear that this is a visual inspection and test operation only.

The objective of this is to look for symptoms of problems. In the end, I report that symptoms were or were not found; I do NOT discuss anything having to do with internal condition. There will be little risk associated with reporting on whether the engine exhibits any symptoms, or that it does or does not perform satisfactorily.

I would not recommend that anyone lacking a solid background or experience with a wide range of diesel engines do this. Instead, by necessity, most busy surveyors end up establishing a relationship with a trusted and competent diesel engine surveyor. If you are in an area where there are no independent engine surveyors, it would be wise to attend a diesel engine training course or two,

Fig. 11-2. Contrast this Crusader engine with the Mercruisers shown on facing page.

preferably one that concentrates on diagnostics rather than repair.

When working with an independent engine surveyor, there are a couple of important points to bear in mind. This has to do with the laws of contractors and subcontractors which, in many states says that if you hire someone on behalf of your client, you are responsible for the caliber of the subcontractor's work or his fee in the event you have a collection problem.

Gas Engines

Gas engines are a different matter. Because of their greater simplicity, it is possible and within reason that a well-trained surveyor can cover gas engines within the scope of the hull survey. The prerequisite is that he have a good working knowledge of V-8 gas engines plus outboards if he deals with these. Fortunately, there are numerous books on engine troubleshooting and repair on the market that are frequently revised and updated. For outboards, you can either try to get your hands on an older dealer shop manual. They won't give up their current ones, and they are prohibited by dealer contracts from letting go of the old ones, however . . . . where there's a will, there's a way. Or you can buy the after market manuals such as Seloc or Chilton. Thorough study of any of these is enough to give you a good grounding.

For mid sized vessels, it can be quite a stretch to complete both the engine and hull survey components of the survey in one day, particularly if significant

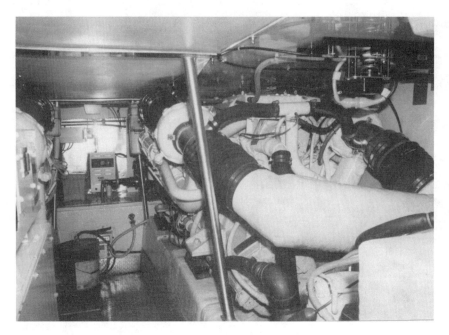

Fig. 11-3. Larger engine rooms can present the surveyor with quite a challenge. Though surveying the engines may not be his job, he is responsible for everything else in these cramped spaces.

travel distances are involved. Because of this, the surveyor needs to take care that one part of the survey doesn't suffer at the expense of the other by ensuring that you will have adequate time. Some surveyors don't cover the engines at all, advising the client that he needs to get a specialist (usually a local marina mechanic) to check out the engines. My experience is that clients are usually not very happy with this response.

Other surveyors tell the client that they do not perform full technical engine surveys but that they will look over and performance test the engines to the best of their ability, much as discussed earlier. Clients are a lot happier with this response than the former. The down side of this is that the survey effort is not complete (meaning a full machinery survey has not been made) and one need be wary of the associated risks.

A third way is to conduct a complete engine survey including compression test. Clients are most happy with a surveyor who does this. All three ways are not without their problems, and the biggest problem with doing complete surveys is the time factor. It's hard to do complete engine surveys and survey the boat all in one day, and, if you drag it out into a second day and charge for part of a second day, your fee is probably going to generate complaints.

The only way to resolve this problem is to have an understanding of how long it takes to survey certain kind of boats as well as being able to charge for your time. After all, your time is really what you are selling, but you have a limited amount and unless you manage it efficiently, you're not going to make it. For example, it's unlikely that a surveyor will be able to survey a 38' gas motor yacht type with generator in one day. A 30 footer, yes, no problem. But the bigger boats can lead to serious scheduling, as well as cash flow problems. In other words, how you handle it comes down to a matter of efficiency. If you're not maintaining a busy schedule, then it may not matter. But if you are, underestimating your time will lead to serious scheduling conflicts and a loss of income.

Gas engine surveys can go very quickly, or they can turn out to be major time burners when doing compression test. Like when you have a pair of engines jammed in a tight compartment and it's near impossible to get the spark plugs out, or the plugs may be rusted or installed so tightly that you can't remove them without breaking the plugs. When compression testing, we run into all sorts of unanticipated problems so we need to be sure that we're going to get fairly paid for our work. The compression test is the most important part of an engine survey as it will tell more about engine condition than anything else. Thus, to try to forego it is to do an incomplete survey.

Pricing Engine Surveys

All gas inboards are basically the same General Motors V-8 engines with differing types of marinization equipment hung on them. Therefore, in theory they are easy to survey. In reality, all sorts of problems can crop up to derail your carefully conceived scheduling. Outboards are even easier to survey and compression test rarely pose any significant problems other than dead batteries or faulty starting circuits.

Since time is money it pays to have a good idea of how long it's going to take to do each kind of job. The engines are the same, but the boats they are installed in are not. For example, twin engine stern drive boats will usually take twice as long to compression test as a comparable inboard installation. This is because the engines are usually jammed together and you can't reach the inboard spark plugs. You will also find that there are inboard installations where it is impossible to get at the outboard bank of spark plugs for compression testing. The more boats you are familiar with, the less likely one is to make big pricing mistakes.

For gas boats, my survey pricing always includes at least a basic engine survey. This is included in the fee quote. I do it this way because people generally don't like to deal with a fee plus add-on charges. They feel most comfort-

Fig. 11- 4. With the increasing use of aluminum parts, patches like this one on an exhaust manifold will become commonplace.

Fig. 11-5. Heat exchanger tank end plate leaks are commonplace. There's a big clue as to the nature of the problem here. Can you identify it? It's the badly balooned hose at lower left indiating that the heat exhanger is badly plugged up.

able when they are quoted a flat rate charge that includes everything. I charge extra only for compression testing, and this I do at a per cylinder rate. Since I am not familiar with all boats, and I don't want to get caught short undercharging, doing it on a per cylinder rate help solve this problem. The client is always informed in advance that there is the possibility that I cannot test all the cylinders for a variety of reasons.

Why Engines Wear Out Prematurely

With only marginal care, car engines seem to last indefinitely. Such is not the case for marine engines. The wet marine environment and corrosion is the reason why. Take note here that the saltwater environment is far worse than fresh water. Boat buyers are prone to placing too much emphasis on engine hours, thinking that hour meters are a good indicator of engine condition and wear. Not so. Because boats float in water, engines are vulnerable to corrosion damage and most of us are aware of the reasons why engines with low hours are more likely to be in poor condition than engines with higher hours.

With engines that receive infrequent use, gravity and evaporation will remove the coating of oil on cylinder walls and other internal parts. This exposes the metal to atmospheric corrosion. Also, whenever an engine stops, there are always at least two cylinders with the exhaust valves completely or partially open. This leaves the cylinder open to the very wet environment of the water-filled exhaust piping, and when it's salt water, this can be particularly damaging.

Thus, engines that are run more frequently are less exposed to this situation; they suffer from less internal corrosion.

So it is that a five year old boat with only two hundred hours on the meter is of greater cause for suspicion about its condition than, say, a comparable boat with six hundred hours.

Normal Engine Life

V-8 inboard engines will typically have a longer engine life than stern drive installations and the reason is due to engine location. A mid engine installation is usually in a more protected environment than a rear engine installation.

All things being equal, engine life of a well cared for closed cooling system gas engine can exceed fifteen years, though this is fairly rare. It's equally rare to see as much as 2,000 hours. Moreover, Crusader engines are the only ones that I have ever seen this kind of life span. None of the others ever seem to make it that far. The average life span is closer to 8-10 years and 1,000 hours or less. This has to do with the quality of the marinization of the basic engines.

Sea water cooled engines have about half the life span of closed system

Fig. 11- 6. Head gasket leaks are easy to spot if one can get visual access.

Fig. 11-7. A graphic illustration of the effects of infrequent operation in sea water environment. Each time the engine was run, stopped and allowed to sit for a long period of time resulted in these corrosion rings on the cylinder wall.

engines, though this can vary with engine size. Big block engines typically have heavier castings and will outlast smaller engines.

There are four basic ways that water can get into a marine engine: failed manifolds and risers, through the exhaust system, plus deck leaks and condensation. The first three are pretty much self-explanatory. Internal condensation is a little recognized problem that occurs as a result of large atmospheric temperature changes from cold to warm. When an engine block cools and the atmosphere becomes warmer, water vapor within the crankcase will condense on the colder metal. An easy check for condensation problems is to remove the valve cover caps and look at the valve train for rust before starting it. Also run your finger along the upper inside of the valve cover surface. If it's rusty, this could indicate condensation damage or water intrusion into the engine by other means. In any case, it's a bad sign that needs to be investigated further.

Getting Started

Boat owners and brokers like to run the engines before the surveyor arrives, usually to ensure that the engines will start. This, however, puts the surveyor at a disadvantage by not only possibly covering up problems, but now he has to work around hot engines. Thus, the surveyor should request of the owner that the engines not be run before he arrives.

Before starting the engines, not only should one do the basic safety checks, but also do a complete visual inspection and look the engines over carefully for evidences of fuel, oil or coolant leaks. Make note of these telltale signs for rechecking during the sea trial.

Oil leaks may be slight or profuse and it can be hard to tell just by looking at the oil trails. Before sea trialing it's a good idea to note potential areas and wipe away existing oil trails so that you can get a better idea of how strong the leak is with the engine under load. If there are oil trails on the hull under the engine, I'll try to wipe down a part of it so that I can see if the oil trail reappears. The two main culprits are valve covers and crankshaft seals.

Only after performing the necessary cold checks and ensuring that there are no fumes in the compartment should the engines be started. It's always wise to open up the compartment as much as possible to let it ventilate.

Engines should start easily and idle smoothly. Anything less than quick and easy starting means that something is wrong. New engines will usually start with less than one complete revolution of cranking. Any well-tuned engine should do nearly the same.

Visual inspection of inboard installations usually goes rather quickly, but stern drive engines can be hard to see because they are usually jammed close together. A mechanics mirror and flashlight will help

Basic Diagnostics

The following is a list of the various tests that can be done:

- Compression test
- Cooling system pressure test
- Crankcase oil analysis
- Dip transmissions with magnet
- Full speed test
- Backdown test of engine mounts
- Single engine load test
- Infrared pyrometer scan

Fig. 11- 8. The effects of excessively slow speed idling. Carbon build up on pistons becomes impacted in piston grooves, heats up and melts the piston. This will eventually result in catestrophic failure.

Compression Tests

Compression tests are potentially dangerous due to the fact that unburned gas is being run through the engine. Great care must be taken not to allow any fuel vapors to escape. Open up the compartment as much as possible to allow any fumes to dissipate. If you smell gas, immediately stop and let the fumes dissipate before proceeding. Remove only one spark plug at a time and replace it when finished with that cylinder. Do not make the mistake of removing all plugs at once. Not only will you be pouring gas fumes into the engine compartment, but you'll have trouble getting the ignition wires sorted out.

Before testing, make sure that the ignition wire from the coil or solid state control unit is grounded to the block in such a way that it will not arc and cause sparks. Avoid the use of clip-on remote starter buttons; these things usually generate a lot of sparks at the clip connections. The safest thing is to have a second person to do the engine cranking.

WARNING! Beware that excessive cranking with the ignition disabled will fill the exhaust system with unburned gas vapor which can explode should the engine misfire. To avoid this, do not restart the engines immediately, but allow about 30 minutes to allow the fumes to dissipate.

Warm up engines until the exhaust manifold begins to feel warm. Race the engine up to 2000 RPM to be sure oil gets to the upper cylinders. You need not run up to full operating temperature and risk getting serious burns. Keep in mind that the spark plugs are sandwiched between the uncooled exhaust ports. The difference between cold tests and hot tests will be a maximum of 10%, not more and usually less. For a warm test, the difference is insignificant. However, it is imperative that the engine be run and the rings oiled prior to testing.

Compression tests can be made with an engine running. However, this will damage the bicycle valve in the compression tester fairly rapidly, so if you plan to do engine running tests, keep a package of replacement valves on hand. My experience is that engine running tests result in readings that are about 10% lower.

Many engine marinizers do not give the compression in psi in the engine specs. The vast majority of all GM block V-8 marine engines have a new compression of about 150 psi which translates to an 8.5:1 compression ratio.

All large outboards with the exception of most 225-250 HP engines also will have a compression of 150 psi. The higher horsepower engines will have 7.5:1 ratios which is around 120 psi. If in doubt, contact an engine dealer who may be able to provide the right number.

Compression testing will reveal low compression, but not the cause of low compression, which could be either worn rings or worn valves. There is a big difference in repair costs between the two, so the surveyor will want to be able to advise the client what the problem is. This can be determined by retesting low reading cylinders after injecting some oil into the cylinder. Rather than carrying leaky oil cans around, I carry a length of transparent plastic tubing used to suck some engine oil out and then blow it into the cylinder. If the pressure comes up substantially, the problem is worn rings. If the pressure does not rise significantly, then the pressure loss is worn valve seats, meaning that only a valve job is necessary to restore good compression.

What is the minimum acceptable pressure? Manufacturers vary in their recommendations. In my opinion, the 100 psi put forth by Mercruiser in some of their literature is unacceptable. Most engines, all other things being equal, will run fairly efficiently down to about 110 psi, but below that incomplete combustion and power loss becomes excessive.

Compression variations between cylinders should be minimal, not more than 10%. Substantial variations cause engine imbalance, vibration and progressive loss of engine life.

When only one cylinder with very low compression is found, the probability is for broken rings or a damaged valve. When multiple cylinders are very low, but a few have normal compression, chances are there is a leaking exhaust riser putting water into the engine. Adding oil to the cylinder results in only slight pressure increase.

What happens when, for whatever reason, you can't test all the cylinders, is the compression test compromised? No, the test is compromised only to the extent of the numbers of cylinders that can't be tested. If it's only one, what are the odds that one cylinder is bad? But, say you can't reach an entire bank of cylinders; now you don't know the condition of 50% of the engine. On the other hand you do know the other 50% which is 50% better than nothing. So, the bottom line is whatever little you can do is worthwhile and provides some clue as to internal condition.

Visual Inspection

Making a thorough visual inspection of an engine is one of the most important aspects of the survey since there are many internal problems that will manifest externally.

Check for leaking crankshaft oil seals. Symptoms include the inside of bell housing being wet with oil; oil drip stains under bell housing or at front end. Hand wipe under side of engine before seal trialing to check for leaks on very oily engines. Make sure it's not just leaking valve cover gaskets.

Crankcase pressure. This test works in lieu of performing a compression test. It should be done with engines at full operating temperature. Close off all valve cover breathers and remove oil dipstick. Place your thumb over the opening for 30 seconds. If crankcase rapidly pressurizes and oil flows out dip stick, chances are there are worn valve guides. This is usually confirmed by excessive smoking from valve covers. If, during the sea trail, there is heavy smoking from the valve cover openings, this indicates heavy internal wear, either blow-by from rings or valve stems or both.

Cooling Systems

Overheating is a frequent problem because cooling system maintenance is often neglected. When it comes to cooling systems, cleanliness is all important. Systems can become contaminated for many reasons. When a system begins to develop sludge and other deposits, this can vastly reduce heat transfer capabilities through the castings, thus making an engine eternally prone to overheating unless those deposits are removed. The primary deposit types are rust pitting, iron oxide deposits and contaminates such as calcium, silt and sand. With raw water cooled engines, sand, silt and iron scale can accumulate in the lower block water passages. Over time, it is possible for these passages to completely fill up with debris, resulting in an engine that runs hot at the lower block. The infrared pyrometer is capable of diagnosing this condition when very high temperatures are obtained at the bottom of the water jackets, just below the freeze plugs.

Yet another form of inhibiting sludge comes from excessive ratios of ethylene glycol in the cooling system. Although rare, this happens when an owner, rather than taking the time to properly mix his coolant ratios, simply keeps topping off the system with antifreeze. This will show up as a gummy green residue in the heat exchanger tank. The reverse of this condition is a lack of rust inhibitor that will result in suspended iron oxide that will build up on water jacket walls and heat exchanger. This can be detected by running your finger around the inside of the tank. Both conditions can result in chronic overheating. Another telltale is when the plastic system reservoir looks to be very dirty.

- Check cooling system for contamination with oil or carbon. Both contaminants can indicate a cracked block, leaking oil cooler or bad head gaskets.

- Check closed systems for signs of salt around reservoir cap. Leaking heat exchangers can result in sea water going into fresh water side. The telltale is if the tank starts to overflow when cap is removed.

- If you're going to be doing engine surveys, you should have a cooling system pressure tester and pressure test the cooling system for internal leaks.

- Heat exchanger end plate leaks. This very common problem usually results from exhaust riser rust scale blockage that causes a rise in internal water pressure. In an effort to stop the leaking, owners and shade tree mechanics will try overtorquing the end plates which will either cause them to distort or crack.

- Perform a single engine load test by running one engine up to cruise speed. Cooling system is in good condition if temperature holds steady. Rapidly rising temperature indicates a fault in the system and will even show up a tendency to overheat that will not show with both engines running.

- Check all cooling system hoses. There should be no kinks, cracks or abrasions. Squeeze the hoses hard. If they crackle, the hose is either imbrittled or there is a heavy build up of scale. Steel wire reinforced hoses should not be used on saltwater engines.

- Check for drive belt tension, wear and misalignment. This is foretold by rubber particles all over the front of the engine. Rapid belt wear is usually caused by misalignment between engine and pump pulleys. This can usually be determined by sighting, lining up the two vee grooves and checking to see that the pulley sides look to be parallel.

- Check circulating water pump housing for leaks and unusual noise. Shoot the pump shaft with the infrared gun; if it's getting warm, then the seal is leaking and the bearings are going bad.

Gasket Leaks

Particularly on sea water cooled engines, check the head gasket surface located up under the exhaust manifold. Look for heavy rust at the interface; also be sure that any rust is not caused by leaks from above, such as from a riser joint. If rust is present, reinspect with engine running for any signs of percolation such as bubbles emanating around the gasket joint. Pay particular attention to this on sea water cooled engines.

Exhaust Risers

Leaks occurring at the exhaust riser to manifold gasket, no matter how minor, signal the onset of trouble. If this joint is leaking to the outside, chances are it is also leaking to the inside. In a sea water environment, water is migrat-

Fig. 11-9. There can't be much doubt about what's happening here with such distinctive rust trails from the riser gaskets.

ing under the gasket and will corrode the gasket surface, meaning that even the slightest leak is going to get progressively worse and ultimately will put water into the exhaust manifold and possibly the cylinders sooner or later.

Cast iron risers have relatively short life spans. Once a gasket surface starts to leak salt water, the casting has to be replaced. This is because the salt water will erode the gasket surface so that a gasket will not be able to seal it again.

Mercruiser and many after market castings are known to fail in few years or less, while Crusader risers generally last longer. Risers of any kind rarely last more than 5 years. One should never assume that a riser is in good condition just by looking at it. Iron castings may be of poor quality and be quite porous. Note that Crusader risers and manifolds always have casting dates on them, others don't.

Carburetors

Carburetors have a limited life span. As the carburetor body gaskets age, they shrink and start leaking. Rough idling is often the result of water contamination of fuel which will cause corrosion damage to needle valves, but it can also be caused by leaking gaskets. Leaking gaskets show up as gummy residue on the exterior of the unit.

Remove the flame arrestor and check the butterfly valves for corrosion. If heavy corrosion is present, this usually indicates a water leak from above is entering the carburetor.

Engines should idle smoothly at 600 RPM, which is the manufacturer recommended low idle speed. If it requires a much higher idle to keep the engine from stalling, something is wrong.

Exhaust Emissions

After starting the engines, check the exhaust outlets for oil or fuel discharge. Carburetor or injection overfueling will show a rainbow sheen on the water surface. A carboned up engine will usually result in carbon black on the water surface. A very light blue or white exhaust emission means that the engine is burning oil. Overfueling results in gray to black smoke.

Carbon Monoxide Hazards

CO is indeed a serious and dangerous hazard and it's remarkable that there hasn't been more trouble with it than we've had. With the relatively small number of fatality cases that have occurred, there does not appear to be a cause common to numerous cases. Non fatal cases occur with greater frequency than is reported since the symptoms of headache and nausea are often not recognized as CO poisoning.

CO poisoning occurs for a lot of reasons. The surveyor should be particularly on the alert for problems with improperly installed generators with exhaust outlets that could result in blow back into the vessel, its cockpit, doors, windows, ports and even sink drains.

Also be alert to the station wagon effect and whether or not the boat seems to be unusually prone to pulling exhaust fumes back into the cabin area.

Engine compartments should be nearly air tight to interior spaces. They rarely were on pre 1985 boats and only occasionally do we find late model boats where there are major openings into the cabin spaces. Beyond this and examining the exhaust systems, there is not much more a surveyor can do.

Unfortunately, high quality CO detectors suitable for use in testing exhaust systems are very costly and require frequent and costly recalibration. For this reason, there is no history of surveyors routinely using them as the cost is excessive.

Pyrometer Checks

When performing a survey, I record numerous engine temperatures on a preprinted form. The infrared pyrometer or temperature gun is a very useful tool for locating engine problems.

To perform a pyrometer survey, you need a good working knowledge of the engine. The procedure is to shoot engine temps at identical locations on both sides of both engines. This starts with taking a shot at or near the combustion area of the cylinder block or exhaust manifold port. Temps off the usual high will indicate incomplete combustion or a cooler burn.

If you can locate the water temperature sender, shoot the temp of the casting in way thereof and compare with reading of boat's gauge.

The pan oil temperature should be in the range of 190-220F with engine under load. Temps higher than this will indicate a fouled oil cooler. Check temp of oil entrance and exit from cooler and note the difference. Oil coming out of cooler should be significantly lower. If little change, cooler is bad.

Sweep the exhaust manifolds for hot or cold spots. All four manifolds should fall within a range of about 10%.

Check exhaust riser temps as these are most prone to rust and scale blockage. Riser temps should be very close to same temp as cooled portion of the exhaust manifold. Hot spots will indicate blockage and the need for replacement.

Exhaust hoses, crossovers and other pipes. Perform spot checks of the top side of all hoses and pipes. Objective is to make sure that the upper side is receiving cooling water. Check at both idle and cruise speeds. Beware of older boats with cast iron exhaust system elbows and "Y"s; these things rust out on the bottom side of the castings where it's hard to see and are capable of sinking the boat.

For transmissions, perform the same oil cooler tests as above. Shoot the temps at input and output shaft bearing bosses on aft side of gear case after running for a while. Generally, transmission temps should be below 150F.

Pencil thin magnet sticks are available at Sears and are perfect for dipping transmissions to see how much wear metals are laying on the bottom of the box. When the magnet comes out all fuzzy with iron filings, there is a serious wear problem. Same goes for chips and flakes, which means gear damage.

Stern Drive Boats

Occasionally engines are found that are mounted too low in the hull so that water backs up through the exhaust and floods the engine. With the boat afloat, make a quick check by noting the height of risers relative to the waterline. If it looks dangerously close, measure the actual distances. The engine risers should have a minimum height of 8" above normal floating water line.

Engine oil pan too close or in contact with bilge water. Are there water lines showing on the oil pan? Is it badly rusted? Will the bilge pump keep the water level sufficiently low?

Launching from trailers on very steep ramps results in water backing up through exhaust.

Leaking hatches and motor boxes leak water onto engine, sometimes into engine.

Vee Drive Installations

Oil pans are subject to corrosion because the stuffing box is under the engine. Stuffing box must be fitted with a splash guard to prevent oil pan from rusting out.

Weak engine mounts allow engine to move too much, causing constant stuffing box leakage.

Lube Oils

All too often, the engine oil has been recently changed because the boat is for sale, in which case the oil should be checked after the sea trial. Finding emulsified oil, meaning oil contaminated with water, is rare because it takes a lot of water to noticeably contaminate 5 quarts of oil.

Check the oil for fuel dilution by a simple smell test; diluted fuel will have a distinct gasoline smell. Rusty oil dipsticks indicate that water is getting into the crankcase somehow. Usually this is a condensation problem, but could be something worse. Using the paper towel viscosity test (to see how fast the oil spreads) is not reliable. This is because differing kinds of paper will behave differently. If you use the same type of paper for all such tests, then perhaps the results will be valid for determining fuel dilution.

Oil Analysis

This can be a good tool in the hands of someone who knows how to use it. However, there are a lot of pitfalls to anyone using it without a good background in metallurgy. First, the purpose of oil analysis is not for one-shot oil analysis but for long-term engine condition monitoring. It requires controlled conditions to get reliable results. Little or nothing can be determined from an oil sample for which the period of use is unknown. Next is the issue of who is interpreting the results? Are you qualified? Do you know what wear metals are in the particular engine and in what proportion they should appear? What does 400 ppm of iron mean?

On the other hand, oil analysis is very useful for determining contamination with water, glycol, salt and other compounds that should NOT be there. But beyond that, unless you have some good training on the subject, or you are just using it to locate contaminants, a surveyor best steer clear of attempting to interpret an oil analysis.

Electrical Systems

Wiring should be neat, orderly, well secured and most especially protected from vibration and hot manifolds. Connections should always be of the ring terminal type and splices should be butt connectors and never wire nuts or twisted, taped splices.

Gang connectors are vulnerable to corrosion as the sockets trap and hold water. It's best to pull them apart and check visually. Other important points to check are the starter motor cable and solenoid connections, which should not be rusty. If they are, cleaning and repair should be mandated. Also look out for starter motors situated under leaking heat exchangers as this is very common.

Check that alternators are charging. Most boats today have inexpensive voltmeters rather than ammeters, which makes it a bit more difficult to determine if the alternators are charging properly. The meter should read at 12 volts or above. If it's less, chances are that the unit is not charging. On most set ups the charge rate should be 13-14 volts.

Sea Trial

Sea trials should not be conducted on any boat where the engines are not in satisfactory running condition. Not only do you not want to get stuck with a break down, but we should remember that we don't down this boat and we don't want to put ourselves in a position where we could get blamed for causing damage. If there are any hazardous conditions, or the machinery is making unusual noise, or there is any indication of a possible break down, I advise the client that I will not be responsible for the operation of the boat and abort the sea trial.

This often leads to a problem where the seller then starts some kind of rush repairs. That would be fine except for one thing; you're either going to be delayed in completing the survey, or the repair efforts are going to interfere with your other survey efforts. Beware that for many boats, someone working in the engine compartment makes it impossible for the surveyor to continue with his work. Either way you are facing a pay cut as a result of lost efficiency. The simple fact here is that the boat isn't ready for survey and sea trial. Now you're going to find out why those preliminary agreements you made, or did not make, with the client are so important. The last thing in the world you want to hear from the seller is "We'll have it fixed by 4:00 PM." Ah, so this means you have to work until six or eight o'clock to get the job done. Have that happen to you twice a week and you quickly understand why some surveyors have a hard time making a reasonable income. What has happened is that the seller's problems have now become your problems; it's not your fault the engine doesn't run but you are going to pay a penalty. These inevitable situations have to be anticipated and covered in advance with the client lest you go broke.

During the sea trial, and preferably at a cruise speed, the engines should again be visually inspected, being aware that faults will show up under load that will not show when stopped or under no load. That means we check for coolant, oil or fuel leaks a second time.

Evaluate and record overall performance through a range of speeds. This is usually done in increments of 500 RPM.

Many surveyors record the boat's engine gauges at either cruise or full speed. With the infrared gun, record your engine temperatures versus the vessel gauge readings.

Evaluate operation of engine controls, particularly for stern drives and outboards. Note any uncertainty about shifting or neutral idle problems with the controls. Be sure that with stern drives, the gears engage positively without skipping and much "clunking." On inboard boats, check over the exhaust piping for leaks wherever visible.

See the Sea Trail chapter for further details.

Chapter 12

Fuel Systems

Fuel systems in pleasurecraft are regulated by CFR Title 33, Part 183, Subpart J and apply to all boats with gasoline engines. Small passenger vessels come under 46 CFR, Subchapter T. Voluntary standards are published by the American Boat and Yacht Council, H-24 and H-33, as well as NFPA Standard 302 and Underwriters Laboratories Inc., Standard UL1102. Surveyors typically regard these later standards as mandatory minimums.

The survey of fuel systems, particularly fuel tanks, is problematic from the standpoint of a significant lack of conformity between the CFR regulation and the voluntary standards which, although they have a similar intent, have considerable differences in actual requirements. The surveyor, in the course of providing his usual services, is not certifying as to compliance with either the regulation or standard. He is prevented from doing so for a variety of reasons, the foremost among these being the inaccessibility of all parts of the system, combined with the limited range of the fee for service requested by the client. Simply stated, the scope of the survey does not permit the surveyor to dismantle portions of the vessel to gain accessibility. Nor does he have the ability to determine materials composition from visual inspection in order to verify compliance with various materials standards such as the typing and grading materials.

Scope of Survey

The surveyor who is performing a pre-purchase or insurance survey is charged mainly with evaluation of those parts of the fuel system that he can see, and those materials he can identify by sight. In a large number of surveys that he will perform, his ability to inspect the complete system, especially fuel tanks,

Fig. 12-1 The foamed-in aluminum fuel tank with its numerous problems. In this case, the deck hatch leaked water into the tank cavity. The foam filled margins along the sides of the tank are filled with water, seen at left.

will often be extremely limited, and often too much so for comfort. It's quite common that fuel tanks are completely inaccessible for inspection, along with significant parts of the fuel supply system. Faulty fuel systems are responsible for creating dangerous conditions and costly repair remedies, conditions which are of the utmost concern to the conscientious surveyor. Unfortunately, the manner in which systems are installed in vessels conspires against the surveyor being able to fully evaluate and advise his clients of the actual condition of the system, or whether it meets both regulatory and voluntary standards.

Gasoline systems, of course, represent an explosion hazard. While diesel systems only rarely are ever associated with fires, they do represent a very real pollution hazard to the owner when systems leak and fuel is pumped overboard by bilge pumps. This is a fairly common occurrence that the surveyor should be alert to.

Marine surveyors should be conversant with CFR Title 33, Part 183, Sub-part J and the two voluntary standards. While he cannot "survey" the system to a standard, knowledge of the standards will assist him in identifying visual evidence of noncompliance and faulty installations.

A thorough system survey within the limits of the scope of a pre-purchase survey consists of visual examination of every part of the system possible. He should use his sense of smell to check for vapors, as well as his sense of touch by

Fig. 12-2. The same tank shown on facing page after it was pulled out. Top of tank is at left. Dark areas are the original black paint with which the tank was painted. Only about 50% of the foam remains adhering to the tank. Where water got between tank and foam, severe corrosion occurred.

running his hands over joints and connections to check for leakage. The use of mirrors is useful for looking around corners or inspecting tank bottoms that are exposed. Since fuel systems behave differently under varying conditions, the system should be inspected during a sea trial and with the vessel in a static condition. Vessels held for sale may not have been used for long periods so that evidence of leakage and other problems may have evaporated or otherwise disappeared in the interim. This will leave a gummy residue if the leak has existed long enough. There's nothing like putting a system to a test for showing up defects. Therefore, it's always a good idea to check out a system before, after and during operation.

Fuel Tanks

Aluminum and fiberglass are the prevalent materials in use today for powerboat tankage. It's interesting to note that most of the higher quality boat builders opt for fiberglass tanks over any other material. Fiberglass has long been the standard for Bertram and Hatteras for a good reason - reliability and corrosion resistance. Well constructed fiberglass tanks have an extremely low incidence of defect or failure as compared with metallic tanks which are subject to the very difficult problem of corrosion prevention. Of the thousand or so Bertrams and Hatterases the author has surveyed, only a few have showed up problems of leakage, all of which involved the manner of attachment of fittings.

H24.10.2 is one of the least complied with of the ABYC standards:

The tank(s) shall be installed in such a manner that means for maintenance or replacement is provided or indicated so it can be accomplished with a minimum of disturbance of the boat structure.

This is of little consequence for fiberglass tanks which rarely have a problem, but for aluminum tanks, thousands of boats require major surgery when replacement is required. The surveyor should be cognizant of this when dealing with boats having aluminum tanks.

Aluminum Tanks

Aluminum is a good material for both gas and diesel fuel tanks so long as the tanks are properly designed and installed. By far, it is the most widely used material for tanks, water and fuel. Unfortunately, the material has gotten a bad reputation as a result of increasing numbers of tank failures caused by corrosion. This is indeed unfortunate because such failures are preventable by good design. Properly installed, aluminum tanks can last the life of the vessel; improperly installed, they can fail within a few years.

Aluminum is fairly low on the scale of nobility so that it is vulnerable to both galvanic and crevice corrosion. Galvanic corrosion can occur when steel, brass or bronze fittings are used as tank connections, incompatible materials are used for straps, or when a tank is set on a platform containing screws of incompatible materials and so on. Crevice corrosion can occur anytime the tank is in contact with a foreign material and becomes wet or traps water. Common examples of this are tanks sitting on wood decks, water pocketing under securing metal straps, water laying on a dirty tank top, or a tank sitting on top of neoprene straps which traps water between the two materials.

Crevice corrosion occurs when water is trapped in small pockets or crev-

Fig.12-3 Fuel gauge sender on aluminum tank. Notice what's missing here? Originally installed with steel screws, all but one have corroded away. These senders can be made of steel, zinc alloy and occasionally stainless steel.

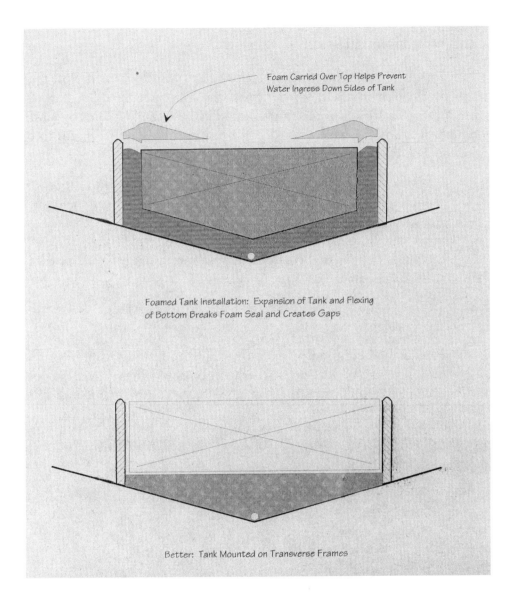

Foam Carried Over Top Helps Prevent
Water Ingress Down Sides of Tank

Foamed Tank Installation: Expansion of Tank and Flexing
of Bottom Breaks Foam Seal and Creates Gaps

Better: Tank Mounted on Transverse Frames

Fig. 12-4. Top: This cross section view of a foamed in place aluminum tank helps illustrate why this installation leads to corrosion problems. Bottom: Tank installation without foam provides for better air circulation.

ices in such a manner that it becomes starved for oxygen. Chemical reactions turn the water from ph neutral to highly acidic, and it is this acid that does the damage. It can occur virtually anywhere water becomes trapped and unable to evaporate. Metallurgists refer to these as corrosion cells.

Foamed Tank Installations

The worst of crevice corrosion problems occurs with foamed in place tank installations. Foaming tanks into bilge cavities is a widespread practice, particularly in boats under 30' and is the single largest cause of tank failures by far. In my opinion, foaming fuel tanks in place is a terrible practice that ought to be abandoned. The following are a few of the problems:

1. Fuel tanks expand and contract as they are filled and emptied. Although foam is supposed to adhere to the side of the tank and keep water out, more often than not the movement of the tank breaks the bond and allows water to migrate between tank side and foam. Once there it is trapped and creates a corrosion cell that can quickly damage the tank and result in leakage.

2. Tanks installed under decks are prone to water leaking down from above which often provides a constant source of wetting.

3. Tanks mounted in deep bilges are subject to wetting from bilge water. Although tank cavities are usually blocked off, it's nearly impossible to maintain waterproof integrity of a compartment in a high

Fig. 12-5. The ongoing problem with this tank is easy to identify by the corrosion deposits appearing along the edges. Mounted directly onto a deck, the underside traps water coming in from a leaky hull/deck joint.

speed vessel. It only takes a minor breach, a crack, pin hole or even wicking through glass fibers that are not fully wetted out with resin, to create a capillary effect that brings water into the tank cavity.

4.   As the low point in the vessel, bilges become contaminated with all sorts of chemicals, from leaking battery acid, petrochemicals and often chlorinated cleaning agents such as scouring powders that are often used to clean decks. The chemical stew found in bilge water can not only be corrosive to aluminum, but often breaks down the foam which is intended to protect it.

5.   The bilge spaces between deck and hull bottom create an extremely high moisture environment. With the sun beating down on the deck during the day, bilge temperature levels can reach 130°, creating an environment in which the air is completely saturated with water.

6.   Low nighttime temperatures, followed by sudden deck surface heating by the daytime sun will cause cold tank surfaces to sweat. Condensation then accumulates within the tank cavity, dissolving crystallized salts from the marine environment. Over time salinity levels within the tank cavity increase to high levels.

Foamed in place tanks appear predominately in open runabouts where the tanks are located beneath the cockpit sole. The ABYC standard requires that there be a removable deck plate to facilitate tank removal. Unfortunately, more often that not, the deck plate is the major culprit in allowing water to leak onto the tank. Unless the deck and hatch cover are extremely rigid, flexing of these components will usually result in a break in the caulking seal that lets the water in. Another common source are the plastic access ports to the valves and fittings. Fitted with o-ring gaskets, these access ports are supposed to be water tight but experience shows that usually they are not. It only takes a little bit of dirt or sand working its way into the gap to break the seal and allow water to pour into the cavity.

When dealing with foamed fuel tank installation, the surveyor needs to give serious consideration to protecting his client from this serious hazard. Prudence dictates that the surveyor should create a standard warning clause to be incorporated in every report dealing with foamed fuel tanks. The clause should warn of the corrosion hazard, the surveyor's inability to inspect the tank, and the potential consequences of not knowing what the condition of the tank is.

Aluminum tanks show up with varying degrees of the tank encapsulated in foam. They are found completely foamed (all six sides), foamed only up to the top, or foamed only around the base. Of these, tanks foamed only around

Fig. 12-6. The ultimate nightmare. Two aluminum tanks improperly installed in a custom sport fish. Both tanks were boxed in with plywood, then the cavity was filled with foam, creating a perfect water trap.

the base offer the greatest potential for trapping water since expansion and contraction of the sides will inevitably break the seal and allow water to work its way to the bottom. Tanks that are foamed up the sides to near the top are little better since this also traps water between foam and tank and stringer. The better installation is where the foam extends up the sides and over the top to some degree as this will at least inhibit water from running down the sides (Fig. 12-4). It will, however, trap water on the top but at least it has the chance of evaporating whereas water trapped between foam and tank does not.

Salt water leaking down from the deck will result in an increasing accumulation of salt as the water evaporates and leaves the salt behind. The increasing level of salt concentrates the electrolyte and increases the rate of corrosion whenever a galvanic cell is present. Occasional rinsing off with fresh water will at least reduce this potential. If the residue of scouring powder is found, the owner should be advised not to continue using it since chlorinated cleansers only aggravate the problem.

Deck Mounted Aluminum

Tanks mounted on a wooden deck pose nearly as much trouble as do foamed tanks. The only advantage is that you can see the sides, but not the bottom.

Wood is very good at absorbing water, even from the atmosphere. In high humidity environments, equilibrium level of water content can be as high as 15% of the weight of wood so that what might appear to be dry wood is actually quite wet. Even worse, as wood is alternately wetted with salt water and dried, the salt content gradually increases over the years. The bottom line is that metallic tanks should never be mounted directly in contact with raw wood at any point on the tank. On the other hand, tanks set on top of fiberglass laminated wood will do just fine so long as there is not a wide, flat surface that will trap and retain water.

ABYC requires a 1/4" gap between the tank and deck, yet the method of achieving that gap is equally troublesome. The use of neoprene or rubber strips presents the problem of creating gaps which, by means of the capillary effect, is very good at sucking up water and retaining it in a manner that sets off crevice corrosion. Another problem is that the rubber may have a high amount of carbon in it that is galvanically incompatible and actually causes galvanic corrosion. This system will work fine so long as there are no water leaks onto the tank or mounting surface. The surveyor should be looking for evidence of water leakage when inspecting this type of installation. Experience has shown

Fig. 12-7. It would be hard to find a better testimonial for why fuel tanks should not be mounted directly to the bottom of the hull, or made hull integral. This tank is glassed in place directly on a natural hinge point of the bottom, an unfilled bottom strake. The tank is now a hull frame and has fractured. Fancy aluminum facings help to conceal what has happened here.

that unless a boat has a chronic leak above such a tank, as when installed under a cockpit deck with a hatch opening, tanks that are mounted on plastic or aluminum strips perform well and corrosion failures are rare. When tanks are mounted under cockpit decks the failure rate goes up dramatically since cockpit hatches almost always leak.

Engine room mounted tanks that have the required 1/4" gap perform very well. If they do not have the required gap, even small leaks that work their way under the tank can cause trouble as Fig. 12-5 reveals. However, engine heat and the high volume air flow promotes rapid evaporation of water so that wetting of properly mounted tanks will dry quickly, unlike the high moisture environment of the under-cockpit installation where moisture is ever present.

Beware of aluminum tanks that are particularly long relative to their width. Mounted on top of flexing stringers or frames, long tanks are more susceptible to weld fracturing and baffle failures caused by hull-induced stress. Tank beds should be inspected for any signs of disturbance or working.

Iron Tanks

Iron tanks have a notoriously poor performance record resulting from its susceptibility to corrosion. Rarely used anymore, they will be found in older Oriental boats, and become increasingly dangerous with age. Unless coated

Fig. 12-8. This fellow thought he had a fuel tank condensation problem. Installing fuel fillers at low spots on decks is not a good idea.

Fig. 12-9. The USCG requires these protective bowls under filter sight bowls. They prove to be quite a nuissance and many people remove them.

with something like coal tar epoxy[1], iron is vulnerable even to atmospheric corrosion. When mounted in direct contact with wood, the results are usually disastrous. Even equilibrium moisture levels in wood will cause painted iron to corrode. Iron tanks must be kept absolutely dry and ideally should be coated with a material like coal tar epoxy or other soft coating which does not crack or flake. The tanks are best mounted on fiberglassed frames and be completely exposed for adequate air circulation.

Iron tanks are rarely used in domestic boat building anymore and are most often found in Oriental imports. Most of the time these tanks in Oriental boats are found completely covered with a soft, water absorbent acoustic tile so that no part of the tank is visible. This is a particularly risky situation for the surveyor: if there are deck leaks, or tanks are mounted next to a stuffing box, the acoustic material will absorb and retain water. When encountering such installations, the surveyor would be wise to incorporate a carefully worded clause in his report detailing his inability to determine the condition of the tank and why.

Stainless Steel

Rarely used in North American boat construction, stainless tanks are most often found in European and Oriental boats. These tanks have three major shortcomings: crevice corrosion, weld failures and excessively thin wall thickness that results in severe expansion and contraction and related problems.

The author has had little experience with stainless fuel tanks in power boats since they are most often found in sailing vessels where the tanks are small. They are most often used for water tanks in power boats where their service record, at least in my experience, has not been good. Stainless is subject to crevice corrosion to a degree similar to aluminum, in addition to which weld joint failures and baffle failures seem to be the most common complaints. As with all metallic tanks, stainless should not be in contact with wood or dissimilar metals, though they often are. Nor should it be installed in ways that create crevices that trap water.

ABYC does not permit stainless tanks unless they are cylindrical with domed heads, and with good reason: The low minimum sheet thickness requirement allows for tank walls so thin and flimsy that the G-forces generated by slamming of the hull can cause these tanks to balloon severely. In turn, bellowing of the tank walls breaks loose baffles and stresses weld joints. Good examples of this sort of failure are often found in Oriental imports with large water tanks mounted in the forward section where pitching and slamming forces conspire to damage them.

Metallic Tank Mounting

The critical factors for installing a tank are where and how it is installed. Under open cockpits where the tanks are likely to get wet is the least desirable. Experience has proven that wing tanks in the engine room have the least difficulty with corrosion. However, the mid and forward sections of the hull experience the greatest G-forces from hull pounding so that providing a stable platform becomes most important. It's preferable that tanks not be mounted directly on top of stringers because of the energy transference upward into the tank that will unduly stress the tank. Ideally, the tank mounting deck should be on a glass-covered wooden cradle that will absorb some of the impact load to the tank.

The mounting system should be fully inspected to determine whether there is any disturbance to the mounting base, as well as loosening of the securing system such as metal straps and base chocks. The discovery of loose or damaged mounting systems is not at all uncommon and it may well thwart a ruptured fuel tank when such conditions are found.

Tanks improperly mounted under cockpit decks on plywood decks can often be easily corrected by lifting and shimming with strips of 1/4" plastic to get the tank away from contact with wood. The problem with the pair of tanks shown in Fig. 12-5 was corrected in just a few hours time.

Bilge mounted tanks need careful consideration as to whether the tank is likely to be subject to standing bilge water. Occasional immersion is rarely harmful, since water by itself is not harmful to aluminum. I've seen many cases of tanks in contact with very oily bilge water that had no corrosion at all. Lacking this coating of oil, prolonged immersion can produce the same results as an unprotected aluminum hull and *will be subject to stray current corrosion*. A tank located only 2" above the bilge is obviously going to be wetted frequently, while a tank 6" high less frequently. Centrifugal bilge pumps will usually leave up to 2" of water in the bilge, but by installing a diaphragm or neoprene impeller suction pump, with the float switch properly located, the problem of frequent water contact can often be eliminated or at least reduced without the need for remounting the tank.

During the sea trial, the surveyor should be able to get an idea of whether the tank gets wetted when boat trim changes. I do not suggest that exposed tanks (other than foamed installations) that are infrequently wetted require any remedial action. That would mean a tank that gets wet as a result of bilge pump failure does not. Tanks that get wet every time a change in trim occurs do need corrective action.

Fig. 12-10. Due to stress at the connection, flex hoses tend to crack with age at this point. This severe cracking was only visible when the hose is forcefully bent as shown here.

Fig. 12-11. One weakness of copper fuel lines is shown here where the pipe is in contact with wood which will get wet and cause rapid corrosion. These pass-through holes should be fitted with plastic grommets.

What about wetting from above? So long as the tank does not have any condition that creates a corrosion cell, water can leak onto that tank indefinitely without damaging it.

Fuel tanks should never be mounted directly on the skin of the hull (Fig. 12-7), yet occasionally we find this to be the case. The use of hull-integral fuel tanks in fiberglass boats is a spectacularly bad idea and fortunately it's not often found in production boats. I've seen a few from Italy and Taiwan, including some where fuel migration through the hull laminate has occurred. Incomplete resin saturation of glass fibers makes them prone to weepage through the laminate. I've also seen commercial fishing boats and a few sail boats with integral glass tanks that have resulted in complete saturation of the hull laminate with fuel oil. Any defect or laminate failure in and around the tank has the potential to case serious leakage problems. Cored hulls have been found that were completely saturated with fuel from stem to stern. Beware, beware beware!

Systems and Materials

Fuel Lines

The most common materials in use for fuel lines are copper pipe and flexible hose that is U.S.C.G. rated for marine use. All of the name manufacturers produce good quality material.

One of the best aspects of CFR 33 is that nearly fifteen years ago it required the labeling and dating of fuel tanks and fuel lines, a feature that is of great help to surveyors. Having actually set a real, honest-to-goodness standard for materials and construction, most of the problems that were encountered in the past with substandard materials have been eliminated. However, that is not to say that someone at some time will not pick up a piece of unidentified material and use it for a fuel line repair or replacement.

Copper Tubing

Copper, when correctly installed, has a history of exceptionally long service life, even when used in the most adverse conditions. It performs admirably even when constantly wetted. This is why Subchapter T, 46 CFR, *Small Passenger Vessels* requires the use of annealed copper only for gasoline fuel lines. Yet, like most metals, it is subject to crevice corrosion. Its primary weaknesses are corrosion from contact with wet wood and galvanic corrosion resulting from contact with dissimilar metals. Joints are susceptible to loosening and damage caused by vibration when such connections are not properly secured.

The routing of copper pipe is important since the material should never be in contact with holes drilled in wood or laying on raw wooden decks that are frequently wetted. All points where copper tubing passes through wood bulkheads should be fitted with protective plastic grommets or shielding. When mounted on flat wood surfaces, the wood should have at least two coats of paint to prevent the wood from absorbing water.

Since gasoline has very low viscosity, connections are easily checked by simply running your fingers around the joint. Slight weepage will usually result in fuel evaporation faster that it can leak so that the joint won't be fuel wet. However, evaporation will leave a build up of resin or gum that will feel sticky and serve as a warning of the leakage. Any connection with a sticky residue should be flagged for service.

When non-annealed copper tubing corrodes, it creates an unusually thick scale so that even minor corrosion can appear to be more severe than it really is. The degree of severity can be determined by scraping away the scale with sharp instrument and gauging how deeply the material is pitted. Copper tubing has a rather thick wall compared to its diameter so that light surface pitting, say as much as 0.025", is acceptable. Copper is not particularly prone to cratering like many other metals.

Pay particular attention to the various fittings used in the overall system. Copper systems should only use brass or bronze fittings, never stainless or galvanized. Be particularly alert to copper tubing used in conjunction with aluminum tanks. No part of the tubing must ever come in contact with the tank. Copper pipe laying against the top or side of an aluminum tank can quickly burn a hole through the tank. Further, the connections to the tank require a proper galvanic isolator. Aluminum tanks should never have brass nipples threaded into them. An acceptable isolator is a stainless or galvanized connector. In other words, copper to stainless to aluminum.

Fuel Hose

Fuel hose is required to be marked as to type and date. If the hose is not marked, replacement must be recommended with approved material. The surveyor is not charged with certifying that the proper material is being used, only that the material contains the proper U.S.C.G markings. In recent years, various fuel additives such as ethanol and others have created quite a firestorm of controversy over the effects of these additives on fuel system components. Many of these additives are known to cause damage to synthetic materials and for that reason it behooves the surveyor to pay particular attention to fuel hoses. The following is a description of damages most commonly found.

Embrittlement — Hoses become stiff with age or as a result of hardening caused by chemical additives. Check hoses by bending, particularly at low points where fuel collects. If hose makes a cracking or crunching sound, it should be replaced. Especially check for cracking at points of attachment.

Dissolution — This occurs when the material actually begins to be dissolved by an additive and the material becomes unusually soft, mushy or tacky to the touch. The surveyor should know what new hose feels like so that he can gauge what damaged hose feels like. Hose that is dissolving feels too soft and bends too easily. Dissolving hoses often result in fuel system damage from gum or even large pieces of the inner wall sloughing off and fouling carburetors or injectors. Squeezing the hose should yield considerable resistance.

Vibration, chaffing — The most common fuel line damage of all, fuel hoses need to be protected against normal engine vibration. Fuel lines should always be secured to a solid surface Hoses should never be draped one over the other and should never span open spaces where they can get snagged. Check all points where hoses pass through openings in any type of surface.

In addition to visual inspection, the best way to test fuel hose connections is to simply pull on them. The ones that slip off need attention.

Delamination - Fabric reinforced hoses have been known to delaminate.

When the inner ply separates, the vacuum draw of the fuel pump may cause the walls to collapse, shutting off the fuel supply. Delaminated hoses usually feel very soft when squeezed. Fuel hoses should be considered anytime there is a fuel supply problem.

Mechanical damage — cutting, crimping, crushing, melting. This type of damage occurs as a result of inconsiderate routing. After chaffing, fuel line damage most often occurs as a result of being placed where it gets frequently stepped on, such as on a deck or edge of a stringer in the engine room. Hoses shouldn't be bent around sharp corners and never draped across engine manifolds, intake or exhaust. Remember that gas engine intake manifolds have heat riser passages that get very hot. Be on the alert for hoses laid on decks inside lazarette hatches where equipment may be stored on top of them, and be on the alert for signs of pinching or crimping. Poor engine performance is often traced to fuel supply restriction due to crimping of the hose or copper pipe.

Aging of Hose Of course it takes a long time before we learn how well the products of any given manufacturer hold up. Fortunately, I can say that the fuel hose produced by all major U.S. manufacturers has shown to hold up well, generally lasting about ten years before serious signs of aging appears. I recommend replacement of all hose ten years or older, regardless of appearance.

Fuel Tank Senders

Fuel sender units and the means of attachment to the tank often provides a means of fuel leakage. Sender mount plates are often found of steel or zinc alloy, both of which corrode rapidly. I frequently find senders that are leaking. Fasteners are often found to be of steel or brass or even wood screws. The use of wood screws will allow fuel to leak by the threads. Neither of these materials should be used and, when found, replacement with stainless steel and properly threaded machine screws should be recommended.

General Routing

The difference between a neatly installed fuel system and a sloppy one often translates to reliability. A builder who doesn't care how it looks probably doesn't care how it performs. Neatly installed systems usually mean that the installer cares enough to ensure that it's done right, so be particularly alert to slipshod installations.

Whether gas or diesel, fuel lines should never be routed in bundles of wiring, nor should they make contact with primary battery cables to the engine starting motors. If a wire short circuits, as engine starting systems occasionally do, it might burn through the fuel line and start a fire that will be nearly impossible to extinguish. The general rule is that fuel lines should not contact electrical circuits, motors or other electrical equipment. If they do, rerouting should be recommended. Occasionally owners or installers will find fuel lines a convenient way to route a new electrical line by wrapping the wire around the fuel line. Not a good idea.

Fuel lines of any type should not be laying in the bilge or routed beside stuffing boxes where the spinning shaft will throw water on them. If there's no choice of routing through wet environments, it's best to recommend one of the shielded types of hose, or to install a conduit over it.

Particularly in small boats where space is at a premium, fuel lines should never be routed above or near batteries. Unfortunately, they often are. When found near batteries, it should be recommended that the lines be rerouted. Hydrogen gas given off by batteries causes embrittlement of hoses and severely corrodes copper and other fittings.

For obvious reasons, fuel lines should never be mounted on the under side of deck and directly above an engine.

Valves

The earlier ABYC standard requiring positive fuel system shut off valves has been rescinded and replaced with one that requires physical testing in order to prove whether or not it meets their standard. There is virtually no mention in this standard of valves or anti-siphon devices in fuel lines. Instead, the standard resorts to the peculiar language of stating that the fuel supply system must withstand breakage for 2-1/2 minutes without leaking more than 5 ounces of fuel. That's a mighty strange way of setting a standard because who knows how much a system will leak if there's a break. Just to put this into perspective, a 5/16" I.D. fuel hose six feet long will hold five ounces of fuel, as if the surveyor is supposed to know how much fuel every size fuel line will hold, and whether or not it will siphon from the tank.

Further, the standards now permits siphon breaks, one-way check valves. These little gizmos can be incorporated into a fitting the size of a small elbow, and usually are. This makes for a situation where the surveyor cannot determine whether anti-siphon devices exist, or whether they are functioning. If the device malfunctions or gets clogged up with debris, there's no way of knowing if it works. The only requirement for anti-siphon protection is with the use of electric fuel pumps. For all practical purposes, this standard cannot be evaluate by the surveyor in actual practice.

Electric Fuel Pumps

The use of electric fuel pumps on gas inboard boats is a very dangerous proposition that the surveyor should be fully aware of. Electric fuel pumps on gas inboard boats ought to be banned, but they're not. Electric fuel pumps are usually found on outboard or race boats, but occasionally we find someone foolish enough to install them on inboards.

The problem is this: If there is no means to shut off the pump when the engine stops (particularly if it stalls) then the pump will keep on pumping fuel and possibly overflow the carburetor if the flow control valve sticks. There's no way for the surveyor (within reasonable limits) to check the system to be sure that it's properly wired and set up. True, it is *supposed* to have an internal pressure switch and the system is *supposed* to regulate the pressure between pump and carburetor. But disaster looms should any element of the system fail. As a former race car driver, I've seen plenty of horrible fires caused by electric fuel pumps that failed to stop pumping gasoline when they should have: I lost two cars to fuel pump-caused fires myself, so I am very prejudiced against their use. The result can be a gas-fed fire that cannot be stopped. Because of the problem of water and debris in fuel, the pressure regulating mechanisms in these systems cannot be considered as absolutely reliable.

Fuel supply lines on gas boats rarely have leakage problems because they operate off a suction from the mechanical engine fuel; they're not pressurized except between engine pump and carburetor where there's a steel fuel pipe. But when an electric pump is added, the whole system is then pressurized and this greatly increases the risks for leakage, in addition to the potentially disastrous problem of pump shut off failure.

When electric fuel pump systems are encountered, it's prudent to advise the client of these dangers and let him decide whether he wants to live with it. In any case, be sure to protect yourself.

Fuel Fill Systems

ABYC H24.12.6 is another commonly ignored standard: *All components of the fuel fill system shall be accessible.* In reality, few are. The great danger, of course, is that fuel fillers are usually jointed segments with the potential for leakage that, when filling, could put gas or diesel fuel in the bilge.

Fuel filler pipes and deck fittings cause more problems than a novice surveyor might imagine. The fact is that fuel tanks and decks are not rigid structures but usually move to some degree. Imagine a big sport fisherman smashing along through a heavy sea and it becomes easy to envision the fuel tanks and decks shuddering. For that reason, some degree of flexibility has to be provided between tank and deck fitting. Unless the fuel fill system has been thoughtfully designed, it's quite likely to cause problems.

The most common problem, and one that is often never discovered, occurs when the fuel filler plate is mounted on a deck that holds water. Most fuel fill plates have threaded caps with o-rings. Can we imagine that, when the deck plate is submerged, this little o-ring (the one that is never inspected) will really keep the water out? While hundreds of boat owners curse marina operators for having water in their fuel, the greater likelihood is that their deck plates are leaking! There's really no way that anyone can check a deck plate for leaks short of taking the plate off and water testing it. But if you find a fuel fill plate mounted in a valley, the odds are quite high that it's leaking.

Tank corrosion and fill hose leakage problems can often be traced to a situation in which the tank is so tall that the top is too close to the deck. In this case, the hose sleeve connector is so short that it cannot sufficiently take up the slack when a side deck flexes, or the tank wobbles a bit, as they usually do. This is likely to cause the hose to loosen at the clamp joints and leak when the tank is filled. Fuel wetness or a residue of gum or varnish on top of the tank is an indication of this possibility.

Flexing of the deck can also result in loosening of the deck plate and allow water to leak in under the flange. This can be deadly because the tank spud may be zinc alloy, or it may be fastened to the tank with steel screws. Add a little salt water to these dissimilar metals and the result may be the failure of the flange or the fasteners. That's why it's a good idea to shine the flashlight on top of the tank area and check these components.

The location of the fuel fill is equally important. I once poured 10 gallons of gas through a fishing rod holder located three inches away from the fuel fill. Other people have also had this terrifying experience. Obviously, rod holders should never be mounted next to a fuel fill even though many are. Rod holders look too much like fill plates. You can either recommend that the rod holder be moved (the hole that it leaves is a bit of a problem) or have the client affix a large, plastic label plate or warning, such as the type made by engraving shops. At least this will head off the client from saying, "You didn't tell me!" It may also head off a terrible accident.

Fuel fills next to tuna tower legs. Ever see a gas fuel fill three inches from a tower leg and wonder what would happen if the tower got hit by lightning? Better to at least check to see if the tower leg is grounded. Although I've never heard of a boat blowing up because of this, it has got to be a possibility. It's hard to imagine that lightning traveling though a near empty gas tank that is mostly fumes wouldn't result in an explosion. Possibly it's happened but nobody ever figured out that that was the cause. There's no standard covering this situation, but there is a standard that tower legs should be grounded.

A.B.Y.C requires that *"all components of the fuel fill system shall be accessible."* How many really are? Probably less than 50% of all boats that I survey. Another problem with fuel fills is the hose sleeve connectors that connect the tubular nipples. If the joint is not tight, it will leak fuel at the bottom connection. If it's not accessible, we can't even check for leaks, rusty hose clamps, or broken bonding wires. Follow the axiom that if it can't be seen, write it up.

Tank Vents

It is a very common problem that fuel tank vents are improperly installed for the following reasons.

- Vent holes are aimed forward or up, take in spray or rain water.

- Vent located aft, low on hull side and goes underwater while underway.

- No riser loop in vent hose; hose runs downhill to tank.

- Badly designed cheap plastic fittings incapable of keeping water out.

Large Systems

Vessels with three or more fuel tanks can have some pretty complicated fuel supply, transfer and return systems. Sometimes these systems are not well designed, or the systems may be quirky. I've had clients run out of fuel and then complain that I didn't advise them about weird idiosyncrasies such as incomprehensible valving. Tracing such systems out and determining how they operate is not part of the usual pre-purchase survey. Some of the things to watch for are:

- Lack of adequate labeling or operating instructions.

- No tankage plans available.

- Lack of fuel transfer capability when it's clearly needed.

- Inconsiderate tankage placement causing trim and performance problems.

- No positive means of determining fuel reserve and reliance on electric gauges.

- No internal access for inspection or cleaning.

When yachts having an unusually large number of tanks is encountered, it's best to ask for and review fuel system plans. If there are no clear tankage plans or operating instructions, the client should be warned of this fact. At least advise him that the operation of the system was not clear and that he should get instructions from the owner or captain.

---

[1] Coal tar epoxy is the generic name for the black mastic used to coat bottoms of aluminum and steel vessels that is sold under various trade names by paint companies. It particularly good at protecting metals because it is very adhesive and remains soft without drying to a brittle consistency.

Chapter 13

Exhaust Systems

Surveying exhaust systems is one of the more critical aspects of completing the marine survey, not only because exhaust systems bear directly on the safety and seaworthiness of the vessel, but because surveyors so often encounter systems with either faulty designs or systems that utilize substandard materials.

The vast majority of boat builders today utilize good quality materials that are able to withstand the test of time, corrosion, heat and pressure. Yet there are a sufficient number of builders that make either substandard or faulty systems that the surveyor should constantly be on the lookout for them. Unlike most other types of vehicles, boats alone have exhaust systems that travel considerable distances *inside* the vessel. For this reason, faulty systems can threaten the vessel and its passengers with hazards of fire, sinking, engine damage and, worst of all, carbon monoxide poisoning. The following are the major design requirements:

- Contain and channel exhaust gasses safely from engine to an appropriate hull exit.

- Materials must be able to withstand constant immersion and be galvanically compatible.

- Materials and joints must be able to withstand internal pressurization.

- System design prevents water back surge into engine.

- System materials should be able to withstand short term overheating without suffering catastrophic failure.

- System design should not result in excessive exhaust back pressure that can cause engine damage.

The introduction of fiberglass pipe and mufflers has gone a long way toward eliminating most of the exhaust system problems of the past, which were directly related to the use of metallic components that were highly subject to the effects of various types of corrosion. Rarely do we find metal mufflers, flanges and connectors in new boat construction, although they are occasionally found on custom or import boats.

The use of fiberglass pipe joined with sections of high temperature, reinforced exhaust hose known as "sleeve connectors" creates a rugged and highly reliable system which, depending on the quality of the exhaust hose, can last for decades. So, too, can fiberglass mufflers if they are well made.

The weakness of most systems is to be found in the manner in which it is designed and installed, and it is here that the surveyor must examine and evaluate the system with utmost care. But before we get into details of system design, lets first review some of the basic components and materials.

Materials

Fiberglass Pipe

Constructed of heat resistant and self-extinguishing resins, fiberglass pipe has proved to be the most ideal material for marine exhaust systems. Although requiring exhaust water for cooling, this material has been known to withstand the loss of cooling water for short periods without experiencing catastrophic failure. Pipe can be sectioned and easily formed into angles and elbows.

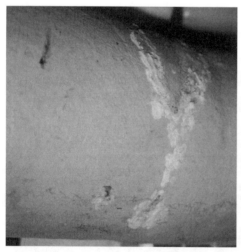

Fig. 13-1 Fiberglass pipe is great stuff as long as it's not made of mat. The stuff is too porous.

Fig. 13-2 Exhaust hose is prone to vibration damage. Just touching against this plywood corner resulted in complete penetration.

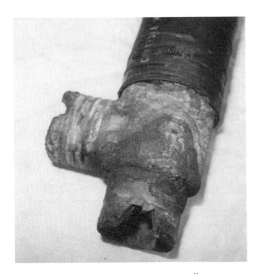

Fig. 13-3. Iron elbows can outwardly appear in good condition. Be sure to look on the underside where it may look like this.

Fig. 13-4. Crevice corrosion is always a problem when hose is joined to aluminum pipe,

Manufactured on a male mold, it is usually smooth on the inside and rough on the outside. Joint surfaces have to be hand smoothed to create a leak-proof joint. Leaks at joints are most often caused by failure to smooth the joint surface.

Exhaust Hose

Semi-flexible, heavily reinforced exhaust hose that is specifically manufactured for exhaust use is a proven material for most installations so long as it is adequately supported and fully water-cooled. Because of its high cost, its use has largely been supplanted by fiberglass pipe for long piping runs and is now primarily used for making sleeve connectors between sections of pipe. Most exhaust hose is made of reinforced butyl rubber so that a constant flow of cooling water is necessary. The material is self-extinguishing but will burn as long as the heat source is constant. When used alone as the primary exhaust piping, exhaust hose needs to be thoroughly supported along its length, as well as precisely fitted to all connections. If it is not precisely fitted, there is a high potential for chronic leakage no matter how hard hose clamps are tightened.

Good quality material can last indefinitely if not damaged by heat. However, in recent years the quality of some products on the market seems to be declining as builders opt for ever cheaper materials. Lower quality material has the tendency toward embrittlement which makes it susceptible to cracking when stressed. The larger diameter hoses are most prone to ply separations or delaminating. Pressing hard against the hose with a blunt instrument, or even squeezing it with your hands, is one easy way to check the condition. When hose is aged or even burned on the inside, it will usually make a distinct cracking sound when compressed.

Beware of this material when located beside, and particularly above, batteries. Rubber can be quickly and severely degraded by the hydrogen fumes given off by lead-acid batteries. Rubber hoses should be routed as far away from batteries as possible. Any degree of kinking or any form of mechanical stress on this material should be avoided. This means that hose should never be formed into a sharp bend. A bend is too sharp when the material begins to buckle. Hose sleeve jointed sections of rigid pipe should always be properly aligned. Misalignment will cause unnecessary stress that causes cracking and leaking joints. Watch for plastic (clear) wrapped hose from the Orient; the plastic wrapper on some samples of this hose was found to be flammable and should be stripped off within three feet of the engine. Otherwise, most of the hose that I've seen from the Orient seems to be remarkably good quality. Also watch for delaminated sleeve connectors; highly stressed connections often result in ply separations. In this case the hose will feel very soft when squeezed.

Stainless Steel

In late model boats stainless is most often found in risers, elbows, flanges and male connectors. The use of stainless in exhaust systems continues to be problematic. Even so, considering the cost/benefit ratio, stainless will continue to be the material of choice for metallic parts. Because stainless is anodic to carbon rubber, mating it to hoses containing carbon rubber can result in severe galvanic corrosion at the hose joint. Hose joints to stainless components are also subject to crevice corrosion at the point where the joint traps water between the hose and pipe. The use of stainless in systems that are partly or completely immersed in sea water will suffer all the same problems as underwater metals. It is the undersides of pipes and weld joints that require the most careful inspection for leaks. All parts of a wet exhaust system need to be tied into the common bonding system but very often they are not.

Cast Iron

Still used in gas engine installations, cast iron can be found in risers, elbows, tees, crossover pipes and occasionally cast iron mufflers. Cast iron works well in systems that are not continuously submerged, and it is not unusual to find iron components that have lasted for decades. But cast iron does not do well when completely, or even partially submerged, or utilized in low-lying areas of the system that collect and hold water. Another weak point of cast iron is that it does not withstand extreme temperature changes or temperature differences within the same part. A typical example of this is an exhaust riser that has cooled and uncooled sections. Heat transition zones from hot to cool deteriorate rapidly. Cast iron should only be used for gas engines and never diesel systems. The high sulfur content in diesel exhaust combines with water to create sulfuric acid to which iron is highly vulnerable.

Aluminum

This material works reasonably well in thoughtfully designed systems, but tends to fare poorly in systems where the weaknesses of aluminum have not been considered. Aluminum is highly anodic to carbon rubber so that clamped hose joints are vulnerable to galvanic corrosion. Crevice corrosion is another serious problem at hose-to-metal joints that are submerged. Heat affected zones around welds have also proved troublesome. As with cast iron, aluminum should not be used on horizontal systems that are submerged. Vertically oriented underwater exhausts of the type commonly found on large aluminum yachts have few problems, mainly because such exhausts are large enough in diameter that the coatings on the submerged part can be maintained.

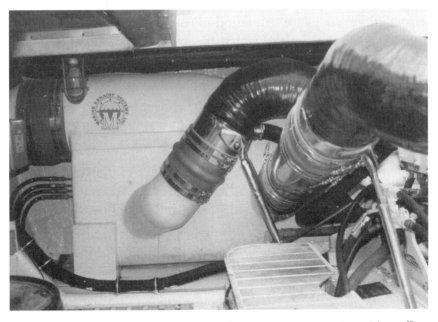

Fig. 13-5. These days manufacturers are becoming very creative with muffler design. There are so many new designs around that we can only guess at their effectiveness. This one is made by Marine Exhaust Systems, Inc. but many others are made by boat builders themselves.

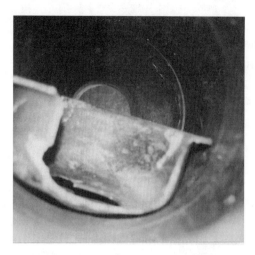

Fig. 13-6. One problem with mufflers is the problem of broken baffles. Shown here is a an older Vernatone muffler with broken baffle. When let loose, these can block the system, resulting in high pressure that can blow the system apart and cause engine damage.

Copper

Rarely used anymore, annealed copper can still be found in older vessels, most often in sailboats and imports. Annealed copper has performed very well when the designer knows what he is doing. But copper is near the bottom of the galvanic series and is highly anodic to most commonly found metals in exhaust systems and machinery. Whenever copper is encountered in marine exhaust systems it should be viewed with suspicion and subjected to thorough evaluation. Copper-nickel alloys are still found in engine exhaust risers and can also perform very well so long as the system does not retain sea water when the engines are shut down. With upsweep risers that hold salt water in the pipes, internal corrosion drastically reduces their longevity.

Mufflers

As with fiberglass pipe, fiberglass mufflers have eliminated most of the problems associated with marine mufflers. Automated laminating processes have enabled manufacturers to produce reliable and cost effective products that can last the lifetime of the vessel. But, like any good idea, never-ending attempts to make products cheaper often ends up producing poor quality products. Increasingly we are finding mufflers that fail early on in their operating life.

Marine mufflers serve two primary functions: reducing noise and preventing water back surge through the system. On production boats, they are found in two basic styles, the tubular and the water-lift type. Both types of mufflers are subject to high internal pressures, temperatures and vibration from exhaust

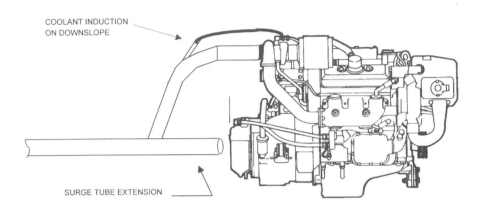

COOLANT INDUCTION
ON DOWNSLOPE

SURGE TUBE EXTENSION

Fig. 13-7. Keeping water out of the engines is a key element of good system design. The surge pipe extension is one means of preventing water from backing up and overcoming relatively low risers. The surge extension allows backsurge to flow past the main exhaust pipe, rather than up it.

pulsing that can cause failure.

Tubular mufflers

These mufflers rely on baffles for noise reduction and to restrict water back surge through the system. The most commonly experienced problem with these mufflers is the breaking loose of the baffles. This can be caused by overheating, poor design or an undersized exhaust system. When baffles inside the muffler break loose, they can block the exhaust, causing high internal pressures that can cause engine damage or even cause the exhaust system to blow apart. The best way to check mufflers is to simply shine a powerful flashlight up the exhaust. Most mufflers manufactured within the last 12 years use conical or spheroid baffles. Older mufflers often have flat plate baffles which are dangerous from the standpoint that they can completely block off the opening when they break loose.

Baffles that have come adrift will usually show up sitting at odd angles to the muffler orifice. Over a period of time, loose baffles will eventually break up from exhaust pulsing, and unless they completely block the exhaust and blow the system apart, the pieces of baffle will eventually be expelled. When you find mufflers that don't have any baffles at all, it's because the baffles have broken up. Baffle damage can be caused during winter lay-up as a result of water laying in the bottom of the muffler that does not drain out.

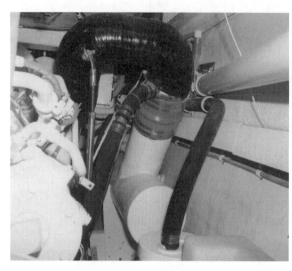

Fig. 13-8. Sport fishermen require all the back surge protection they can get. Shown here is an extra high riser with surge extension. This designer was taking no chances with a pair of engines valued at over $100,000.

Evidence of loose or broken baffles can also show up as a rattling noise within the muffler. Make it a point to get close and listen to the mufflers while the vessel is operating at lower speeds. Exhaust systems for very large diesels often times do not get adequate cooling water to the upper side at lower speeds. Keeping in mind that it is exhaust pressure and pulsing that creates the fine water spray that cools the system. At lower speeds this mixing sometimes does not occur. When this happens, overheating will result. If you don't have an infrared thermometer to take the temperature, simply place your hand on top of the muffler while cruising along at idle speed, after allowing sufficient time for the system to reach operating temperature. The best time to perform this check is after a sustained full speed run. If the muffler is being adequately cooled, its temperature should be less than 150°. If it burns your hand immediately, suspect a problem and investigate further.

Fig. 13-9 . Oops! Supporting that exhaust pipe with plastic coated wire wasn't such a good idea. The wire slipped through the cable clamps and down she went. Providing solid support for exhaust systems is not a matter of insignficance.

Water Lift Mufflers

This type of muffler is commonly found on generators, sail boat auxiliaries and low-powered diesels in trawlers. They are not suitable for high performance diesels as they create too much back pressure. The water lift muffler uses a water chamber for sound reduction and is a very effective method of preventing back surge if properly installed. The primary shortcoming of this type is that it creates higher back pressure than tubular mufflers and generally should not be used with diesel or gas engines of more than 200 HP and never with high performance diesels, no matter what their horsepower. Although muffler manufacturers make these mufflers with orifices up to six inches I.D., they can only be used in a system that has been designed by a trained engineer who has empirically tested the system. Several boat builders have attempted to use these mufflers without performing the necessary engineering with disastrous results. High back pressures cause engine valves to burn and systems to blow apart (Fig, 13-9).

To perform their function properly, water lift mufflers have to be installed at the proper height between engine and maximum vessel load water line. This is especially important for trawler style yachts and sail boats where engine placement is below the water line. When not properly placed, water back flow can fill up the muffler and back up into the engine. Water lift mufflers remain full of water when the engine is stopped. Vessels located in freezing climates should be checked for evidence of freezing damage since most manufacturers do not supply drain plugs on these products. It should be fitted with a drain if it doesn't have one.

Bottle Mufflers

Small, molded plastic mufflers that look like convoluted bottles are often used on generators with some degree of success. Unfortunately, they occasionally show up on trawlers and other boats with larger engines. Such mufflers may assist with noise reduction but do little or nothing to prevent back surge. They are simply too small to be effective. Be suspicious when you find these mufflers on engines over 50 horsepower.

Back Pressure

Excessive back pressure caused by faulty exhaust system design is frequently - I stress, frequently - responsible for shortened engine life. The most common causes of back pressure are undersized pipes, selection of wrong size muffler

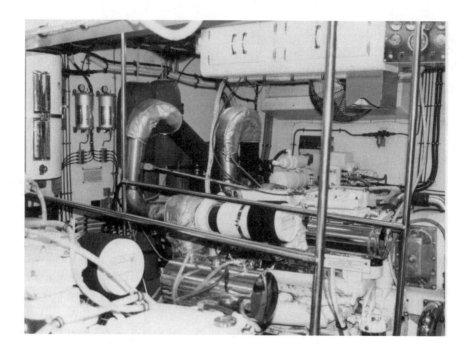

Fig. 13-10. Wet risers are not often used anymore because of the problem of internal leakage. These very tall risers are capable of putting several gallons of water into an engine.

(particularly water-lift types), and hull side ports that lack a fairwater (a fair water here is defined as a raised ridge or eyebrow located at the leading edge of the exhaust port that causes the slipstream to deflect away from the exhaust port). This later situation is most common. A hull side exit port that is below the water line while running needs to have a fairwater added at the leading edge of the port to create a slipstream of air into which the exhaust gases can escape. This can be determined by simply looking. If it doesn't have them, then fairwaters should be added. The incidence of high pressure that I am finding is running around 20-25% of all surveys of boats with side exhausts. So, if your engine surveyor is not measuring the exhaust back pressure, you should ask him to do so.

Exhaust Risers

Exhaust risers are among the most troublesome of all machinery components. Along with the muffler, the engine exhaust riser's purpose is to prevent back surge into the engine, and a well designed boat should have both. There are three primary types of risers: Water jacketed upsweep or horizontal risers, water-jacketed down sweep risers and lagged, non-jacketed risers.

Lagged Risers

Lagging, in marine parlance, means insulating. This type of riser can literally last the lifetime of the engine or the vessel when made of quality material. It eliminates the corrosion problem by not using any cooling water. Normally they are fitted with a low cost water-induction arrangement that can simply be replaced when it corrodes and starts leaking. The lone drawback is the need for effective insulation to prevent both injuries and fire hazards. Since asbestos was banned, there has been no low-cost material appearing to take its place. Fiberglass wrapping is now the standard.

On high horsepower systems, simple fiberglass wrapping has generally proved to be inadequate. For large dry systems, manufactured "blankets" or jackets should be used. One of the latest developments is a laminated fiberglass with high temperature resin, produced under a patented proprietary process. It's good looking, effective and expensive but will outlast other types of insulation. Exhaust blankets are very effective at reducing and even eliminating heat radiation through the system. Like most all insulation, these expensive blankets deteriorate with age. The primary culprit is vibration which causes the insulation to break down. By the time high quality blankets are about 8 years old, they will have lost about half their insulating quality and will need to be replaced.

Dry insulated turbochargers have been a major source of serious boat fires. Fortunately, recognizing this hazard, most engine manufacturers have switched over within the last ten years to water-cooled turbos that completely eliminate this hazard. Yet many insulated turbochargers are still in use and their insulation should be inspected carefully. The insulation on these turbos tends to get compacted on the top with the insulation being squeezed out and falling down around the underside of the turbo. The outside temperature should be checked with an infrared thermometer or, if you don't have one, by simply holding your hand an inch or so above the turbo after the engine has been run hard. Outside temperature should be below 300°. Anything higher than that and the insulation should be replaced. If you don't have an infrared thermometer, test by holding your hand one inch above the insulation with the engine running under load for at least a half-hour. If you can't hold your hand there for more than 15 seconds, the insulation should be replaced.

Keep in mind that while there may be no flammable materials in contact with the exhaust at the moment, at some point in the future there may be. On one occasion I found a 5 gallon plastic oil bucket hard up against a hot exhaust elbow, smoldering away and about ready to burst into flames. This is precisely

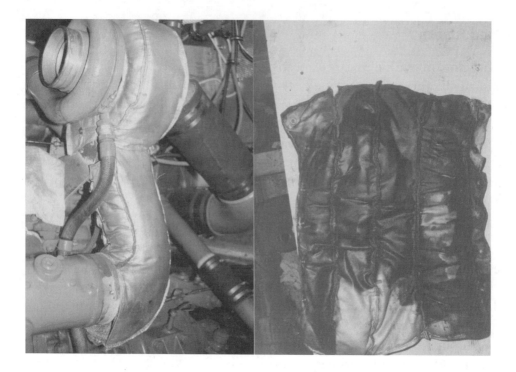

Fig. 13-11. Watch out for oil leaks into blanketed hot exhaust sections as this is capable of causing serious fires that are near impossible to extinguish.

the sort of thing the surveyor should be on the lookout for. We should also keep in mind that the flash point of most lubricating oils is about 600°F. It is not unusual for insulation to become saturated with oil from engine leaks and the insulation can act as a perfect wick for vaporization and combustion. Any time insulation is found saturated with oil, immediate replacement should be recommended.

When encountering dry insulated systems, the potential fire hazard should not be underestimated. No materials of *any type* should be in contact with the exhaust. That includes control cables, cooling and oil hoses and wiring. When located close to deck beams or any other structure for that matter, the threatened surface should be protected with aluminum sheathing and a layer of insulation under that. Aluminum is very good at dissipating heat and goes a long way toward protecting vulnerable materials.

Water-jacketed Risers

As shown in Fig. 13-10, upsweep jacketed risers retain saltwater in their jackets whether the engine is running or not. That means that the risers are subject to all the corrosion problems of other underwater metals. Even worse, if

Fig. 13-12. Failure to allow for engine movement is a common cause of leakage. Here, the sleeve connector is too short to allow for movement.

the riser develops a leak, the water can enter the exhaust manifold and even find its way into the cylinders or damage exhaust valves. In the past, water-jacketed risers have been a major cause of diesel engine damage. In the last ten years, use of the jacketed up-sweep riser has declined dramatically, being replaced with dry insulated pipes. Most production builders are aware of the dangers and engineer their systems to avoid it. Yet many older boats and yachts still have jacketed upsweep risers and the surveyor has to contend with them.

When examining this type of riser, the first thing to look for is evidence of leakage on the outside. Jacketed risers are usually bolted directly to an uncooled section of manifold, thereby creating a heat transition zone. This is the area most susceptible to developing leaks. Often times we find patches welded on the outside of the pipe. If a riser has been leaking on the outside, it is far more likely to have developed leaks on the inside. Patched up risers should be viewed with great suspicion.

Look for dates etched on the riser. Most of the major manufacturers include a name plate and, when they repair risers, will inscribe the date near the name tag. Some include the date of manufacture. All too often, owners of older boats seek to avoid the costs of making replacements or proper repairs. When performing pre purchase surveys, there is only one way to deal with these old risers and that is to recommend that they be removed, inspected internally and pressure tested by a fabricator who has the necessary jigs to do that.

Jacketed Down-sweep Risers

This type of riser is little more than a water induction elbow for the remainder of the exhaust system and are usually fabricated of stainless. The only hazard that this type presents results from the fact that they offer no back surge protection whatever. These systems should be equipped with both good mufflers and surge tube extensions. If well made, these elbows should be very long lasting. When leakage develops, it's usually the result of the use of lower quality stainless steel.

Gas Engine Risers

Diesel engines, with their long-stroke, high profile cylinder blocks, offer a degree of surge protection by their height alone. But the low profiles of gas engines make them considerably more vulnerable. Gas engine risers tend to be short and stubby. Their main purpose , apparently at least from the manufacturer's point of view, is to provide salt water induction into the system for cooling of the exhaust piping. In and of themselves, most tend to do little to prevent back surge and for that reason gas system design needs to be carefully evaluated. If the boat builder is not aware of this, and does not provide additional back surge protection in the form of mufflers, then we got a problem.

But whether it's gas or diesel, small engine risers, when poorly designed, can cause chronic engine overheating problems. The manner in which cast iron corrodes is at the heart of the problem. The oxidized material from cast iron can expand up to ten times the size of the original material. The usually small water passages in these risers can become blocked with iron scale. This restriction of water flow can cause two things to happen. First, the reduced cooling water flow through the risers results reduced water flow through the engine and can raise engine operating temperatures to overheating. Second, the lack of cooling water flow to the exhaust system likewise causes overheating or risers, manifolds and piping, even to the point of starting a fire in the exhaust system.

This is particularly true when exhaust hoses are attached directly to the riser, as most are. Gas engine risers should become suspect when leakage begins to occur at the base gasket surface, or when overheating of the exhaust piping immediately after the riser occurs. Over time, water tends to wick out under

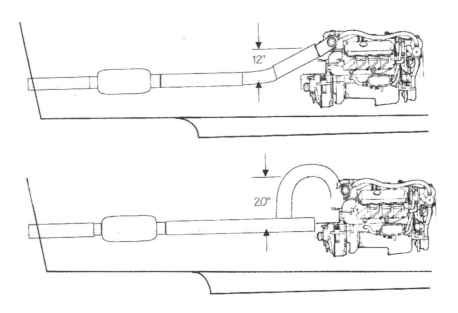

Fig. 13-13. This drawing highlights the differences between a system with back surge protection and one without. Whether it's a motoryacht, sport fisherman or stern drive boat, the basic principles are the same, starting with the location of engine relative to the water line.

these gaskets. Excessive weepage often coincides with the rate of internal corrosion.

Stainless Steel Risers

Stainless is now the overwhelming material of choice for diesel manufacturers. The fabrication of stainless risers is costly and requires a high degree of skill in both the design and welding process. Riser pipes usually cannot be welded on the inside and therefore exact alignment and precision welding are necessary to produce a quality product. The degree of welding difficulty means that a very high percentage of risers have small welding defects that will eventually turn into leaks.

For dry risers or down sweep jacketed risers, these pin hole leaks pose little threat of water entering the engine, but leaks that occur in jacketed risers that retain water can result in costly engine damage. The pin hole leaks that develop in dry risers are far less serious and are amenable to spot weld repairs so long as there is not a condition of general erosion. It is okay for these risers to be repaired repeatedly over the years since the source of the leakage is almost always localized corrosion pits, and not general degradation of the metal.

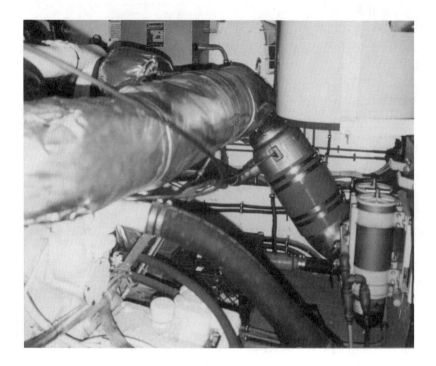

Fig. 13-14. This riser is seven feet long. The slightest bit of engine movement is greatly magnified by the long lever arm. This makes it hard to keep joints sealed and often causes problems with turbocharger joints. It needs a bellows at the joint that only has a hose sleeve.

It is an interesting phenomenon that leaks in water cooled risers and pipes have a tendency to start and stop. As pin holes develop, there are times when the minute hole becomes blocked with scale or carbon, only to start leaking again at a later date. Whenever we find rust stains and rust trails on risers or pipes, even though there may be no evident leakage at the moment, all signs of previous leakage should be treated as leakage that will recur. We should not assume that just because it is not leaking at the moment, that it will not start up again. It will.

Large System Mounting

The methods of mounting and securing large exhaust systems to an engine are often problematic. Not only do diesel engines generate substantial vibration, but they're also subject to movement on their mounts. In high performance boats, it is not unusual to find engines shuddering or shaking under slamming loads when the hull is skipping off the tops of waves. Engine movement, combined with weight of the system, and often the leverage generated by the system configuration itself, works to stress the joints and connections. Unless one actually takes the time to analyze what is happening during high speed operation, it is difficult to envision the stresses that can be placed on the exhaust system. But these are the primary reasons why we so often find leakage at the system joints.

At some point there has to be a means of taking up the slack between the engine and the exhaust system, whether it be an elaborate riser or a simple straight pipe. The usual method is the slightly flexible hose connector which, so long as it is of adequate length, will generally perform this function fairly well. But it should be obvious that the connectors shown in Figure 13-12 are not of sufficient length to permit much movement. Had this sleeve connector been about one foot longer, it would have easily taken up all engine movement. Large risers may require other methods such as a more flexible accordion-style bellows. Many yachts have chronic exhaust leakage problems directly related to a lack of a flexible connection. Such a system is shown in Fig. 13-14. Notice that in this case, the hose sleeve connector is also too short to allow for much movement. The result is that the shuddering of the engine is constantly breaking the seal at the hose joint. Replacing the short section of hose with a more flexible bellows hose would immediately solve the problem.

Yet large piping systems such as this one need more than just flexible connectors. In this instance, the piping is such a large, one-piece weldment that the leverage of the piping itself is working to tear the joints apart. Systems this large should not be supported by the engine alone but rather supported by the hull or deck with suitable brackets. When very large pipes are supported by the engine manifolds, it can happen that the piping actually begins to loosen the engine manifolds. The best design approach in this instance is that both the engine and exhaust piping should be mounted independently.

System Installation

Systems utilizing horizontal runs of piping from the engine to the stern require that the piping and mufflers be fully supported. One major cause of exhaust system failure is the failure to adequately support the system. It's easy to forget that, when filled with exhaust water, the piping system may have to support hundreds of pounds of water. Exhaust hose, despite its apparent rigidity, can easily kink when subjected to an unsupported span. Ideally, exhaust hose should be supported on a flat deck. If it has to be suspended, the unsupported span should not be more than 24". Exhaust hose should never be supported by cradles as vibration can cause the narrow support surface to chafe through. Fiberglass piping should be supported at no less than 36" intervals. Mufflers should be supported by cradles under *both* ends.

The preferable method of supporting piping is by means of platforms or cradles. But if it is absolutely necessary to use hangers to suspend piping from a deck, the hanger material should be very strong and of sufficient width as to avoid chaffing. If you've ever placed your hand on an exhaust pipe or hose while an engine is running, you already know that the amount of vibration can be tremendous and can cut improperly installed hose and piping through in short order. Rope, string, plastic or any kind of wire should never be used for hangers. Custom fabricated metal hangers are the best bet. Both hose and rigid piping should be inspected for evidence of chaffing at support points and at locations where they pass through bulkheads.

Undersized piping or systems that involve sharp twists and turns are occasionally found to be the cause for poor engine performance. Undersized piping is most often found on boats that have been repowered and the owner did not want to incur the additional cost of upgrading the exhaust system to the proper size. The tip-off that this has occurred is usually found in the form of a reducer nipple somewhere around the riser or manifold that reduces the new engine's larger exhaust to the older, smaller piping.

Another defect that is occasionally found is a system that has been partially replaced where the I.D. of the new and old system don't match. In this case, it is often found that some sort of shim has been used to make the connection, usually a large piece of hose slipped over the smaller. This kind of jury-rig can be deadly, resulting in the system blowing apart or exhaust fumes escaping into the interior.

Generator Exhaust Systems

By far, the biggest problem with generator exhaust systems results from units being located at or below the water line. This is especially troublesome in sport fishing boats where the generator is located in the stern and exhausted through the transom. In this case, wave action against the transom pushes water back through the exhaust. When both the muffler and generator are below the water line, the end result is predictable.

The thing is, however, that a generator exhaust system as described above may exist in a boat for many years without ever having water get into the engine. So long as the generator is running when at sea, it won't happen because of the exhaust pressure. But, on the one instance when the generator is not running, suddenly it fills with water.

In many cases the cockpit deck is so low that it is not possible to put an adequate riser in the exhaust line. The best that can be done is add in line check valves and flappers on the exit port and hope this works. The important point here is that the surveyor identify such situations and advise the client.

The Carbon Monoxide Hazard

It was not until recent years, when the number of carbon monoxide cases increased dramatically, that builders paid much attention to the potential of carbon monoxide leaking into the living quarters. While I don't have any hard scientific or statistical data, my own work with CO detectors seems to show that gas engines put out at least four to five times as much CO as do diesels. Cases of CO poisoning from diesels are unknown to this writer. While high concentrations of sulfur dioxide are sickening, it would appear that the smell is so bad no one can tolerate breathing it long enough to cause injury. Exhaust from a well-tuned gasoline engine is far less noxious and CO is odorless and can overwhelm its victims long before they're aware of what is happening. Thus, the danger appears predominately with gasoline engines.

It would be great if every surveyor could carry a CO detector. Though they are expensive, cost is not the major problem. The type of detector used for detecting leaks and which gives a quantitative reading in parts per million, is a very sensitive device that requires frequent recalibration and servicing. That is where CO detectors become very expensive, since it is recommended that they be serviced twice annually at a cost of around $300.

Lacking a CO detector, the best way to check for leaks is by conducting a thorough inspection of the entire system. Because marine exhausts are water cooled, any part of a system that can leak exhaust gasses is also likely to leak water. Therefore, water leaks translate into gas leaks, but beware that gas leaks can occur without any obvious signs or traces. It's especially important to check the undersides of pipes and mufflers, not just look at the tops. The inspection of the system is best conducted with the vessel running at top speed, or at least cruising speed because it is when the system is hot and under pressure that the leaks are most likely to appear. And, when you're dealing with sea water, leaks always leave telltale traces of salt and other deposits. Remember what was stated earlier about leaks starting and stopping? Don't assume that because a prior leak is no longer actively leaking that it won't start again. Leaks have a sinister way of starting and stopping.

More and more builders are making greater efforts to make sure that engine compartments are sealed off from living quarters. This is only common sense, but there still remain many builders who build boats with engine room bulkheads that are full of holes and allow a free flow of engine room fumes.

Many have large openings that make engine room airflow contiguous with all bilge spaces. Not only does this allow normal engine room odors and engine emissions to travel throughout the hull and living quarters, but is also down-right dangerous.

Particularly in smaller gas powered boats, we often see engine compartments built right into the living quarters — under a berth for example — which makes it inevitable that any exhaust leakage will immediately enter the quarters. It's not easy for the surveyor to condemn a boat in which a berth is situated directly over a gas engine. Yet how can the surveyor turn the other way at the prospect of child going to sleep on top of an engine that may be leaking CO into the living quarters. Some of these small, stern drive cruisers with so-called "aft cabins" have precisely this arrangement.

Some of the most highly publicized cases of CO poisoning have resulted from the placement of gas generator exhausts in the hull side, rather than the transom. Or in instances of aft cabin boats having stern exhausts but windows or ports that allowed the wind to carry the exhaust back into the boat. Others have occurred from placing the generator exhaust outlet next to a head sink drain and fumes were transmitted into the stateroom in this manner. By now nearly everyone knows about the "station wagon" effect and how, when conditions are just right, exhaust fumes can be blown or carried back into the boat via the cockpit. I wouldn't suggest that it's the ultimate responsibility of the surveyor to prove that a vessel is safe against this hazard. No empirical studies have been done that I know of, and we really have no basis for evaluating such conditions except for our awareness of those instances where it has occurred. But it's only common sense that the surveyor should be on the lookout for these conditions whenever surveying gas powered boats:

- Gas generator exhaust should always have transom exits.

- Check that exhaust port is not near a sink drain or bilge pump discharge.

- Be alert for boats that have too much of a tendency to draw fumes back into the cockpit and cabin.

- Pay special attention to gas generator exhaust system components, particularly the cast iron exhaust elbows and manifolds that can leak without any evidence. Water induction iron risers are particularly susceptible to developing leaks.

- Be alert for engine compartments that have openings into the living quarters.

- Generator and engine exhausts should never utilize the same exhaust pipe.

The surveyor should pay particular attention to gas boats with generators which have centrally located engine rooms where a leak in the generator exhaust is likely to put fumes into the living quarters. Unlike older boats, most late model boats today are air-conditioned and more and more of them have fewer and fewer opening windows. This cuts down on the amount of external air transfer. When vessels are underway, the internal air transfer is substantial; propulsion engines suck in huge amounts of air and blow it out the exhaust. Any leaks around the engine are likely to be soon expelled. But at rest the amount of air transfer in the living quarters is likely to be reduced to zero, a factor which greatly raises the exhaust poisoning hazard. Going to sleep with the generator running to power the air conditioning, at a mooring or at a dock, can be a dangerous thing to do.

Back Surge Protection

Every year hundreds, and perhaps thousands, of boat engines are severely damaged by water backing up through the exhaust system. Most often this occurs simply because of the carelessness of the builder or designer. Engines have to be protected from this hazard, but it's usually the design criteria for interior space that causes engines to be mounted so low, or have insufficient space for adequate risers that causes the problem. And when we do discover the problem, it's often not easily or cheaply solved.

Properly designed risers are the first line of defense against wayward sea water. But because the designer wanted 6'4" headroom in the salon, we often find that the engine doesn't have adequate risers. He may have brought the deck down so close to the engines that higher risers couldn't be installed. Instead, the designer may have tried to compensate by adding mufflers or exhaust surge extensions. A combination of both will usually do the job so long as the risers are not too low. Surge extensions, as shown in Fig. 13-8 allow water that is forced up the exhaust pipe to travel past the riser, rather than surging up a curved elbow directly into the engine. Virtually all sport fishing boats should have surge extensions to protect against this hazard when backing down. Alone, mufflers will not prevent water from backing up: they only retard the travel of water somewhat, nor is that their designed purpose. But they do help.

The best way to check for adequate riser height is to simply locate a through hull fitting on the side of the hull in way of the engine room. Note it's height above the water, and then transpose that height measurement to the engine room, measuring the height of the riser above that point. Be sure to measure to the bottom of the inner passage and not the top. Once this is done, the obvious question is how much is enough. Again, we don't have any empirical data to fall back on. It depends entirely on the system design and the surveyor's knowledge and experience. For a 6" diameter pipe with both surge extension and muffler, an effective height of 12" is probably enough. But for that same diameter pipe that has a sweeping slope up to the engine with only a muffler, water surging up the pipe can easily overcome the muffler and an 12" slope. See fig.13-13.

Systems that have the piping sloping gradually up to the engine should be viewed with great suspicion. One has only to visualize the working of a manometer to realize how easily water can run up this slope. If you know how a manometer works, then you know how water in an exhaust pipe will behave. Most of the time we see boats sitting quietly at their docks and unthreatened by the effects of storms and wave action, unaware of what can happen when a boat is docked stern-to a body of water with considerable fetch. Waves slamming up against a transom for a period of time can drive water up the exhaust considerable distances and overcome both mufflers and low risers. Both rolling and pitching, while moored, docked or drifting at sea, can sufficiently change the trim angle to permit water to surge up the pipes with considerable velocity. All of these possibilities are among the factors a system must be designed to protect against.

Flappers

Installing flappers on exhaust ports is a fairly effective means of protecting against back surge, particularly on small gas powered boats where design considerations make it very difficult to achieve adequate riser height. It's best, wherever possible, that flappers not be the sole means of protection, for flappers are highly susceptible to being torn off by wave action and particularly hard backing down. The most common type are clamp-on, rubber flappers which usually have a rubber hinge and are rather weak. Never-the-less, for small gas inboards, it's better to have them than not.

Beware of flappers that have the flaps screwed onto the flapper body with stainless steel screws into rubber. Galvanism between metal and rubber corrodes these screws quickly. If clamped onto a stainless transom flange, remove the flapper body and inspect the flange for severe corrosion at the point of attachment that may be caused by galvanism or crevice corrosion.

Underwater Exhausts

Usually found only on larger yachts, exhausts exiting through the hull have only one significant shortcoming and that is the tendency to increase exhaust back pressure at idle speeds. A yacht with an underwater system will naturally create a suction and tend to draw the exhaust out of the system once it gets moving so that the underwater system is the most efficient of all types so long as it is moving forward. By the time the vessel is going ten knots or so, virtually all back pressure is eliminated. Above ten knots, the system is actually aiding in the removal of exhaust emissions by creating a negative pressure.

At idle at the dock, however, the system needs to be equipped with a suitable by-pass arrangement. Otherwise, it not only creates excessive back pressure, but causes a most unpleasant rumbling sound and great splashes of water as the large exhaust bubbles burst on the surface. Some yachts are equipped with electrically controlled by-pass valves, either automatically or manually controlled. These function with varying degrees of success depending on design. But a well-designed fixed system can function perfectly with no need for valves: the speed of the vessel will automatically control where the exhaust exits.

Boats with the transom exhaust ports that are completely submerged are waving a red flag at you. The ports may be wrongly located or the vessel may be badly trimmed, but in either case, a submerged exhaust poses serious hazards. System joints become much more prone to leakage and corrosion damage because the system is now submerged in an electrolyte. Due to increased back pressure, long periods of engine idling can result in burning of engine exhaust valves. A submerged exhaust may also mean that the engines are in danger of taking a big gulp of water due to insufficient riser height.

Hull Side Exhausts

Putting the exhaust out through the side of the hull is a great way for the builder to save money, but it usually results in major aggravation for the owner. Not only do the hull sides become blackened with oil and carbon-based soot, but water spray oxidizes paint and gel coat, and wind can blow fumes into windows and ports.

Systems with chambers or conduits built into the side of the hull should be approached with great caution, regardless of the hull material. The surveyor needs to remember that the hull is now actually part of the exhaust system and therefore must rely on a steady and adequate flow of cooling water to keep the system — and the hull — from becoming severely heat damaged. Over the years I have encountered at least a half-dozen such systems with major damage from overheating. If the system can be opened up for inspection, the surveyor should do so, or at least make that recommendation. If the system cannot be opened up, it's only prudent that the surveyor should fully describe the situation and the potential problems in his report.

Hull side exhaust chambers and ports are usually installed with fiberglass taping and a lot of fairing, which accounts for why we so often find blistering and cracking around exhausts ports. Such ports should also be inspected from the interior to determine if there is water weeping through the laminate or fairing material. Accumulations of salt deposits and water stains on the interior indicates a potential problem. Quite often the joint is disturbed or not adequately bonded, leaving a porous bond that weeps.

A number of builders have attempted the use of external exhaust cowlings running down the side of the hull. These can pose some grave dangers. The first of these is the damage that can be caused should the system lose cooling water. Without cooling water, the ducts can heat up to 600°F or higher, more than enough to set the fiberglass on fire. And even if cooling water is never interrupted, it's highly likely that inadequate mixing of exhaust gas and water will occur to insure that the ducting is evenly cooled throughout. In other words, the ducting is likely to be cool at the bottom but hot at the top. Bear in mind that the larger the chamber is, the less likely adequate mixing will occur. Finally, external cowlings are likely to be damaged when a vessel is hauled with a travel lift. Exhaust cowlings may be either bonded onto the hull or it may be simply screwed on. When such a cowling extends far from the hull side, it's going to take a major part of the load from the lifting slings. Both the cowling and the hull side to which it is attached must be sufficiently strong to bear these loads. When they are not, it is usually the cowling that crushes under the pressure of the straps.

Transom Attachments

A lot of boats sink because of problems with the attachment of the exhaust piping to the transom. It's very poor practice to run a length of fiberglass pipe through a hole cut in the transom, and then just apply caulking around it. Unfortunately, a lot of boats are built this way. High end boats usually have the exhaust pipes heavily laminated into the transom opening. Others may have a fiberglass or stainless flange plate which is fine so long as it is properly installed. But stainless plates may suffer from crevice corrosion behind the flange and at the point where they pass through the transom, particularly if the hull is cored and water is entering the core. On purchase surveys, it's best to recommend

Fig. 13-15. T-bolt clamp broken after only six months service. Utilizing three pieces of metal sandwiched together and spot welded, it creates its own crevice corrosion failure mode.

that the stainless flanges be pulled and inspected.

Long runs of fiberglass pipe should not be rigidly affixed to the hull. A 10" diameter pipe with an even large muffler, when full of water, can weigh hundreds of pounds. Even when well supported, this weight can cause movement that can result in cracking at the transom connection. The through-transom pipe section should not be more than a few feet long, and should be joined with a sleeve connector. If a long length of pipe is found, it should be recommended that the pipe be sectioned and joined with a sleeve connector so as to relieve the stress on the transom joint.

Hose Clamps

The use of thin gauge, 3/4" wide worm screw driven common hose clamps have performed fairly well for gas engine exhaust systems. But for diesel systems, where pipe diameters range from 6" to 12", heavy duty clamps should be used. One type of heavy duty clamp, shown in fig. 13-15, is a toggle or T-bolt clamp. At first glance, it looks like a great clamp until you see what crevice corrosion does to these things in a very short time. For clamping in a wet environment like under a cockpit deck, the worm screw clamps are probably a better choice.

Chapter 14

Electrical Systems

Surveying the electrical system in the course of conducting a pre-purchase survey does not mean performing a full-scale electrical system analysis. Rather it is a more cursory inspection and general test operation that includes an attempt to determine if the systems meet basic requirements within reasonable limits, meaning within the surveyor's physical ability to do so, and within the definition of the term "survey". It also includes the search for defective, damaged or substandard installations.

One of the greatest advances in marine safety and standards in the last 20 years has been in electrical systems. Even 20 years ago it was very common to find poorly designed systems with substandard components. Today, it is rare, although that is not to say that a few builders don't do a pretty bad job of it. However, most of the problems posed by electrical systems appear in older boats, not so much because systems deteriorate, or were poorly designed, but as a result of years worth of substandard alterations, additions and repairs. In other words, jury-rigged wiring. It almost seems axiomatic that whenever new electrical equipment is added to a vessel, the wiring is strung out helter-skelter, patched and pieced together in whatever manner is most convenient, and with complete disregard for its appearance or safety.

When old circuits are no longer needed, the wires are cut and left in place so that no one knows whether they're hot or dead Old boats are usually full of discontinued circuits. When new circuits are added, the power feed is often doubled up on a circuit breaker, or even taken directly off a battery. Sometimes an in-line fuse is added at some bizarre location where no one will ever find it. And on an on. These are among the many things surveyors have to contend with.

The question inevitably arises as to what is safe and what is not. Quality builders don't go to all that trouble of making painstakingly neat wiring installa-

Fig, 14-1. There will be days when this is what the surveyor is faced with. The back side of a main electric panel on a $1.5M new yacht. It's hard to believe that anyone could have this little regard for high voltage systems on a yacht.

tions that hardly no one ever sees for nothing. Neat, intelligible electrical systems go to the heart of safety and ease of maintenance. Sloppy wiring systems can be extremely difficult to search out when something goes wrong. Sloppy wiring always poses the danger of accidental damage. It is also an indicator of a builder who has little regard for safety.

A well-designed electrical system is one that is neat, orderly and intelligibly laid out in such a manner that circuits can be quickly searched out for faults. As you have probably noticed, the better builders usually have the circuits numbered and the wires properly color coded. Wiring that takes off in all directions and disappears into innumerable and inaccessible holes does not qualify for a well-planned system. In fact, it is the hallmark of no planning. For the most part, care in installation equates with care in design and planning. Most high production boats have pre-engineered systems. That means that a trained electrician designed the system *before* the boat was built, not during construction. Most builders create a substantial part of the electrical system "on the bench," so that every boat of that particular model has more or less the same identical system. How often this is true is usually dependent on the size of the produc-

Fig 14-2. This well-designed, pre-engineered electrical system was obviously done with great pride and care. Contrast this with the photo on the previous page.

tion run. If it's only a few boats, or custom built, more than likely the system was not pre-engineered, but "wired up" as the boat is being built. Or, in other words, a seat-of-the-pants wiring job. This is the type that the surveyor has to be most careful with. One look at photo 14-1 leaves little doubt as to which type of system this is; the result speaks for itself. This is an Egg Harbor 54 sport fish built at the time the company went bankrupt and apparently didn't have the resources to do the job right.

The question this situation poses for the surveyor is not so much a matter of standards, but what kind of advice does the surveyor owe the client. Would a client expect to get a mess like that in a million dollar plus yacht? Would he anticipate that the surveyor would advise him that such a system is, shall we say, not exactly what one might expect? Every surveyor has to come to his own conclusions about the nature of the advice he gives his clients. Ultimately, the deciding factor becomes not only a matter of safety and standards, but also a matter of whether the client might face some degree of economic loss for which he might blame the surveyor for not advising him about.

A boat full of jury-rigged wiring not only poses electrical hazards, but also a potential nightmare for the owner (whether he is doing work himself, or paying someone else) if basic rules of electrical circuitry are violated. In addition to the probability of design errors, sloppy wiring becomes very difficult to search out, repair and maintain. With such systems, finding the source of a simple problem can turn into a costly predicament.

The most common problems associated with electrical systems do not stem so much from failure to meet standards such as the ABYC rules or the National

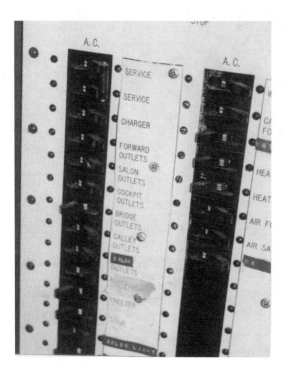

Fig. 14-3. This panel has seven of twenty-four breakers relabeled. When there's been this much jiggering on a panel, it's a clue that all is probably not well.

Electric Code, but violation of simple rules of common sense. While it is not the purpose of this chapter to provide an education on basic electricity, anyone who calls himself a surveyor should already be well-versed in basic AC and DC systems, and there are plenty of good books and seminars on the subject to keep our education up to date. The emphasis of this chapter is to review why things go wrong and what to look for to prevent that from happening.

Stray Current/Galvanic Corrosion Problems

Stray current is current that escapes from the insulated confines of electrical system components and ultimately finds its way to the immersed underwater metals where it causes what is known as true electrolysis. Galvanism is a very similar form of corrosion caused by current generated by dissimilar metals. The difference between the two types of damage is a matter of severity; stray current is far more damaging and rapidly occurring than galvanic corrosion.

It is fortunate indeed that stray current problems on fiberglass boats are far less pervasive than what we used to experience with wood boats. The main reasons are that plastic boats leak less and the hulls are non conductive, unlike wood which, when wet, is conductive to some degree. Plus, boats have better electrical systems today. In surveying several thousand boats, my experience has been that something like only one or two percent of all inboard powered

Fig. 14-4. Light up your life; go ahead and touch that interior grade circuit breaker mounted on the exterior of the boat. This owner did and got an unfree trip to the hospital. We see builders do some dumb things, but this one is rooted in profound ignorance.

boats experience stray current problems at any given time. For outboards and stern drives, the percentage will be considerably higher due to higher sensitivity of the aluminum castings involved.

Stray current damage is usually easily discernible. Because it occurs so rapidly, the end result is that the eroding surfaces of metal will almost always show bright, whereas the slower process of galvanism leaves a dull appearance as oxides are not carried away from the eroding surface fast enough to leave a shiny surface.

When conditions of serious underwater corrosion of metals is encountered, surveyors usually do not consider it their provenance to determine the cause, though we will almost always be asked. Electrical system studies can take a matter of days. It is important that the surveyor be able to identify the type of corrosion damage and be able to recommend the appropriate remedial measures, such as conducting a full system analysis, or whether it's a matter of just making a few minor changes.

In this chapter we will discuss what the surveyor can or should do regarding the electrical systems, as well as discussing some of the more common system faults that we routinely encounter.

Clean Dry Environment

Just because wires have insulation doesn't mean that current can't escape from the conductor. Try putting a fully charged automotive battery on a damp concrete floor. Come back a week later and see if it's still fully charged. If not, where did the stored power go? Did it disappear into the air? No, it went right out through the battery casing and into the damp floor. Right through what one would consider a very good insulator, plastic. The same thing can happen with wiring that's been routed through pockets of water or bilge water that could be highly acidic or alkaline. In the tropics, plastic wire insulation is attacked by fungus in wet environments and degraded. There is also the problem with the use of inferior grades of wire that are not suitable for marine use. For these reasons, wiring and all electrical apparatus must be installed and routed in clean, dry environments. It's a natural thing that boats leak, but if wiring is not intelligently routed, it may well be exposed to water and develop stray current as a result. Wiring should never be routed through bilge water, or under or near weather deck hatch openings.

Proper Securement

In addition to being properly routed, wiring must also be well secured. We shouldn't forget what happens to loose wiring on a vessel in heavy seas. It bounces, and in bouncing may be damaged by contact with abrasive surfaces or stress and damage end terminals and connectors. Wiring that is not reasonably well secured against this kind of movement is not safe.

Connections

Because of the stress imposed on electrical circuits, only ring terminals and butt connectors are acceptable types of connectors. Wire nuts and twisted, taped wire connections are absolutely not acceptable, nor is stranded wire wrapped around a screw terminal. Spade connectors are often used on engine instruments and should be crimped to prevent slipping off. Spade connectors should never be used for anything but instruments, and even that's not a good idea.

Fig. 14-5. The older the boats we survey, the more likely we run across conditions like this. When things get this bad, there's little choice but to make a general recommendation that the boat needs rewiring. There's little point to itemizing dozens of faults.

Wire Splices

It is a necessary evil that some degree of wire splicing must be tolerated on boats, but their number should be kept to a minimum. Older boats are often found with numerous wire splices made with butt connectors. Butt connectors are not good because the crimping tool often cuts through the insulation and can result in an exposed conductor, corrosion and stray current, particularly in a wet environment. Furthermore, splices in wires create resistance, results in increased power demand and can cause overheating. A few spliced wires here and there is acceptable, but when we find dozens of them, the client ought to be advised. Ideally, wire circuits should run unimpeded from connection to connection. When excessive wire splices are found, rewiring should be recommended.

An even worse type of connector that is now showing up is the crimped wire nut shown in Fig. 14-7. Unlike a conventional wire nut that is screwed on, this one is crimped. The fault with these things is that these little cups capture and hold water.

Fig. 14-6 . Unacceptable. High voltage, solid stranded, interior grade wire with taped spliced connections, not adequately secured and directly over an engine.

Steel Junction Boxes

The use of steel boxes on a boat are a spectacularly bad idea for obvious reasons. Not only do they rust, but a damaged wire or water entry into the box can result in a short circuit that electrifies the box. I've gotten my fair share of jolts and I believe that steel boxes should be banned. Nice molded plastic boxes cost about two bucks and should be the material of choice.

Conduits

A lot of plastic conduit found on boats does not meet the NEC or ABYC standards for heat and fire retardancy. This includes most of the black and gray ribbed plastic conduit in use today. Some of this stuff is so flammable that if you set fire to it, it will act like a gunpowder fuse, burning from one end to the other. I've had fire cases where plastic conduit spread the fire from one end of the boat to the other, even passing through small holes in bulkheads. The simple way to test this material is simply cut off a piece and set fire to it. It should be self-extinguishing. This stuff should absolutely never be used on engines; even hot manifolds can set it on fire. In one case, an overheated transmission set the plastic conduit on fire which then traveled throughout the boat. Wiring conduits should have the same temperature ratings as the wiring itself, 105°C.

Corrosion

It is a fact of life that boats by their very nature leak. While it's easy to say that electrical installations should always be installed in a dry location, the real-

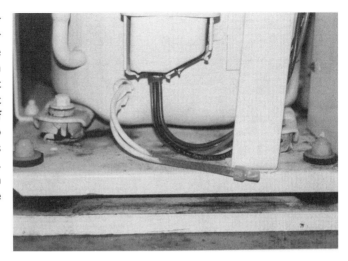

Fig. 14-7 . Go fiugure! Air conditioner manufacturer brings a hot wire out of the compressor spliced with an open crimp and leaves it laying on the chassis that runs like a river of condensation. Needless to say this little beauty was lighting up the whole dock. Best to test the charge on the grounding system before you touch anything.

ity is that for many types of equipment this can be very difficult. Sure, it's easy to find dry locations in the cabin areas, but try installing electrical equipment in the aft bilge, under cockpit decks with numerous hatches, most of which leak like a sieve.

This is an issue that the surveyor constantly faces. Items like trim tabs, bilge and other pumps all have to have wire connections located in an unfavorable environment. Ideally, the number of splices needs to be kept to the bare minimum and be located in an intelligent manner as possible. That means that splices shouldn't be located immediately under a hatch, or so low in the bilge that water is going to get at them. A recent new product called Liquid Electrical Tape has shown to be much more effective at sealing wire splices than shrink wrap or Ray Chem connectors.

Salt and corrosion bridges are a common source of stray current in these areas. It is usual to find terminal blocks lo-

Fig. 14-8. This is what happens with most of the plastic conduits found on boats that I have tested. It doesn't merely burn, but burns fiercely and spreads the fire by means of dripping burning, melted plastic as shown here.

cated somewhere on the inside of the transom. Positive and negative connections are often located side by side. These often get wet, leaving a salty corrosion residue on these surfaces that can then result in current bleeding across the terminals, resulting in either stray current or a power leak from a minor short. Not to mention high resistance connections that are the primary cause of DC equipment failures.

Whether it's a corroded terminal block or a single butt connector located in a wet environment, the problem has to be addressed. It is best to recommend that exposed terminal blocks be placed in a plastic junction box of the type that are now inexpensively available. Exposed and corroded wire splices usually can be quickly cut back and respliced. It is often believed that shrink wrap or Ray Chem type connectors are water tight but they are not. I've cut apart many of these splices and found the wire inside corroded. Probably the best way to seal butt connectors is with Liquid Electrical Tape. This stuff really seems to work.

Bilge Water

Judging by the number of boats I find with electrical equipment installed only a few inches above the bilge, builders apparently believe that bilge water never splashes around, nor do bilge pumps ever stop working. If you've ever looked at what happens to a few inches of water in the bilge of a boat that is going thirty knots or more over choppy water, then you know that electrical equipment can't be gotten far enough away from bilge water. And yet so often we find pumps and motors only inches away.

The usual attitude toward this situation is that, well, the builder built it that way so it must be okay. But it is not okay. Sooner or later the bilge pump is going to fail, or the water is going to slosh around and damage that electrical

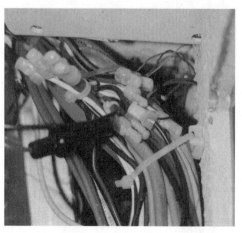

Fig. 14-9. Here's another builder who didn't know how, or was unwilling, to predesign a complex electrical system. All these splices exist because this boat was wired seat-of-the-pants. Meaning, "as built".

equipment. It's not enough for the surveyor to say, well, the equipment works now, so I'll say nothing about it. What the surveyor is faced with is a condition of imminent potential equipment failure that should be reported to the client. Then it's up to him to decide to make the appropriate changes.

Understanding Grounding

Both AC and DC power require an earth potential to complete the circuit and permit electrical equipment to operate. The DC system on a car does not use an actual earth ground but the car's chassis as a ground. On a boat, the negative battery cable is grounded to the engine which, because it is connected to the shaft, is in contact with water. Here the water is not the ground, but the metallic mass of engines and drive gear.

AC system neutrals and ground are wired back to an earth potential ground. But the AC ground (never the neutral) is also tied to the vessel's DC negative, usually through a common grounding buss. Thus we have DC ground plus the vessel's bonding system and the AC grounding or bond tied together. The reason for this is a matter of safety to persons on board, the reason being that it is necessary to provide ground fault protection for virtually all high voltage that can find its way into the DC side. Hence, the DC side is tied back into the dock ground as well. Of course, this does provide the potential for corrosion since all the underwater metals are now tied into the dock ground.

Many people argue that this results in preventable corrosion problems, further arguing that the AC to DC ground should be removed (this argument

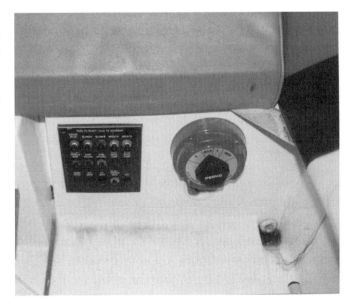

Fig. 14-10 . Having a panel installed at the bottom of an open cockpit may be amusing to you and me, but the client won't appreciate the inevitable unhappy ending of this sad affair.

has been made repeatedly on Internet forums). They say that this creates a hazard to swimmers around the boat, which is true. But it's also true that it is an even greater hazard to occupants on the boat, and it's much less likely to have people swimming around in a marina where boats are plugged in. ABYC stands by their standard calling for an AC to DC ground connection.

Dock Ground Problems

For decades boaters have blamed bad marina wiring for corrosion problems that emanate from boats that all use the same common dock ground. What ultimately happens (or at least this is the latest theory of it) is that we have boats that are all connected together with a common wire. If our boats are all the same and have the same underwater metals, then what we have is a neutral cell. But, of course, all boats are not the same, and for a variety of reasons they will be at differing electrical potentials. Some boats are at a higher electrical potential than others, which means that the boat with the higher potential is going to have a corrosion problem. In this case, it would be an aluminum boat, or any boat with lower nobility metals underwater. Now we have an active corrosion cell set up by means of the dock ground. That means that if there were two boats side-by-side, one protected with zincs and the other not, the boat with the zincs would experience very rapid zinc loss.

So why don't we just disconnect the AC ground connection to DC ground? Wouldn't that solve the problem? Again, it's an issue of electrical shock protection for passengers, and since safety comes first, we have to live with the problem or find a solution.

This may explain why one boat owner will complain loudly about "bad" dock wiring and corrosion, while most of his dockmates don't have a problem. The problem is actually his, and he needs to do something about it. When conducting a survey, if the surveyor is performing the survey in the affected marina, he can easily test the grounding circuit current to prove the point. Then, when the boat moves to the yard for haul out, try plugging in and testing again.

Galvanic Isolators

These simple and relatively low cost devices provide an effective solution to dockside grounding corrosion problems, assuming that the right type of unit is used and is installed correctly. Isolators consist of two diodes, one wired in each direction, which need more than 1 to 2 volts of power before they become conductive. Thus, the diodes will not pass on these very low voltages back through the grounding wire. The important point to note here is that ground isolators will only protect against very low voltage leaks; for major stray currents they will not.

There are however two additional important points that the surveyor should take note of. The first is that if there are two shore power inlets there must be an isolator on each of them. This is made apparent by this next point. Isolators need to be installed immediately inboard of the shore receptacle.

The new ABYC standard for isolators will require that they be rated for the amperage rating of the shore power. Since circuit breakers are rated to trip at 1.3 times the rated amperage, that means that a 30 amp shoreline requires an isolator rated for 40 amps. There are many isolators in use today that do not have this kind of capacity with the result that they can become very hot and can cause damage or fires. Try to check the rating of the unit, or at least check the temperature with the system in operation under load.

Outboard boats and stern drive boats that are kept afloat, particularly those kept in marinas, should be equipped with isolators if they have shore power systems.

Surveying the System

AC System Check Out

Regardless of the size of the vessel, the first step in checking out the electrical systems is to take some time to specifically size up the systems. If we're surveying a late model 50 footer by one of the major production builders, we're not likely to have much trouble with it because the systems on these yachts are usually very well done. But if it's a custom, or a boat that we are not familiar with, we will need to search the systems out for their major components and get a general understanding of the way the system works.

- Locate main and sub panels.
- Determine power sources, dockside and generators.
- Determine how the main switching system operates.
- Make sure shore power system polarity is correct.
- Make sure that generator power polarity is correct at service outlets.
- Determine the load capacities of each system.
- Determine whether there is metering (volts and ammeters) for every power source.
- Determine generally the total possible power demand (primary high

draw appliances such as those with heating elements and air conditioners).

Open the main panel and test the voltage of the bonding system (green wire). Or you can do this at the dock side connection if there is an independent grounding conductor. There should be no voltage at all and this will ensure that there is not a system ground fault that could electrocute you. Don't ever believe that this is not possible; on two occasions I've been seriously shocked from high voltage in grounded components that were energized.

Once we have familiarized ourselves with the system layout, then we can begin to performance test the primary and secondary circuits. The objective here is solely to determine whether the system can carry the load. We'll be looking for breakers that overheat and pop, as well as notable voltage drops on the line volt meter.

Ground Circuit Test

To test the ground circuit, plug the shore cable into the boat receptacle but not the dock. Turn off generator if it is on. With a multimeter set to ohms, connect one probe to the shore cable ground (green) and the other to any service outlet grounding socket (half round opening). The resistance reading should be low. Also note if there is a shore power ground isolator. If so, the reading will be significantly higher. Do the same for both cords and outlets if it has dual incoming lines.

Line Voltage Drop

For a single line circuit, say a 30 amp shoreline on a small boat, this is very easy. If there is no panel meter, use an available service outlet to get a reading from your multimeter. One by one, we turn the appliances on, watching what happens to the line voltage. Systems that are under wired or have high resistance connections (including the shore power receptacle) will result in a substantial voltage drop. On this size line, one burner on a stove, plus water heater and single air conditioner should bring amperage draw close up to the maximum 30 amps. The line voltage should not drop below 105 volts or about 10%, assuming that the original no load voltage was in the normal range of 115V - 120V. If it drops below 100V there is a serious problem that needs to be searched out promptly. The shore power receptacle is always the first place to look, and where the problem will usually be found.

Next, find the back side of the receptacle and check to see if the line is getting hot. This is a great place to use the infrared thermometer, especially if you can't get at the back side. Then check the shore cord itself to see if it's heating up at the boat and dock end. The connection at pier side must also be checked because there could be a high resistance connection there, too. If there is a service outlet on the dockside, use your meter and check the voltage there as well. If it is okay, if the problem is not there, then it's on the boat somewhere.

Now go to the main panel and use the thermometer or feel the face of the circuit breaker to see if it's heating up. Chances are it will be. Worn out breakers are prone to overheating and should be replaced. Nine times out of ten, all high voltage problems originate between the shore power dockside connection and the main panel breaker. The usual exceptions to this are defective appliances such as faulty air conditioning compressors and AC pump motors.

For more complex systems on larger vessels, we use the same procedure for each power source. What we have done is a very simple but effective rudimentary check of the main power supply. Do the same for the generator inputs on each of the primary circuits. When checking the temperature of each of the main panel breakers, be sure to give them sufficient time to heat up, about fifteen minutes or so. In the meantime, you can be doing something else. I always make it a point to check the main panel voltmeters against my meter since a lot of these things are adjustable and people fiddle with them. Sometimes they're way off. Once this is done, you've now completed a reasonably good main power supply system check that should turn up any major problems.

Normally, this is as far as troubleshooting should go, the purpose only being to identify the existence of a problem, not to diagnose or solve it.

Circuit Breakers

A top quality circuit breaker may cost as much as $60.00 while a cheap one only $15.00. Is there a good reason for this? You bet. Cheap breakers are just that: cheaply made and they're not likely to last long. Good quality breakers will usually show the manufacturer name on the back while cheap ones don't.

Circuit breakers should not be used as ON/OFF switches though many builders do this. Why not? Because breakers use contact points similar to ignition points in a distributor. When the breaker is thrown on an energized system, this results in arcing between the points. Over time, the points get pitted, high resistance occurs and the breaker must be replaced. Frequent working of the pole switches causes them to wear out that much faster.

The main panel back side should be inspected for evidence of overheated or burnt wiring, as well as doubling up on breakers. A panel with a lot of new tape labels is usually a good indicator that a lot of alterations have been made, along with the possibility that the system is being overloaded. The inside of the panel should be neat and orderly, not a rat's nest of wiring like that shown in Fig. 14-1. Bearing in mind that boats bounce around a lot, there should be no loose wiring within the panel that can chafe against any of the terminals.

A common tip-off to jury-rigged systems is when we find that the labels on the breakers have been changed, sometimes frequently. We see this a lot on older boats where old equipment has been discontinued and new equipment added to old, existing breakers. The thing we always have to wonder about is whether the old breaker and the wiring is properly matched to the new equipment. Chances are pretty high that it's not.

Anytime circuit breakers are found to trip, this is an indication of a potentially serious problem that should not be ignored. Many people just write it off as a faulty breaker, wait a while and then reset it, failing to realize that there could be a ground fault involved that poses an electrical hazard. Any time a breaker trips, it should be written up in the report. Here's an example of why.

I once surveyed a boat involved in a legal issue on which one of the air conditioners was constantly tripping the breaker. To solve the problem, rather than search out and repair the source of the problem, someone cut the bonding wire at the air conditioner control panel. This stopped the breaker from tripping. Unfortunately, there was a direct short in the compressor wiring which was energizing the boat's bonding system. A young boy stepped aboard the vessel, putting his bare foot on the fuel filler plate and, with one hand holding onto a dock water pipe, was electrocuted. His death would have been prevented by a 20 minute wiring repair. The cause of the short, by the way, was due to the use of a wire nut that was shorting to ground on the wet metal compressor chassis exactly like the one shown in Figs. 14-7, 14-9.

Main Panel Boxes

It is no accident that top quality builders like Bertram, Hatteras and Viking and others use aluminum panel boxes. There always exists the potential for overheating in a panel and a metallic box helps prevent against fires, whereas a panel installed in a wood box will help kindle a fire. Panels installed in metal boxes also help keep water out of the critical area, which leads us to the matter of panel location.

Main panels should be, but occasionally are not, located at a place where there is no chance of water leakage. It is not unusual to find panels located immediately inside doorways where, if the door is left open, the panel gets rained on or subjected to salt spray. Then there are panels located under side decks which have their back sides exposed to the hull side engine room ventilators where salt spray really makes a mess of the electrical apparatus. Or there may be windows or hardware above that is causing leaks into the panel. It is not at all uncommon to find DC panels on small boats located out in the open. Yes, the switches may have those little rubber boots on them, but we know darn well that the inside of these panels are going to get wet anyway. On a boat with outboards or stern drives, this is just asking for trouble.

It is important that panels be inspected for evidence of leakage or a damp environment. If there is corrosion evident on the electrics, this is a situation that must be addressed as circuit breakers are very sensitive to salt spray. Any time rust or corrosion is found on any of the steel parts of the breaker, replacement and elimination of the leakage source should be recommended.

Yet another thing to be on the lookout for is the presence of any exposed screw ends sticking out through any part of the structure where the main wire bundles are located. This is a rather common cause of boat fires. What happens is that after the electrical system installed, either by the builder or as a result of later additions, screws are run into the area around the box that the wiring may chafe against. The installer of the screws is not aware that the screws he has installed are sticking out into the panel cavity or the area of the wire run. I've even found screws run right through wires, so be on the lookout for this.

Power Supply Protection

High voltage systems on a boat need to be treated with a great deal of respect, but are often treated without regard to the dangers. ABYC and NFPA 302 standards call for line protection for any main power feed from the boat side receptacle to the main breaker that has a wire length over 10 feet. Most of the top builders install fuses directly at the shore power receptacle, and for good reason. This is because of the high probability of high resistance connections between shore power cable connectors or corrosion in the boat side receptacle. High resistance can cause fires. Circuit protection helps prevent fires.

Power supply fires caused by this condition are fairly rare on small boats with a single 30 amp shore service, but on larger vessels with 50 amp service, the number of fires caused by high resistance connections increases dramatically. Therefore, it is very important that this leg of the system be fully checked out. If there are no fuses at the receptacle, it is wise to recommend that fuse protection be added. One of the quickest ways to check the shorepower system is with the infrared thermometer after loading the system up to near its maximum draw. If connections start to heat, it's surefire indication of a defect. I include a standard recommendation in all my reports that shore cable connectors should be dismantled and inspected on an annual basis.

Occasionally we find circuit breakers located at this point on the *outside* of the vessel, or at least in a damp environment such as in a cabinet inside an open cockpit. Such a location is likely to corrode the breaker and cause it to stick in the ON position so that it won't trip under any circumstances. It is not advisable that circuit breakers be used at this location for this very reason. Cartridge fuses are the best bet because of their greater reliability.

Because shore power connectors are exposed to weather on one side, it is always wise to try to inspect the wire connections on the back side of the receptacle, even if one has to pull the panel face to do so. The risk of fire is just too high to ignore this critical point. I would estimate that 25% of all receptacles that I inspect have significant amounts of corrosion and electrical arcing damage on the terminals. If the terminals cannot be inspected, then it is a good idea to make a blanket recommendation that the power connections (on both receptacle and shore cord) be dismantled and inspected. All my reports include a standard recommendation that ALL cable ends and connectors should be serviced at least annually.

If the boat is equipped with a generator, make it a point to check the shore power receptacle to be sure that it is not energized when the generator is running. This can happen as a result of incorrect wiring or switching. The reason why it should be checked is that people often leave the shore power line still connected to the boat when they leave the dock. With the male prongs exposed, the shock hazard is obvious. The less obvious hazard is that some one may inadvertently touch the prongs inside the receptacle.

What Is Electrolysis?

There is probably no other nautical term that is more misunderstood or misused than this one. The myths of electrolysis persist despite the best efforts of experts to set people straight, perhaps because people want quick and easy explanations for a complex subject. As relating to boats, electrolysis is corrosion damage occurring to metal as the result of an induced current from an outside source.

Hang around a marina for a while and it's amazing the variety of stories one will hear about the problems with "electrolysis" caused by other boats and bad wiring. The real story is this: All boats in the marina use the same grounding or bonding system (green wire) within the dock system. If one boat has a significant ground fault (AC or DC current) this bonding system will become energized and back feed into other vessel's bonding system. The amount of voltage isn't much but, then it only takes a volt to cause (true) electrolysis. Installing an isolation transformer on the grounding system is an inexpensive and effective way to prevent current back flow into the vessel's grounding system.

Despite the endless and often misguided talk about electrolysis, having surveyed over 4,000 yachts, I can testify that the incidence of stray current damage to underwater metals of boats is very, very low. One of the reasons for this is that, technically, AC current does not cause electrolysis[1]. That statement may shock you, but the commonly accepted myth that AC current causes electrolysis is false. It is possible that AC stray current leaks can cause corrosion damage if it encounters a naturally occurring diode that will convert it to DC current. In which case, it is not AC current that is causing the damage directly, but does exist as the root cause.

Stray current leaks are typically very low voltage amounts in the 0.50 to 3.0 volt range. AC current at these voltages is rather easily converted to DC current by natural diodes such as crystallized salts which can appear in wire connectors or corroded wiring. It will also cause corrosion damage at points where dissimilar metals are joined, but never on a lone piece of metal by itself.

So why do so many problems of rapid zinc loss and corrosion damage through marina dock grounds persist? Because the dock ground system easily becomes energized with low voltage DC current by means of the galvanic potential of boats, as well as stray current leaks from individual boats. One boat with a full 12 VDC stray current leak will be somewhat protected by the marina grounding system, but it will pass its problem onto its neighbors.

Therefore, if a vessel does show signs of stray current corrosion, and before assuming that stray current problems originate from the marina or other boats, and before going to all the trouble of installing an isolator, it's best to have the boat's electrical system checked out for internal leaks. Remember that it only takes one small wire with bad insulation in a wet environment to cause stray current. Only one.

The surveyor can perform a cursory check for DC current leaks during the haul out by measuring the current flow from underwater metals such as shafts to ground. Of course, the assumption here is that the offending circuit will be energized at this time, which may or may not be the case. The average reading I have obtained from checking hundreds of boats is in the range of 0.20 to 0.35

volts DC without any corrosion problems becoming evident. This is the base electrical potential of the boat. Boats with galvanic problems will usually read around 0.50 volts which is moderately damaging. At this voltage paint won't stay on underwater metals and zincs will disappear rapidly. Significantly more than 0.50 volts is an indication of a stray current problem that should be aggressively checked out by a professional.

Sub Circuits

Beyond testing basic equipment operation, there is not much the surveyor can do with all the secondary circuitry short of making a rudimentary examination. Here are a few additional points.

- High voltage lines should *never* have splices. Wiring must run uninterrupted from source to electrical equipment. If a splice is absolutely necessary, then it should be made with a proper terminal connector inside a nonconductive junction box. There must be no chance of the wiring splice getting wet. Butt connectors, wire nuts and taped, twisted wire connections are an absolute no-no on high voltage circuits. Be especially alert for taped connections hidden in large wire bundles.

- Check that all major equipment (particularly air conditioners and pump motors) have the green bonding wire in place and that connections are free of corrosion.

- Check extra closely all equipment that is located in wet or potentially wet environments.

- Be sure that no electrical equipment or wiring is set deep in the bilge where it is likely to be exposed to high bilge water.

- Be on the lookout for circuitry routed through particularly wet environments. Wiring should not be laying on the bottom of the hull, tank tops and the like.

- Check all points of passage of wiring through bulkheads, partitions or panels. Check for points of chaffing or pinching.

- Check the backs of all circuit breakers for more than one power feed. A single breaker should never power more than one piece of equipment.

- Wiring should never be routed with metallic piping, or tubing carrying petrochemicals such as hydraulic lines. Beware that hydraulic lines under high pressure can jump around and cause damage to wiring. Be sure that hydraulic lines for stabilizers, bow thrusters, windlasses or davits are not routed with wiring.

- Be alert for substandard wiring such as solid strand or interior grade wiring. It's amazing how often high voltage equipment is found wired with audio speaker wire! Permanent equipment should never be wired with portable equipment pigtail plugs (two or three prong standard service plug) to service outlets. If the face of the plug gets wet, it will probably short across the spade connectors to ground.

- Watch for evidence of corrosion and water getting into AC electrical service outlets. Wet outlets can also short across terminals and energize the bond.

- The use of service outlet expanders should be condemned.[1]

AC Generators

On a pre-purchase survey, generators are tested for proper operation by performing a few simple tests. Generators come in several different types, including brushless and brush types, alternator and armature types. Very small units are usually the alternator type. Most marine generators have brushes carrying the generated power off the armature slip rings. More generators are needlessly scrapped and replaced by virtue of worn or damaged brushes or other rather minor problems when they could have been repaired at relatively low cost.

Voltage and frequency output are regulated by engine speed. The safe operating voltage will be indicated on the spec plate. The frequency should be 60 Hz, but should not very beyond 59-61 Hz. Most marine generators are governed at 1800 RPM but some few will be 3600. These are a lot less desirable because of the excessive noise the engines make.

Of course, heavier loads will reduce engine speed, and therefore voltage and frequency. Therefore, I always test and record the output at no load, half load and 75% load. My rule of thumb is that a properly operating generator should have a voltage drop of no more than 10% of the no load value when loaded to 75% of its total Kw rating.

Wattage = Volts times Amps, or conversely, Amps = wattage/volts. Therefore an 8 Kw generator is theoretically capable of delivering 69.5 total amps (8,000 watts/115v). In reality, the engine may not be able to carry that very heavy load (for the same reasons you don't run boat engines at full speed all the time) but it should yield 75% to 80% with no problem.

When voltage and frequency are low, the first thing to check is engine speed. Faulty governors (exhibited by engine surging) and fuel supply problems are most common.

A very common problem with generators in smaller boats is water damage. All too often, the unit is mounted too low in the bilge so that the electrical end gets wet. It often happens that the armature cooling fan blows into bilge water that creates a spray that wets the whole unit. Armatures and windings are rather tolerate of water, but slip rings, brushes and various other controlling electrical apparatus are not. Thus, when units have a lot of external rust, as many do, it should not be assumed that the unit needs to be replaced as repair is often possible.

Generator Output

Perform a load test on the generator by turning on appliances until there is a power demand of 75% of total rated output. If there is less than 10% voltage drop, the unit is in good shape. If there is a 10% voltage drop at 50% load, the unit needs a general tune up and possible brush replacement.

It is a little recognized fact that problems with motors, compressors and electronics on boats experiencing premature failure are usually related to low voltage and frequency problems. Be specially altert to this whenever a numbers of pieces of faulty equipment are found; the cause may be due to operating the vessel's entire electrical system on low voltage or frequency.

Service Outlets

When ABYC first recommended the use of ground fault current interrupters (GFCI's), these devices, not intended for marine use, were set at such a low trip rate that they were constantly tripping and thereby became more of nuisance than a benefit. Within a few years, manufacturers recognized this and increased the trip voltage and eliminated most of this problem. However, some of these GFCI's are still around, particularly in older Hatterases where they continue to harass the owners.

GFCI's are recommended for locations such as galley, heads and open spaces where electrical shock hazards are highest, but I recommend them for universal usage because any outlet can potentially get wet and short across the terminals.

Service outlets on the exterior of the vessel are not prohibited by ABYC or any other standard for that matter. However, it is undeniably foolish to place high voltage outlets on the exterior of a vessel where they are likely to get wet, even if housed in a so-called weather resistant housing. None of these housings can withstand wind-driven spray or water hose pressure when the boat is washed down, and they invariably get wet inside. In performing a survey, I'm not willing to take the risk that someone won't do something foolish like plug an ungrounded electrical device into one of these outlets and get electrocuted. I do not wish to stand in front of this loaded gun. Who's to say that a salt water corroded GFCI is going to trip? Who's to say that the ground and bond wire connections are not so badly corroded that there is no ground protection and that the device operator becomes the only available ground? Not me!

DC Systems

Batteries

The primary reason why so many boaters have trouble with batteries is due to improper battery installation and substandard circuitry. By far, the leading cause of battery drain is due to batteries being mounted in wet environments. It was mentioned earlier about what happens when a battery is set on a damp concrete floor: even the best quality batteries will discharge right through the casing. It should come as no surprise that the same thing happens in boats. It is very common to find batteries mounted directly on the bottom of the hull, on a platform contiguous with the hull that is wet, or under hatches that leak so that water drips onto the battery. Batteries are also found in boxes that are filled with water.

Batteries with top-mounted terminals suffer from the problem that, when the top of the battery gets wet, dirty and damp, this will generate a current flow from positive to negative terminals, thereby discharging the battery. For that reason it is imperative that battery tops be kept covered, clean and dry. It's more than just a matter of protecting terminals against accidental short circuiting across terminals. This is why batteries should be mounted in good quality, covered boxes. A good quality battery box (not one of those $15.00 jobs with the belt buckle strap that no one can figure out how to work) costs about $80.00. Compared with the cost of replacing batteries every few years, a good quality battery box is a good investment that saves money and aggravation.

Battery Location

Finding a good location for batteries, particularly in a small boat, can be a problem. As a result, they end up in some truly awful locations where they can't be reached for service, are exposed to water, or pose a hazard from acid leakage. Not only do fumes emitted during charging damage everything around the battery (even when it's in a covered box) but leaking acid can severely damage surrounding woodwork.

In one instance involving a 40' yacht, the owner had added extra batteries under the dinette seat, sitting on a teak and plywood sole. Although he screwed the battery boxes down to the deck, he failed to realize that the screw holes he made in the bottom of the box would leak acid. Not only did the leaking acid badly damage the sole and surrounding joinery, while at sea the boat rolled severely and the batteries broke loose, tore out the entire side of the dinette, and crashed into the side of the galley causing about $5,000.00 worth of damage. Right there are two good reasons why batteries should never be mounted on the main deck or cabin soles.

Another common fault is the mounting of batteries directly on the bottom of the hull. Make no mistake about it, the batteries will discharge right through the damp hull laminate; fiberglass is only an insulator when it is dry. The ideal location for a battery installation is in the engine room where it is dry, and on a fiberglassed deck well above extreme bilge high water level. This would typically be 12 to 18" above the bottom of the bilge.

The following is a list of typical DC equipment power demands that can be used to make a general assessment of whether battery capacity is adequate or not.

Adequate Battery Capacity

General Equipment Amperage Draw

ITEM	AMPERAGE
DC refrigerator	10
Small water pressure pump	7.5
Large water pressure pump	16.0
Electric head	20 – 35
PAR bilge pump	8
Rule 2000 bilge pump	8

Rule 3700 bilge pump	13
Radar, small	25
General electronics, total avg.	15
Running lights	3
Small windlass	30
Medium windlass	50
Autopilot	15
Search or docking lights	7
DC interior lights	10
Blowers, small	3-7
Bait well pump	5-7

Insufficient battery capacity is most often a problem in gas rather than diesel powered boats. It's hard to understand why a builder would offer a 34' boat at a price of $250,000 with a pair of cheap car batteries that cost him no more than $50.00. But they often do. Not only are many of the batteries provided with smaller boats cheap, but usually are of insufficient amperage capacity for the overall system. As will be pointed out in the BILGE PUMPING chapter, the surveyor needs to learn to estimate battery ratings by the physical size of the battery, rating of 50, 60, 80, 90 A.H. and so on. This is because battery manufacturers choose to keep us in the dark by using all sorts of rating code numbers that change frequently. Therefore, if one is not up to doing much research on battery ratings, just gauge the physical size of the unit and quality of the casing. This is possible because the size and thickness of plates determines the physical size of the battery itself. Car batteries, though they often bear the moniker "auto/marine," are still car batteries and usually don't last more than two years.

Batteries come in two basic types: Cranking batteries and storage batteries. Cranking, or automotive batteries are intended to give short bursts of high amperage for engine starting. They are less good for delivering smaller amperages for longer periods of time, which is the strong suit of the deep cycle battery.

Automotive batteries are only suitable for outboard boats that don't have much in the way of electrical equipment. All others should have storage or deep cycle batteries. Cranking batteries are distinguishable by a CA or CCA rating

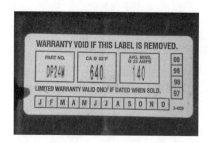

Fig. 14-11. This battery shows a dual rating, cold cranking amps and reserve power expressed in minutes (140) at 23 amps. Usually, only the better battery manufacturers will display any rating at all.

(cold cranking amps).

Storage batteries by necessity have thicker, heavier plates and will be larger and heavier than comparable cranking batteries. They will usually have an ampere-hour rating (AH) with a code like C10, C20, which is the period of hours a battery can deliver 5 amps (100 AH).

The better, or perhaps more honest, battery manufacturers will provide several ratings while their lesser counterparts sell batteries that say nothing about capacity on the units.

One can learn to quickly estimate whether battery capacity is adequate by learning to estimate power demands of major equipment items such as DC refrigerators, heads, bilge pumps and the like. Do not include engine starting motors because this rating is rarely shown. Take the time to read the labels on these items of equipment and learn what their general power demand is. Use peak load, rather than continuous load ratings if this number is given. Do this for a year or two and you will quickly learn to size up a boat and estimate what its power demands are versus power supply. It's also a good idea to figure the capacity of batteries more than one year old at half their A.H. rating which declines very rapidly relative to age. A boat that has 100 A.H. power supply with 80 A.H. power demand has inadequate capacity. As we can see from the above table, the total amperage draw can very quickly add up.

As a general and very simple rule, major equipment demand should not exceed 50% of total battery capacity.

Generators should always have their own starting batteries and, although most do, some are started from the main battery banks. There is not much point in not being able to start the generator because the main system batteries are dead.

Battery Charging

The use of portable battery chargers on boats should be strictly forbidden. These are usually automotive units that do not completely shut off when the batteries are fully charged, but continue to trickle charge and "cook" the batteries. In addition, they are dangerous from the standpoint of often not being grounded and are well known to fail and start fires for a variety of reasons. The use of a portable charger as a permanent charger should be written up in the report.

Battery chargers should be designed specifically for marine use and have a "finish voltage" shut off. This is a solid state mechanism that completely shuts off the charger when the batteries are fully charged. Small batteries will have a full charge rate of about 12.5 - 13.0 volts; larger batteries 13.0 to 14.0 volts. This is because larger cells will develop slightly more voltage than those of smaller batteries. All two volt cells, when new, will generate slightly more than 2.0 volts, hence the voltage greater than 12. A good marine charger will sense this and automatically shut off, whereas an automotive charger won't.

Battery Testing

If you have a battery load tester, great. I don't carry one around because it's too bulky. But batteries can be load tested with a multimeter simply by putting the meter on the battery and cranking the engine. If the battery is fully charged and drops below 9 volts it is weak; if below 8 volts it is definitely on its way out. A battery that reads only 12 volts fully charged is also weak and will soon fail.

Much can also be told about battery condition by its appearance. Batteries with distorted casings are badly deteriorated and should be replaced. For non-sealed batteries, one can look inside and if distorted plates are visible, it should be condemned.

Terminals

Connections to the battery should be proper lead lugs with professionally installed swaged fittings. The steel clamp type are unacceptable as there is inadequate surface contact with the wire, will result in a high resistance connection and can cause fires. Some battery lugs are fitted with a threaded stud so that the main engine starting cables may be connected to this stud with cables having ring terminals on the end. The main cables should NOT be connected to a battery with ring terminals but always swaged, lead lugs. Engine starting draws very high amperage and the contact surface must exceed the circular mil area of the wire, otherwise arcing will occur. Ring terminals do not provide adequate contact area.

There is really no reason why there should be any power feeds taken directly off the battery. When we find them, it usually means that the main panel has been by-passed and possibly the circuit has no fuse protection, or a hidden in-line fuse at best. The wire leads to the main panel should come off the battery switch, never directly from the battery. When there are leads coming directly off the batteries, there is only one thing to do, and that is to recommend the installation of a sub panel.

One exception to this is bilge pumps. So many boats are so deficient on bilge pumping capacity that I'd rather see a pump wired directly off a battery than jury-rigged into a panel. Further, I don't trust bilge pumps with in-line fuses. When these fuses blow, people tend to replace the fuse with whatever they have at hand, regardless of the amperage (Ever try to read the amperage rating on one of these cartridge fuses? Need a magnifying glass to do it!). I've hauled so many boats off the bottoms of marinas with blown bilge pump fuses that it is my view that a bilge pump without a fuse is probably better than one with. The risk of fire is slim but the advantage is great. In fact, if the pumping system is wired after the battery switch, then if the switch is shut off so are the pumps. Hundreds of boats have sank because of this mistake.

In-Line Fuses

It is unfortunately becoming increasingly common for builders, yards and equipment installers to resort to using in-line fuses when equipment add-ons or alterations are made. This is a practice that ought to be discouraged, if not outright condemned. Several years ago I did a survey on a boat for an owner who was complaining that fuses were constantly blowing and, when they did, he couldn't find them to replace them. The survey turned up 17 in-line fuses, some in places that couldn't even be reached, most put there by the dealer who rigged the boat, despite the fact that there were 6 unused fuses on the panel. The dealer was just too lazy to make a proper installation.

It doesn't take much imagination to figure what happens at sea, in bad weather, or at night, when a vital piece of equipment blows a fuse that needs to be quickly replaced. The practice of installing in-line fuses is foolish and dangerous, particularly when placed in locations that are difficult to find and hard to reach. When we run across situations like this, it is both reasonable and prudent to recommend that these pieces of equipment be rewired to a new panel.

[1] It is permissible for service outlets to be daisy chained off a single branch circuit breaker. For this reason, it is important that the number of service outlets available not be increased. Unlike shoreside systems which use solid strand wiring, boats use stranded wire which has a lower current carrying capacity.

Chapter 15

Plumbing Systems

Small boats, as well as large yachts, can have extensive plumbing systems that need thorough inspection. As referred to here, plumbing means all of the piping, hoses, valves, strainers, filters, tanks, scupper, drain and pumps that conduct water in all its various forms. The examination of plumbing can constitute a major part of the survey since the various components are likely to be scattered all throughout the hull. Regardless of the fact that much of it may be hidden or obscured, making the survey process and servicing of systems more difficult, every aspect of the plumbing needs to be inspected.

When it comes to plumbing, there is just no end to the kind of faults surveyors find daily. Everyone from boat builders to owners and repairmen seem to have a major disconnect from the fact that any plumbing system connected to the outside of the boat becomes part of the vessel's hull and therefore must be treated with respect. But people do loose sight of this fact, and so the surveyor is frequently presented with substandard materials, faultily designs and dangerous conditions. The purpose of this chapter is to highlight some of the more common problems so that the beginning surveyor will be aware of just how pervasive these problems can be.

System Types

Plumbing systems are usually categorized into four types, freshwater, sea water, gray water and blackwater. Fresh and sea water systems are self-explanatory; gray water refers to waste water from sinks and showers while black water refers to sewage systems. Smaller boats usually have three of these systems but large yachts will often separate the gray water from the black water, either diverting it overboard or into a separate tankage system so as not to overtax the blackwater system. Long range cruisers will often utilize a reverse osmosis system and recycle the gray water.

A sea water system is any system that brings sea water from outside the hull into the vessel, usually for purposes of cooling machinery, but can include other uses such as reverse osmosis water conversion, bait wells, airconditioning and sea water deck wash downs. The survey of sea water systems gets the highest priority by surveyors for two reasons. First, sea water is highly corrosive to most all metals and, second, because sea water brings outside water inside, any breach in the system runs the risk of either sinking the vessel or causing damage from the leakage of sea water onto other components. For these reasons, sea water systems need to be carefully designed, utilize high quality materials, and be equipped with sea cocks and strainers to prevent foreign materials such as seaweed, plastic bags and the like, from entering and fouling the system.

Black water systems, of course, interest no one but are capable of causing great discomfort when something goes wrong. Sewage systems can also pose serious dangers to both the vessel and passengers for a variety of reasons. One of those is that some, if not most, black water systems mix sea water with waste. The combination of decomposing fecal matter and sea water can make for a brew of corrosives and acids that is lethal to most metals. Most system materials today utilize plastics wherever possible to minimize the metals corrosion problems. Of all the affordable metals, only high quality bronze for pumps will stand up even reasonably well to the highly corrosive environment found in black water systems, which accounts for the trend to the use of vacuum or diaphragm pumps since these systems eliminate the need for metal housing pump orifices. These pumps expose only the low cost, easily replaced synthetic diaphragms to the corrosive fluids.

Health Hazards

As plumbing systems in boats become increasingly more sophisticated and complex, we're going to have to pay more attention to the health hazards that the containment of sewage on board presents. Only recently has this issue been getting more attention as surveyors, yard workers and even owners have contracted diseases which some, including myself, believe were the result of contamination of bilge water with leaking black water systems. Chief among these are tuberculosis and hepatitis.

Not only do leaking sewage systems pose a hazard, but so does the common practice of draining air-conditioning condensation into bilges. It is also becoming recognized that air-conditioning systems can become extremely foul and may well pose health hazards. The danger here results from the sweating condensing coils over which recirculated air from the vessel interior flows. Most marine air conditioning systems have very poor air filtering arrangements and, as a result, the condensers collect airborne dust that builds up, including all the airborne bacteria and viruses which continue to build up in the system over the years. The end result may a system-based hazard such as legionaries disease. If for no other reason, air conditioning systems should never drain condensates directly into the bilge. One way or another, the condensate should be routed overboard or into a sump box.

Safety Rule: *Never, under any circumstances, place your hands in bilge water or handle components which have been submerged in bilge water (pumps, float switches and other plumbing) without using rubber or latex gloves. Always keep protective gloves in your survey kit and use them when poking around in the bilge.*

System Materials

A sea water system is any system that conducts sea water in or on a vessel, whether it involves a through hull fitting or not. All through hull fittings should be equipped with a proper marine sea cock on the intake side when located below the water line. The intake side of sea water systems should also be fitted with internal, not external, sea strainers, to prevent debris from fouling the system and damaging pumps and equipment.

Only marine bronze and annealed copper are really suitable for metallic components in a sea water system that will provide longevity and reliability. That's why true marine pumps, valves and other components are so expensive. Unfortunately, our work in the field shows that there is a never ending effort to cut costs by using lower quality materials. It's also unfortunate that we do not have a complete code or standard of materials for use in all the various aspects of sea water systems. That means that the surveyor has to function as his own judge of what is acceptable or not, based on his experience of what materials perform satisfactorily and which do not.

Plastics are increasingly taking over the role of expensive metals. Where plastics can be engineered in such a way as to withstand the rigors of marine use, this is beneficial since plastics, unlike metals, are nearly impervious to sea water. That's their strength, but their weakness is their relatively low mechanical strength, vulnerability to ultraviolet degradation and low resistance to vibration, heat and other chemicals such as volatile solvents. Glass fiber reinforced sea cocks, for example, have been listed by Underwriter's Laboratories and are at least acceptable in terms of their mechanical strength, if not their functionality, which seems to leave much to be desired. For some reason these valves seem to freeze up or distort in such a way as they can never be freed and have to be replaced.

Fig. 15-1. Non marine plastic valve threaded onto bronze through hull. Note quick connect plastic hose connector at top.

Fig. 15-2. Plastic garden hose fitting mated with thin brass garden hose fitting on air conditioning sea water system.

On the other hand, PVC piping, initially given a bad rap by surveyors, is proving to be a far better material than anyone had imagined. I was recently surprised to find that it is approved by ABS so long as it is properly installed. In recent years much better grades of resin have appeared on the market, along with thicker wall pipes and better design of fittings such as elbows and connectors. One can safely predict that we're going to see a lot more use of rigid PVC piping in marine systems.

PVC Piping

Over the years I have gained a great appreciation for plastic piping for sea and gray water systems. Not only has it proved to be very durable and reasonably strong, but also quite resistant to the effects of vibration and mechanical stress when correctly installed. Thick wall fittings are now widely available and make for very strong joints that even a moron can assemble. Originally, I was quite leery of styrene glued joints but I have watched them over the years and, quite to my surprise, I've never seen or heard of one failing. Initially, PVC piping started showing up with either molded or cut thread pipe joints. These had a very high rate of failure because the wall thickness of the connector and the pipe is cut in half by the threads and the remaining plastic was simply not strong enough. Vibration and stress caused the pipes to fracture at the threads. Glue joints completely eliminate that problem.

Fig. 15-3. Plastic residential sink drain fitting used for a cockpit scupper. It broke and ultimately sunk a 34' boat.

Fig. 15-4. This plastic bait well pump is designed to be threaded onto a through hull. Problem is, if the pump is bumped hard, it will shear off.

PVC is resistant to many solvents and petrochemicals so that its use around machinery spaces doesn't pose much of a problem. But its low melting point means that it should not be used on engines or any kind of machinery that gets hot. There is also a limit to the amount of vibration it can withstand so that it is not advisable that it be used on engine sea water intake systems.

As a general rule, threaded plastic pipe fittings should never be used unless they are the thick wall variety; glue joints are the strongest and most reliable. Further, plastic should never, under any circumstances, be threaded onto a metal fitting and the reason is this: As metals corrode in the threaded joint, the byproduct oxides expand with great force and can cause the pipe fitting to fracture. Pipe fittings to sea cocks and strainers must always be made with metallic nipples and joined with a hose connector. Another reason for this is that plastic is not strong enough to withstand the stress at a metal-to-plastic joint.

Plastic piping runs must always be supported and never allowed to hang or span open spaces. Inexpensive plastic hangers or clips are now readily available that are even more reliable than the more costly, aluminum/rubber clips that corrode and break.

Copper Pipe

Copper pipe is problematic for sea water systems because it is hard to tell what grade of copper it is since it comes in a wide range of alloys and tempers. Soft, or raw copper tubing of the common variety commonly sold in hardware outlets should never be used for sea water systems. Ideally, copper should not be used in sea water systems unless the quality can be identified. Annealed copper, which is very hard, performs very well. Annealed copper can be distinguished by its bronze color or by scratching the surface with a sharp instrument. If it does not gouge easily, it's annealed and is okay for marine use. Most of the large diameter, threaded copper pipe will usually be of the annealed variety as unannealed is too soft for pipe over one inch.

Brass

Non-marine brass formulations such as yellow brass do not hold up well in sea water. Unfortunately, naval brass, which is alloyed for improved corrosion resistance, is not widely manufactured anymore since bronze is not appreciably more expensive. With the addition of tin, brass becomes bronze, so why bother with it? Therefore, most of the brass fittings available these days are plain yellow brass of the type commonly found in hardware or automotive stores for your smaller variety of fittings. It is yellow in color, quite soft, and should never be used in conjunction with sea water applications.

Fig. 15-5. A bronze strainer and an inexpensive plastic strainer which got bumped and broken. Fortunately, only the mounting braket broke. The label on the side warns against using metal pipe fittings though plastic is routinely found mated with metal.

Fig. 15-6. Believe it or not, this is a new $130,000 boat as done by the builder though it looks like something created by a rank amateur. There are four bilge pump filters being used as sea strainers, three in foreground, one in background.

Bronze

The universal standard for strong, durable marine hardware when the utmost in mechanical strength and corrosion resistance is required. An alloy of copper, tin, zinc and sometimes manganese, it is both cast and forged, as in the case of propellers. Bronze has the advantage of both strength and malleability so that it is not particularly vulnerable to stress cracking caused by bending or vibration. It is also far less susceptible to crevice corrosion than stainless steel. Lacking the influence of galvanism or stray current, bronze corrodes at such a slow rate in seawater as to be almost negligible. Its position on the scale of nobility makes it one of the most noble of common marine metals. Mated to most marine grades of stainless steel, bronze is cathodic.

Corrosion failure of bronze hardware is quite rare and when it does occur, it is usually the result of either true electrolysis or erosion corrosion caused by rapid slipstreams such as frequently found on bronze rudder blades behind propellers. Many people believe that pitted rudder blades are caused by electrolysis but this is incorrect: It's erosion corrosion from the propeller wash.

Quality bronze sea cocks and strainers have been known to last almost indefinitely. When they do fail, it's usually the result of the process of dezincification usually caused by stray current. Dezincification is a condition that is readily observable by the pinkish color of the degraded metal. Stray current will leach the zinc out of the alloy, leaving the metal soft and granular in texture. It will crumble readily when struck or scraped with a blade when the condition is sufficiently far advanced.

Bronze is also vulnerable to crevice corrosion but, in my experience, only in conditions where the crevice is totally starved for oxygen for very long periods of time. Such conditions are often found around strut bolts or around sea cock balls or cylinders that have not been operated for periods of years.

Bronze should remain the material of choice for sea cocks, strainers and underwater gear since the material costs remain reasonable. So far, no substitute has matched bronze for strength and durability.

Stainless Steel

The main problem with stainless is that there is no way by looking at it, to determine its alloy. Stainless steel is highly vulnerable to crevice corrosion and stray current. If you've ever seen propeller shafts completely hollowed out on the end by stray current, then you know how deadly it can be to even smaller stainless parts.

Stainless steel should not be used for piping, elbows or nipples. Hoses clamped onto stainless pipe, nipples or other fittings are likely to cause severe crevice corrosion and, if the hose is carbon rubber, galvanic corrosion. Further, threads cut into stainless are another perpetrator of crevice corrosion. This is less of a problem for parts that are not submerged or do not remain full of water. But stainless equipment such as strainers and valves are beginning to appear on the market. When these stainless components appear, the surveyor should at least recommend that these components be dismantled and inspected internally.

Aluminum

On anything but an aluminum boat, this material is unsuitable for just about all plumbing applications by virtue of its low placement on the scale of nobility. The use of aluminum materials is not often found in plumbing systems except when someone ignorantly pulls a part off a plumbing supply shelf and installs it on his boat. Occasionally aluminum bodied pump housings, or other parts are found in non-marine equipment installed on yachts. Such equipment and materials should immediately be condemned.

Iron and Steel

Galvanized or not, neither of these materials belong in marine plumbing systems because of their vulnerability to sea water. Again, these materials most often show up in after-market repairs or additions, not as original equipment installed by builders. It's not unusual to find galvanized iron and steel pipe fittings, particularly elbows, installed by ignorant owners or repairers in plumbing systems, often mated to threaded plastic parts. The primary danger here results from corrosion around the threads which may fail altogether or the expanding rust scale may fracture the plastic or otherwise force the joint open. Iron and steel plumbing parts are not suitable for marine use and when found should be condemned.

Marine Hose

Quality marine hose is expensive and because of its cost people are always seeking cheaper solutions. It's expensive because it's thick, has heavy reinforcement (more than the one or two flimsy plies found in automotive hose) and is made of quality butyl rubber. Fortunately, companies that manufacture quality marine hose usually imprint the grade and the term "marine" directly on the hose. So far, I haven't seen any hose marked "marine" that didn't appear to be marine quality so we can usually take them at their word.

In the past, wire reinforced hose was widely used and which proved to be rather short lived since sea water would work its way up the wire, cause it to corrode, break and then, under spring pressure, force the wire through the side wall. Fortunately, wire reinforced hose has largely been abandoned. It is still found on large engine sea water intakes where a strongly reinforced hose is needed. However, for most applications such as small equipment intakes, the wall thickness of most hose is strong enough to resist collapsing from suction so that heavy reinforcement is not needed. Exceptions would be large air-conditioning systems with high-powered pumps and fire pumps.

Quality marine hose, properly installed, can last a very long time indeed, and may outlive the vessel itself. We should also be aware that outside appearance is not always an indicator of overall condition. Hose should not be condemned when superficial outside cracking occurs. Surface cracking becomes serious when it reaches the point where the fabric reinforcement is exposed and should be condemned at this point. Overall hose quality has also been declining and I've noticed more frequently that hoses located anywhere near batteries can suffer badly from the hydrogen gas emitted by battery charging. Anytime marine hose is found located above, or near batteries, a recommendation should

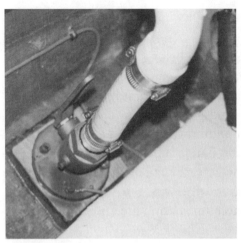

Fig. 15-7. This is the proper way to connect PVC piping to a through hull, with a flex hose section

Fig. 15-8. Bronze siphon breaks, which are spring loaded valves, are highly prone to failure. This is one of the few instances where a plastic fitting is preferable.

be made that it be rerouted.

Marine hose stands up to all kinds of abuse but its weakest point is the point of attachment to a nipple or pipe. For that reason a hose attachment needs a fair lead so that it does not bend at too great an angle Otherwise kinking or severe cracking can result.

A new style of ribbed, flexible plastic hose has made its appearance on the market and, were it not for its rather high cost, would threaten to revolutionize marine plumbing. Good looking in appearance, very flexible and durable, if the price of this material ever comes down, it will most likely become the industry standard as a result of its many virtues. Unlike the spiral-ribbed, gray vacuum cleaner style hose which requires screw-on end fittings that are prone to leak, this material is able to be directly clamped onto nipples because there is no ribbing on the inside. A significant drawback of this hose is that it is so rigid that whatever it is being clamped onto has to closely fit the hose diameter. The material will not compress to make up for any small size mismatches as rubber or poly material will.

Hose Failures

In addition to hydrogen gas attack discussed above, another problem that affects rubber-based hoses is electrochemical degradation or ECD. Dependent on the type of fluid conducted by the hose, a galvanic cell may be set up between the hose and the metal to which it is connected. This leads to ECD, which is usually found closest to the point of attachment. This condition occurs most frequently on engine coolant hoses where ethylene glycol is a extremely good electrolyte and accounts for why engine hoses tend to fail rather quickly. The use of higher quality ethylene propylene rubber will offer superior performance over butyl rubber.

Oil and vibration are the other two enemies of hoses. All but the highest grade ethylene propylene hoses are vulnerable to oil degradation. When hoses become soft, sticky or mushy, they should be replaced with a better quality material. Hoses should never be routed through bilge water or under engines where they will be subject to either biological or chemical degradation.

Improper connection is another killer of hoses. Hose connections to rigid piping or nipples need to have a fair lead onto the connection so that the connection point is not stressed. This usually means that the hose needs to be clamped or otherwise secured into position to avoid movement and vibration. Many people seem to regard recommendations about improper hose connections as being overly nit-picking, but in the long run they can prevent very serious accidents. Example: a 53' Hatteras with stacked air conditioners in the engine room above the port side main engine. The sea water coolant hose was slipped over the coolant copper tubing of the condenser unit. The hose was left hanging four feet above the pump. The hose crimped, cracked and parted at

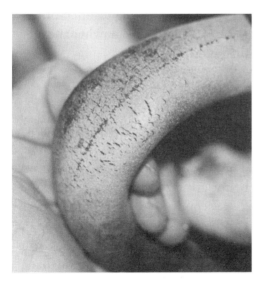

Fig. 15-9. Left: Superficial surface cracking. Often caused by hyrdogen gas from battery charging, this one does not need to be replaced.

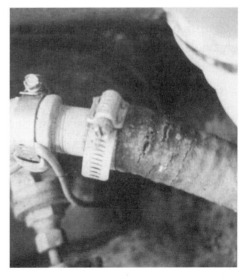

Fig. 15-10. This severe cracking is caused by stress at the end of the pipe nipple. Hoses like this need to be relieved of stress by providing support or a fair lead onto nipple.

the connection, spraying water onto the engine and wrecking it when the engine was started.

Clear, flexible PVC (poly hose) comes in a wide variety of types, reinforced and non-reinforced, and finds its way into all sorts of applications for which it is not intended. This material is very cheap and people use it because it is cheap. Clear PVC is a very poor choice of materials for most marine applications. It is excessively flexible and highly prone to collapsing and kinking; it softens and becomes even more flexible at low levels of heat, and for these reasons should never be used for suction or pressure applications. Under no circumstances should it be used for fuel or oil applications. The nylon webbed reinforced variety has demonstrated a tendency for delamination of inner and outer plies and is also prone to collapsing when used in suction applications.

Marine Sanitation Systems(MSD's)

This is undoubtedly the most unglamorous aspect of the marine survey. Having reviewed the reports of hundreds of marine surveyors, I've found that it is extremely rare that any surveyor even mentions the operation and condition of marine sanitation systems. Even so, I've also found that there is no one more irate than a client who discovers that his toilets don't work, or don't work properly, after the surveyor has completed the survey and has said nothing about it. The good news is that checking out the head system and testing its operation is not a difficult or even particularly distasteful job. Certainly it is nowhere near as ugly a job as the poor soul who has to repair these systems.

Legal Requirements

It should come as no surprise that containment or treatment laws are routinely ignored in some states, whereas in others they are strictly enforced. There are two points that I would caution about. The first is that boats can move from state to state. Increasingly, surveyors are being criticized for failure to advise clients when systems do not meet standards. Secondly, here in Florida, where laws are not enforced, it is very common to find owners who have eliminated or modified their systems in one way or another. Because of Federal laws, a client who purchases a boat expecting it meet these requirements, and yet finds that a system has been modified or even eliminated, would have a legitimate complaint against the surveyor.

Many surveyors are reluctant to report these violations in their reports, probably because they do not like to be perceived as whistle blowers. However,

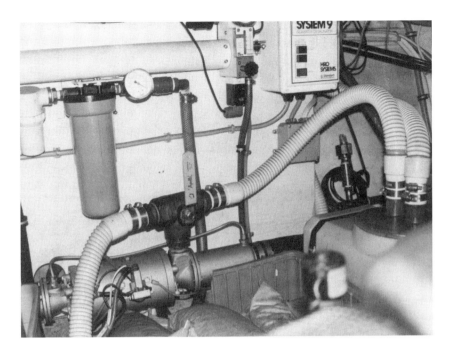

Fig. 15-11. Can you spot what's wrong with this head system plumbing? Yes, the pumps are consigned to pumping uphill, in this case as much as two feet higher than the head units themselves. No wonder the interior of this yacht smells!

surveyors should be aware that throughout the country, the trend is toward increased enforcement and if a state or local government should suddenly decide to come down hard on boat owners, the surveyor who fails to report non-compliant systems may suddenly find himself in big trouble with a file cabinet full of surveys that don't address the problem. Some of these are likely to come back to haunt him. The wise thing to do is to report obvious violations, although this does not mean that the surveyor should assume the position of certifying compliance.

In the U.S., Federal regulations require either containment or treatment of waste. Treatment systems require the killing of coliform bacteria found in human waste. This is typically accomplished by chemical or electrochemical methods. Whereas the ElectroSan treatment systems were once routinely installed on boats, their operation has proved both unreliable and smelly so that this type of system has fallen out of favor and for the most part out of use. Complex treatment systems have proved to be difficult to maintain and unreliable owing to the extraordinarily corrosive nature of waste materials. Metallic components within waste systems degrade very rapidly, thus making the life span of the equipment rather short.[2]

Taking its place is the common holding tank system which poses its own set of problems. Nearly 20 years ago the Mansfield vacuum system was introduced and quickly gained wide application. Unfortunately, this system appeared to have been primarily designed for use in recreational vehicles such as motor homes. The materials employed in the Mansfield system were not suitable for marine use so that these systems degraded very quickly, including the head unit itself. The primary drawback was that the system used sea water in the flushing process. The Mansfield line was rather quickly dropped by most builders that tried it. This system was followed by similar products by firms like Seaward that took the basic idea of a vacuum system and simply brought the system components, including the head unit, up to marine standards. Viola! The corrosion problems were solved and a new and more reliable type of system was now available to replace the common macerator pump driven system.

In my view, vacuum systems have a distinct advantage over push/pull macerator pump systems. That is that vacuum systems are better at clearing the discharge lines of waste, plus the head bowls remain closed off and thereby greatly reduce the unpleasant odors generated by common pumping systems. On the other hand, macerator pump systems typically utilize a dual pumping system, one for bringing in sluice water to the bowl and the other for moving waste out of the bowl. The main drawback of this system is that people don't operate the pumping system long enough to fully clear the discharge lines. This results in waste standing in the pipes or hoses and thus the odor migrates back into the head bowl and escapes. The other problem is that when people do operate the system long enough, it brings so much water into the system that it quickly fills up the holding tank. And, of course, no one likes the job of pumping out the holding tank, and so they flush as little as possible.

The vacuum system greatly reduces these problems because it requires vastly smaller amounts of sluice water to clear the pipes. So little water in fact that they can now use fresh water instead of highly corrosive sea water. And the conversion to a nylon head valve ball has virtually eliminated the problem of corrosion that so plagued earlier systems and caused vacuum leaks. The vacuum system has now proved itself as a highly effective and reliable system when properly installed.

Macerator Pump Systems

The effectiveness and reliability of macerator pumping systems is largely dependent on the quality, and therefore the cost, of the system. Expensive systems such as the Galley Maid Delta system has been in use for over two decades. These heavy duty pumps can easily last ten years or longer so long as the systems are operated frequently. As with most things marine, head systems last longer the more they are used. The reason is simple: the pumps seize up from lack of use. Further, when not used, acids build up within the pump housing that attack the metals. When frequently operated, these acids are flushed away before they concentrate to highly corrosive levels, proving the old adage "use it or lose it."

One of the worst types of mechanical systems is the converted manual head which has a motor drive attached to an old-fashioned cylinder pump, albeit some of them made of plastic. In use for over thirty years, these wonderful devices have a remarkable ability to tear themselves to pieces with their cam and lever arm actuator. Why builders continue to install these dinosaurs is utterly beyond me. Owners particularly appreciate the tendency of the unit to spit the waste back in their faces as the unit chugs and clunks along. But despite the ancient design and clumsy operation, some of these units are made of good quality bronze components that can last a lifetime if they are properly maintained.

Because the bowls sit atop the pump housing, which usually remains full of water, it is necessary that the pump housings be tied into the common bonding system because they are, in essence, submerged. All too often the builders fail to bond the pump housing and this is one of the primary causes of the early demise of these pumps. The surveyor will be doing his client a valuable service if he checks to be sure that the pump housing is bonded.

Keeping the operating mechanism and pump motor fasteners tight will also greatly extend the life of these units. The pump motor base bolts tend to loosen and when this happens the unit begins to tear itself apart. Simple tightening of all the motor bolts and operating system fasteners will prevent this most common form of system failure.

Cheap heads that utilize stamped steel motors and plastic pump housings are hardly worth whatever anyone paid for them. These systems are good for a few years and then usually have to be replaced. Beware of both cheap PAR and Raritan pump motors that are installed below the water line. If electrolysis attacks and corrodes the pump motor shaft and seals, it can result in sea water leakage back through the motor. If you see water leaking out around the pump, it should be repaired immediately as there is a danger that it could sink the boat.

Reverse Siphoning

Surveyors of sailing yachts are all too familiar with the critical point of where and how the marine head is installed vis-a-vis the yacht's waterline.

Reverse siphoning through the head is a serious problem in sailing yachts because heads are so often installed below the waterline. This occurs far less frequently in motor yachts, although it does occur, particularly in deeper draft trawlers. It's good practice to make visual or measured reference to the position the head bowl relative to the waterline. Bear in mind that should the vessel develop a leak and take on a lot of water, once the head goes below the waterline, it can finish off the sinking of the vessel.

The manual or cylinder type head pump is particularly vulnerable to reverse siphoning because people forget and leave the water control valve open. Further, if the head discharges directly overboard, water can back up through the discharge if system parts are worn and the pump stops in the right position with the valve open. Therefore, in addition to taking a visual reference, it's a good idea to operate the pump and then stop it with the valve in the open position, and pump handle up, to test for reverse water flow. If the water continues to flow into the bowl (even though it may not fill it up) there is a problem with reverse flow that needs to be solved, most probably by adding a riser and vacuum break on the intake line.

Moreover, anti-siphon valves are cantankerous devices prone to failure, particularly the bronze valves that corrode and stick in the closed or open position. There are rare occasions when a cheap plastic part is better than a high quality bronze fitting, but this is one of them. The cheap little plastic anti-siphon valve is better than its expensive counterpart simply because it does not corrode in the same way, though the spring loaded check valve can fail. When corroded and stuck bronze valves are found, it's a good idea to recommend replacement with a plastic valve.

System installation

Most failures of head systems to discharge readily are the result of poor installation and the lack of adequate planning. Despite the presence of pumps, gravity provides considerable assist in clearing the bowl and pipes. In reality, most head systems are installed without adequate planning and therefore function at levels below what they were intended to operate. Here are some common faults:

- Head situated below the level of the holding tank infeed piping.
- Excessive piping distance from head to holding tank.
- Piping makes excessive numbers of turns.
- Piping travels up, then down. (Very common)

- Sea water infeed pump above water line and fails or is slow to achieve suction.

- Multiple head system is interconnected and looses suction or back flows one into the other.

- Discharge or water infeed lines have too much riser.

- Stuck check valves in discharge lines to holding tank.

The most common cause of poor system function and bad odors permeating the vessel interior is an improperly designed piping system. Most often, this involves a head situated low in the hull which at some point has a low spot in the piping and thus waste remains standing in the line. The ideal installation, of course, is where the piping has at least a slight downward run to the holding tank so that gravity will assist in clearing the line. This is true regardless of whether it's a vacuum or macerator pumping system.

Valving

Systems with multiple valving for on-deck, overboard and holding tank options are particularly smelly because the alternative piping routes usually retain sewage in the lines when the valves are poorly positioned, as they often are. A good installation is one where the piping runs in as straight a line as possible and utilizes two-way diverter valves installed so as to maintain a straight, continuous flow, and not set up so that there are numerous loops and whorls in the system to cause resistance and pocketing. We often see valves and hosings neatly mounted on vertical bulkheads that, on the surface, looks nice, but in reality causes the system to have to move the waste upward, thereby restricting flow. If the system does not function as smoothly as it should, this is probably the reason.

Sea Water Systems

The use of improper materials and poorly designed sea water systems are the leading cause of boats sinking. While a builder may go to great lengths to ensure that his hull is seaworthy, it is really quite easy to forget that when one pipes sea water into a vessel, that piping system has to be equally seaworthy. For owners, it's even easier for them to forget that a simple mistake can sink their boat. That's probably why we so often find such a hodgepodge of materials used to repair or replace systems on older boats, or to make new installations.

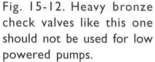

Fig. 15-12. Heavy bronze check valves like this one should not be used for low powered pumps.

Fig. 15-13. Another plumbing mistake: Attaching the strainer directly to the plastic pump housing has damaged the pump. Such connections should always be made with a hose.

Design

The main criteria for proper sea water system design is to prevent inadvertent back flow of water into the vessel. This can occur through careless installation of heads, sinks, showers, bilge pumps or virtually any type of sea water system.

Let's use a shower sump pumping system an example (See Fig. 15-17). In this instance the shower pan and the discharge pump is below the water line and does not have a riser loop. The discharge outlet, let us say, is one inch above the water line. It doesn't take much imagination to realize the many circumstances whereby the discharge could go underwater and result in reverse siphoning.

The type of pump utilized makes a difference, at least in the short run, as to whether siphoning can occur. With a centrifugal pump, as typified by Rule pumps, there is nothing in the pump to restrict back flow. On the other hand, a neoprene impeller pump will prevent reverse flow so long as the pump is in good condition. But when there is excessive wear of the pump impeller, water can then flow by the worn impeller blades and threaten to sink the boat. Thus, regardless of the type of pump used, reverse siphoning remains a threat. The two primary means of preventing back flow are check valves and riser loops and each have certain drawbacks.

Check Valves

Substantial flow restriction and the danger of clogging and sticking are the two problems associated with check valves. The best way to utilize a check valve is to place it as close to the hull discharge as possible. Heavy bronze check valves can severely restrict flow and are prone to corrosion and sticking. For that reason, they should not be used with low pressure pumping systems. Plastic valves on the other hand are light weight and require little pressure to either open or close them and do not have the corrosion sticking problem. But it should be born in mind that any debris in the line, particularly human hair, can easily cause the valve to stick in the open position. It is recommended that check valves always be used in conjunction with a riser loop.

Strainers

The use of inexpensive, low quality strainers of all types is increasingly causing problems such as sinking boats and burning up engines due to water starvation. Chief among these are plastic strainers that are simply not strong enough to withstand the application to which they are subjected. The first point of failure is usually the mounting brackets which, being plastic, are usually not strong enough to withstand vibration or people bumping into them in crowded engine compartments. Many was the time in which I have inadvertently bumped into, stepped on, sat on or backed into a plastic strainer, causing the brackets to shear off its mounting base. On other occasions, a sharp pull on one of the hoses resulted in the plastic nipples shearing off.

Another, and very common failure mode results from threaded metal pipe fittings screwed into plastic nipples. As mentioned earlier, metal should never be threaded into plastic because the expanding metal oxides will eventually cause the plastic to fracture.

In my view, plastic strainers are unnecessarily cheap products that should not be used on boats. The rate of failure is unacceptably high. A number of years ago I encountered for the first time a rather heavy looking swimming pool filter used on an engine intake. This pool filter was vastly superior to any of the plastic "marine" products I had so far seen and so I looked up the manufacturer and called them. It was a small company and when I asked if their filter was intended for marine use, the company owner was appalled to find that his filters were being used for such applications. He stated that he had no intentions that his products be used on boats. Even so, I suggested to him that he might look into this market because his product was significantly better than those on the market intended for marine use. To date, I don't know of any plastic filter for

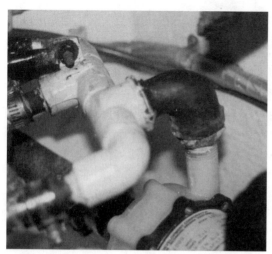

Fig.15-14. A mistake similar to that in Fig. 15-13, this three-way manifold is attached to this plastic pump nipple that will eventually break off. Manifold should be independently mounted and connected with hose.

marine use that would make me feel comfortable with it and I often recommend their replacement with bronze housing units. The small pool pump filters to which I refer have indeed found their way into marine use on such applications as bait well filters and the like. However, for such things as machinery intakes and air-conditioning, the standard bronze marine filter is still the best bet.

Another misapplication of materials commonly found is the small, plastic bilge pump strainer, of the type manufactured by PAR, used as a sea water intake filter. The plastic cover is held in place by a small stainless steel screw of dubious quality that can corrode and disintegrate very quickly. See figure 15-16.

Valves

Marine surveyors have been fighting against the use of gate valves as sea cocks for at least 40 years and still builders persist in their use. So what's wrong with gate valves? The most important complaint is that by looking at the valve, it is not possible to determine what materials it is made of. There is usually no way to tell what material a cheap valve pulled off a hardware or discount store shelf is made of. More often than not, its yellow brass with a steel valve stem that will rust away in a few short years. On the other hand, manufacturers of marine grade bronze sea cocks invariably put their name on their products and usually list them with Underwriters Laboratories so that when we see a marine sea cock, we have good reason to trust in its quality. True marine sea cocks are expensive and I know of no manufacturer that has so cheapened his products as to be dangerous. This cannot be said for generic gate valves that rarely even have the manufacturers name on them.

Furthermore, gate valves do not have the necessary mounting flanges so that they can be properly mated to the through hull flanged nipple and doubler block. Lacking a mounting flange to resist the leverage action of the valve against the doubler block, gate valves are prone to loosening. Finally, because they rely on a threaded screw shaft, the gate valve is very prone to seizing up. For these reasons, surveyors should continue to recommend replacement of gate valves with proper marine sea cocks. Some of the quality valve manufacturers consist of Perko, Conbraco, Buck-Algonquin, and Wilcox-Crittenden.

Within the last decade, nearly all marine bronze ball cocks have been manufactured with the ball in a nylon seat so that the corrosion and seizing problem is vastly reduced.

Plastic Valves

From what I've seen so far, plastic valves, even though approved by U.L. and A.B.S. are no panacea for marine bronze. Plastic valves marketed under trade names such as Marelon and Forespar have proved to be so hard to operate that I've feared shearing them off trying to close them, even when new. What happens to these fiber reinforced plastic valves is that when the securing screws, bolts or flanges are tightened up during installation, the tightening distorts the valve body, making it hard to operate. I've run across dozens of them that with reasonable effort I could neither open nor close, regardless of their age. Quality bronze ball cocks with nylon seats are now so inexpensive that there's no longer any excuse not to use them.

PVC valves from the hardware store shelf absolutely should not be used as sea valves under any circumstances, whether as an inline valve or screwed onto a through hull nipple.

Plastic Through Hulls

Broken plastic through hull fittings probably sink more boats than any other cause. Molded of white nylon, they are highly vulnerable to ultra violet degradation and can crumble into dust within a few years when receiving heavy sun exposure. Of late, apparently some manufactures have recognized this problem and have both increased the size of the fittings as well as having U.V. inhibitors to their plastic formulation. In any case, many of the newer fittings seem to be considerably stronger and less prone to degradation.

Plastic through hull nipples are prone to shearing off on the inside surface and for that reason all such fittings on a boat should be carefully inspected and stress tested. When hauled out, I simply take a screw driver, insert it in the opening and apply a little leverage to see whether it will snap off. Close inspection will often reveal cracking of the plastic inside the orifice. Or, if the plastic is degraded and the outer flange turning to dust it should be replaced.

Vessels capable of speeds over 35 MPH should not use these plastic fittings. Hoses that are loose or suspended by their attachment to the plastic fitting will place heavy stress on the plastic when the vessel is pounding, particularly if the hose is heavy and full of water. It's not very expensive to replace them with bronze.

Air conditioning

The plumbing on most air-conditioning systems generally deserves more attention than it gets. Major faults usually consist of substandard materials installed after the vessel was built, as well as poor layout and design of the cooling water systems. Single unit systems are pretty straightforward but with multiple compressors, shortcomings tend to multiply.

First, be sure that all hoses are well routed and that there are no kinks in the lines. Installers tend to forget that when a hose fills with water, it gets much heavier. Hoses should not be permitted to dangle where motion of the vessel can cause the hose to fail at the point of attachment. AC condenser coils usually terminate with a cut pipe end that may be sharp and cut the hose. The hose attachment should have a fair lead-on to the connection with no bending or kinking.

Some specialty sea water pumps like Teal and Marche pumps have plastic casing pump housings with a threaded nipple at the top. There's nothing wrong with that, but heavy, metallic manifolds should not be attached directly to the pump housing as the weight and the lever arm created by the length of the manifold can easily shear off the plastic nipple. Instead, the manifold should be hard mounted and connected with a piece of hose. This will eliminate the danger of damaging the pump housing (see fig.14-14).

Specialty sea water pumps such as the Marche pumps are magnetic drive so that there is no through-shaft from pump housing to the motor. This eliminates the chance of leaking water seals that damage pump motors. But the impellers are fairly easily clogged and stopped by any debris within the pump housing. If the pump motor runs, but fails to pump water, chances are the pump just needs cleaning.

Beware of commercial air-conditioning systems on yachts. Non-marine AC systems usually use inferior materials and are not suited for marine use, particularly the cooling coils which are often raw copper and may corrode rapidly. The same applies to non-marine pumps which absolutely should not be used for sea water applications. They're often found as cheap substitute replacements.

Very few builders of yachts are unaware that the improper placement of AC coolant lines can be disastrous. However, be on the lookout for after-market installations, custom boats and imports where coolant lines are either poorly insulated, improperly routed behind ceilings or in the overhead. It's fairly common to find these mistakes in cheap refits of older vessels, such as installing coolant lines in the overhead where the sweating pipes can cause serious water damage.

There are many mainline U.S. builders who install air-conditioning units under flying bridge coamings. This is a particularly bad idea because of the danger of condensation leaking into the overhead. Watch particularly for flexible ducting that fills full of water and then dumps a load of water into the salon via the overhead duct when the boat rolls. The best solution to this problem is to increase the insulation on the ducting, as well as to make a small hole to let any accumulated water to leak out. Far better to lose a little cool air than to ruin an expensive headliner or furniture.

If I could afford a half-million dollars for a yacht, I sure wouldn't want to be sleeping on top of an air-conditioning compressor installed under my bed. Amazingly, a lot of builders are now doing this simply because it's cheaper. They're also installing them under various types of seating. Self-contained units have to have means of draining off condensation. If drip pans and drains are not properly designed — keeping in mind that boats are subject to rather violent motion — the condensation is going to escape and cause damage to woodwork and other components. Water stains and damage around bases of berths and seating or paneling is often the result of condensation leakage.

Bait Wells

Primarily found on sport fishing boats, in-deck bait wells can not only be troublesome, but sink a boat if not properly designed. Bait wells should be examined to ensure that the upper edge is water tight to the underside of the deck. It should also be checked to ensure that the deck is not so low that the plumbing to the outside can flood and overfill the well. This is most commonly a problem in smaller boats where cockpit decks are very close to the waterline.

Plastic Transducers

Many different types of underwater electronics such as depth sounders and knot meters come with plastic transducers. And many have failed and sunk boats, particularly when the hull strikes floating objects. Plastic transducers are subject to easy breakage and should not be used. Numerous instances of the large plastic Datamarine knotmeter impeller housings fracturing and sinking boats have been recorded.

Plastic Pipe Fittings.

Household variety plastic fittings of every type and description manage to find their way into boats, placed there by builders, owners and repairers. One recent case of sinking involved the use of a plastic sink drain utilized as a cockpit scupper which broke off (Fig. 15-3), allowing an underwater drain to sink the boat. More commonly, brittle and weak ABS and styrene plastics find their way into all sorts of plumbing fittings such as garden hose connectors, quick release connectors, sprinkling system plastic parts, plastic sink drain fittings and what-not. Since most of these materials are not identified, and were never intended for marine use, the surveyor has to use his own judgment on where and when the use of such fittings is safe - if ever. Clearly, it's not safe to use garden variety plastic fittings on sea water systems, or to use plastic sink drains that can easily snap off, causing the drain hose to drop down and sink the boat. When in doubt, the best policy is to recommend replacement with materials of known quality. It's hardly worth the risk of sacrificing the whole boat, and possibly even its crew, for a few dollars in savings on otherwise inexpensive parts.

Fresh Water Systems

The only serious danger that a fresh water system presents to a vessel is when it is connected to a dockside water system. Unfortunately, few people realize that community water systems can function at widely varying rates of pressure intended to be handled by metal pipes. More often than not, boats don't have metal pipes and high water pressure (60-100 psi) can easily burst hoses, connections and low-grade plastic pipe fittings. In addition, high pressure can also burst or damage water tanks, particularly the thin gauge aluminum tanks that we are seeing with increasing frequency. For that reason, any boat with a dockside water hookup should be equipped with a pressure reducer/regulator which should be located immediately after the inlet connector. Small to mid sized boats are often equipped with cheap plastic regulators that are neither adjustable nor detectable when the regulator fails. These should be replaced when a boat is ten years old or more. I recommend using a brass bodied, heavy duty adjustable regulator such as the type manufactured by Watts or other quality makers.

The ideal piping for fresh water systems is copper, and that's what most quality builders use. Fresh water system pumps should be equipped with a pressure gauge so that one can determine what the pressure is on the low pressure side. A properly designed system will have two check valves: one before the water tank fill and the other before the pressure pump. These check valves prevent the pump side of the system from being pressurized by dockside pressure. These valves are very important because the pump may use a diaphragm and will also be tied into the system with low pressure hose. If not isolated from dockside pressure, these components may burst.

- If there is a dockside water connector, prove the existence of a pressure regulator.

- Prove the existence of check valves to protect the water tank and pump.

- Check the connections to all faucet fixtures, making sure that connections are not made with low pressure hose.

- Connect vessel to dockside pressure and check all hose connections on the pump side of the system. The presence of "ballooning" hoses will indicate either a lack of check valves or a faulty regulator.

Over the years a number of boats have been found with inferior grade plastic water piping, one manufacturer of which has been the subject of a massive, nationwide class-action lawsuit. The most dangerous fault of these systems is the plastic connectors which are weak and prone to cracking and complete failure. When the connector fittings fail, the piping connections come apart and can fill the vessel with fresh water. The surveyor should pay special attention to the compression fitting connectors and examine them for cracks. If cracks are found, then the entire system should be condemned. One manufacturer of quality plastic piping is Imperial Eastman whose systems are not known to fail. Their piping is clearly marked with their name and pressure ratings. Beware of plastic piping with no pressure rating markings. The piping should also be clearly marked "Nontoxic" for potable water use. Plastic piping should always be well secured and no parts of the system allowed to hang free in open space where it can be damaged by vibration, inadvertent snagging or slamming forces.

Aluminum Tanks

These tanks have a generally good service record so long as the tank is not excessively thin wall material such as 0.125". Aluminum fresh water tanks do corrode from inside and out, and for that reason alone the heavier the material the better. Thin wall tanks are also subject to high pressure, as mentioned above, when improperly connected to dockside water systems. Tanks with the sides and top ballooned out are suffering from either freezing or overpressurization. Improperly designed systems are most often found in custom and import boats.

Large tanks installed far forward in yachts have also proved vulnerable to the G-forces of slamming that can cause tanks to rupture. When you find tanks installed in the bow, it's a good idea to check them out for signs of bulging or movement on their beds.

It's best to have water filters installed on the intake side of the water supply lines to the fresh water pump for any type of tank material, but it's imperative for aluminum. Aluminum tank corrosion creates a lot of corrosion debris inside the tank (with the consistency of very coarse sand) that is damaging to pumps, particularly PAR diaphragm pumps and Galley Maid pumps. PAR and Perko make inexpensive little filters that are ideal for this application.

Bilge Pumping

This is a subject to which an entire chapter could easily have been devoted to cover the subject thoroughly. Sailors of the last century obviously knew the importance of their ability to remove large quantities of water from the hulls of their ships as evidenced by the massive pumps with which every ship was equipped. Somewhere between then and now, the understanding of the importance of adequate bilge pumping has been lost. Perhaps it's because most American boatsmen feel comfortable that help is only a VHF radio or cellular phone call away.

As with fire extinguishers, no one thinks much about bilge pumps until an emergency occurs, and then it's too late. To the best of my knowledge, no one has ever set a standard on how much bilge pumping capacity a vessel should have, although I have some very definite ideas about that. Having personally been in situations at sea where the amount of water entering the hull was greater than the capacity of the pumps to discharge it, I can certify that it is not a pleasant experience.

Fig. 15-15. Bilge pump discharge at water line with no riser. After countless years of boat building, you wouldn't think you'd see this mistake very often, but we do.

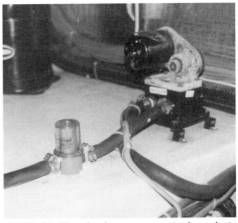

Fig. 15-16 .The diaphragm pump is the solution where complete dewatering of a bilge is needed, or spots where submersible pumps don't fit.

The number and capacity of bilge pumps should always be considered with a view toward emergency situations, not the normal, everyday needs. Nor should we be fooled by the presence of large manual pumps; anyone who has ever tried to work one of these things for more than five minutes knows that only a gorilla could operate one of these things for very long. Manual pumps simply do not supplant the pumping capacity of a powerful electric or engine driven pumping system.

Nowadays, it seems that most builders supply just enough pumping capacity for normal dewatering but not sufficient for even the most minor emergencies such as the common event of a stuffing box or hose coming loose.

So how much is enough? Obviously, we're not talking about a condition where a vessel receives a major hole in the hull. A reasonable emergency condition to plan for would be something like our stuffing box example, a broken plastic fitting, ruptured hose and the like. The objective should be that the pumps will handle this volume of water until such time as the leak can be located and stopped. What happens all too often is that the pumps can't handle the rate of inflow, the source of the leak goes underwater and then cannot be found. At that point, for the want of another bilge pump, the vessel is lost.

Here again, the definition of seaworthiness should come into play in determining how much pumping is really needed. The reasonable criteria would then be any such emergency as is *likely* to occur. This should then be evaluated in context of how the vessel is used; is it a long-range cruiser or a cocktail circuit

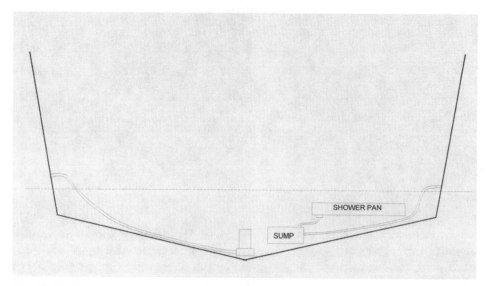

Fig. 15-17 . Two common plumbing mistakes: Bilge pump with no riser loop and shower sump discharge with no riser. Both are capable of sinking boats.

cruiser? The way to determine that is to simply ask the owner or client.

DC Pumping

Battery powered pumps are only as good as the batteries that power them. Smaller boats are frequently deficient in battery power and in many cases the battery system will need to be upgraded just to adequately power the existing pumps. For boats that remain afloat and which have a shorepower system and battery charger, there's not much to be concerned about. But for many outboard and stern drive boats, we often find an inadequacy of both pumps and batteries. These boats are usually found with automotive batteries, which means that they deliver a lot of amps in a hurry, but the ability to deliver power over a more extended period of time will be about half that of a deep cycle battery. A single 60 AH battery that is 18 months old is probably only capable of delivering 30 AH due to deterioration of the plates. Therefore, say with an 8 amp bilge pump, at best one could expect it to drive the pump for four hours. However, as the battery depletes, it will do so at an accelerated rate, so this four hours is theoretical at best, so that our pump will run at full power for something even less than that.

A good rule of thumb for estimating the battery capacity needed is to multiply pump draw in amps by 10 times the number of pumps. Thus a small boat with two 8 amp pumps would need 160 AH battery power, which would readily be supplied by two 90 AH batteries with a comfortable margin. Use this formula only for boats that depend strictly on battery power to stay afloat. Unfortunately, most small boats arrive from the builder with 50-60 AH car batteries, so you're going to be making a recommendation to upgrade. For more information on battery power and quality, see Nigel Calder's *Boat Owner's Mechanical and Electrical Manual.*

Number of Pumps

It is difficult to get a handle on how many pumps any particular boat needs because the basic configuration, size and type of the vessel itself plays a significant role in determining how many pumps are adequate. Regardless, we still need some kind of rule of thumb to serve as a guide. I recommend that total capacity roughly be estimated on the basis of 150 GPH per foot of vessel length for most boats. However, it should be recognized that the number of individual pumps, the compartmentalization of the hull, and their placement is also important. The following table will serve as a guide as to what constitutes a reasonable recommended minimum number of pumps and total combined capacity. Selection of type and placement of individual pumps needs to be assessed based upon vessel trim and the low point of the hull.

Size	Number of Pumps	Total Capacity GPH
16 - 20	2	2500
21 - 26	2	3000 - 3500
27 - 35	3	3500 - 4500
36 - 42	3	6000
43 - 49	3 - 4	8000
50 - 59	4 - 5	9000
60 - 69	5+	10,000+

Primary Service Pump

This is the pump that sits at the lowest point in the hull while the vessel is at rest and will perform all of the normal dewatering. It should be a heavy duty pump capable of handling a fairly large volume of water over extended periods of time.

Stern Pump

The aft bilge pump is rarely the deepest point in the hull with a vessel at rest except for rear engine boats. However, while underway, this pump then becomes the primary pump because of the change in trim that causes all the water to run aft. One exception to this may be semi-displacement hulls with very deep keels or keel sumps. Because serious leaks often occur while the vessel is underway, this pump should be of large capacity and automatically operated.

Forward Pumps

The forward bilges in some yachts are the deepest point while the highest point in others. Depending on the situation, the capacity and placement of the forward should be judged accordingly, adjusted for changes in trim caused by fuel and water load.

Backup Pumps

It is only common sense that all vessels should be equipped with a back up bilge pump. This is not merely for emergencies but in the event of failure of the primary pumps. In recent years we've seen more and more builders supplying back up pumps as standard equipment, but older boats rarely have them. The best location for the main back up pump (if there is more than one) is near the primary dewatering pump. Back up pumps should be mounted and set up to operate when the water level reaches about 6" above the point where the primary pump should turn on in the event that it fails. It is best that the back up pump does not sit partially immersed in normal bilge water where it can get clogged up with sludge and debris and seize up from disuse.

Float Switches

Float switches are often damaged as a boat gets up on plane and all the water in the bilge goes rushing aft. If the float flapper is facing forward, the water will catch it and tear it off its foundation. One solution for this is the covered or caged switch. But surveyors come to dislike these things because one cannot easily test the operation of the pump by lifting the float.

One solution to avoid caged switches is to install the float so that the flapper faces aft, not forward.

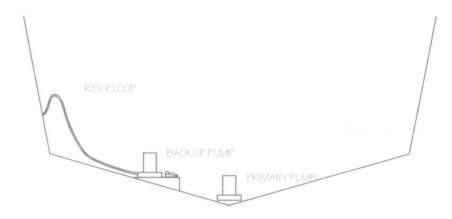

Fig. 15-18. A back up pump arrangement that is proven to work well. The back up is shown off center here for clarity. The pump and switch are raised up so that it is not always in contact with bilge water.

Idiot Lights

Most builders will install Rule pumps with the standard Rule panel switch that contains an indicator light to show that the pump is running. Judging from my own experience, I would venture a guess that these indicator lights have prevented hundreds of serious accidents by warning vessel operators that the pumps are running continuously or too much. If a pumping system doesn't have them, it's a good idea to make that recommendation.

High Water Alarms

Bilge high water alarms are to be highly recommended and every vessel should have at least one float switch activation station. If the vessel does not have a back up pump, the activation switch should be located 10 -12" above the bottom of the bilge, or depending on at what point high water will cause damage. If there is a back up pump, placing the activation switch only a few inches above the pump will suffice. For boats over 35' having a two station alarm system is best with one switch aft and the other at the static water accumulation point.

High water alarms are recommended for all cruising yachts, as well as stern drive boats that are stern heavy. The primary objective is to alert the operator when excessive water accumulates in the stern while underway, which often goes unnoticed before it is too late. With the engines in the rear, you can easily see why stern drive boats need an aft bilge alarm.

Capacity ratings

The capacity ratings of most bilge pumps that I've tested tend to be somewhat to greatly overrated. This means that the pump is rated for pushing water horizontally, not vertically. And this is with a brand new, fully charged battery. Simple capacity tests that I've conducted show that a pump rated at 2000 GPH wouldn't even pump half that much with three feet of static head. This is an important consideration since a bilge pump in a typical 40 footer, including the riser loop, will have to push water up that far. The above recommendations take this into account and is why they may, at first glance, appear to be excessive. In the real world of actual performance, most pumps after installation (considering factors of in-line resistance of hoses and fittings) will not pump to their rated capacity. I'm not suggesting here that a surveyor should test pumping capacity, only that he should be aware of this when assessing the over all number and capacity of the installed pumps.

Riser Loops

The primary purpose of a bilge pump riser loop is to prevent outside water from back flowing into the hull. The fact is a large number of boats sink every year because the discharge outlet is too low to the water line and there is no riser loop. Builders like to place the discharge outlet low to the water because during discharge, the water splashes and makes big stains on the outside of the hull. But consider which is more important: no stains or a sunk boat? Many people seem to think that as long as the outlet is just above the water line, it's okay. But consider what happens when an engine is removed from the vessel for an overhaul, or the boat is subject to wave action.[1]

The fact is that there are all sorts of unanticipated situations where improperly installed discharge plumbing can cause, or contribute to, the sinking of the boat. My recommend minimum riser height (not the exit port) be 18" above the water line. It should be noted that the riser loop does not substantially increase static head pressure because the water falling down the down side of the loop causes a siphon effect that relieves this pressure once the pump gets going. In smaller boats, this height is usually not attainable, in which case a plastic check valve should be used.

Emergency Pumps

Battery powered pumps can never be defined as emergency pumps simply because there is usually inadequate power to run them under the conditions in which they are needed. Emergency pumps must run off either high voltage or be engine driven to be effective and reliable. The best and most cost effective emergency pumps are those which are belt driven from main engines, or the main engine sea water pumps can be equipped with valves and bilge suctions. If both main engines are so fitted, the capacity of emergency pumping becomes enormous and can be regulated by engine speed. Either way, these pumps are only dependent on whether the engines run.

Vessels equipped with an AC generator can also utilize 125 VAC bilge pumps that can serve as an emergency at-sea pump. If there are high capacity air conditioning water pumps or deck wash down pumps, these can also be equipped with valves and bilge suction piping that, with a flip of a valve, can quickly transform it into an emergency pump. This is a very good option since the pump will serve a dual purpose at very low cost.

Sport fishing vessels are more at risk than other type of yacht by virtue of their low, open cockpits and the manner in which they are operated. Fast backing down and open sea navigation makes it common sense that these vessels (regardless of their size) should be equipped with an emergency pumping system. It's not surprising then that we see some of the top builders like Viking and Hatteras installing engine suction pumping systems as standard equipment.

Outboards don't provide the option for either engine driven pumps or AC electric pumps since outboards are rarely equipped with generators to run them This leaves the DC battery system and manual pumps as the only options. Oddly enough, we rarely find manual pumps on smaller boats where they can be of most value. It doesn't take a corps of football linebackers to manually pump out a small boat so that a manual diaphragm pump would be a valuable addition to any small boat.

Why Bilge Pumps Fail

This discussion of why bilge pumps fail is included so that the surveyor will understand it is so important that only quality equipment be used and installations be made properly. It is my estimation that about 80% of all US built boats are equipped with DC bilge pumps made by Rule Industries. These are good quality pumps with a long history of good service. In fact, I recently surveyed a 25 year old Hatteras that still had the original Rule pumps in it. And yet tens of thousands of pumps fail every year and owners are endlessly heard to complain about them. Well, the problem is rarely the pump's fault but rather the fault of the installer or owner to properly maintain it.

There are three primary causes of pump failure. The first is damage wired connections resulting from the wire splices either being located too deep in the bilge where they are wetted by bilge water, or from leaks in the deck above. The second is from failures of the float switch caused by the switch remaining in the up, or ON position after all the water has been discharged. This is usually caused by sludge or debris in the bilge, or interference with other hoses or wires that prevent the switch from turning off. The pump continues running and either runs down the batteries or burns up from overheating. The third cause is float switches that go adrift and cause the pump to run continuously. Yet another common cause is a pump that operates for extended periods off of low battery voltage that also causes the pump to overheat. In any case, the fault is not the pump but installation and maintenance.

The following is a check list to help ensure proper bilge pump installation and operation:

- Bilges must be clean and free of debris and sludge.

- Reversed Wiring. Pumps are often installed with reversed wiring, which will cause the pump to run slower and hotter. For Rule pumps, the white wire is hot, brown is negative.

- Both pump and switch must be solidly secured against movement.

- Float switches must be protected against heavy surges of bilge water causing damage to them.

- Wire connections must be located in a dry location and as high above the bilge as possible. Connection should be coated with a water resistant material to resist water penetration into the connector.

- Connections should be installed in a watertight junction box when installed under open cockpit decks where water from leaking hatches will cause corrosion damage.

- Battery power must be properly matched to amperage draw of the pump to ensure adequate power supply.

- Low voltage and continuous running may cause the plastic pump housing to melt or distort. Check housing for signs of damage, particularly on the top. A small brown spot or dimple indicates overheating.

- Check pump speed and output. If pump runs slow despite full battery power, wiring or pump may be damaged.

- Always check wire connections for corrosion damage. Corroded connections create high resistance and are deadly to pumps.

- Check discharge hose for restrictions such as kinks, crushed hose, improper joints or heavy check valves.

Open Boats

Smaller open boats are most vulnerable to sinking from accumulations of rainwater as well as vulnerabilities from low cockpit decks and deck drainage systems. Every year hundreds of small boats sink because of failed pumps, batteries and boat design mistakes. In recent years the value of small open fishermen has escalated dramatically, to the point where thirty footers can be worth as much as $250,000.00. and be fitted with a vast array of costly equipment. It only makes sense that these expensive craft be fitted with a pumping system that minimizes their risk of sinking.

Calculations show that one inch of rainfall into the cockpit of a 24' open boat can amount to as much as 90 gallons of water. Should this rain water fail to be discharged overboard for whatever reason, sinking of the vessel in a moderate to heavy rainfall is a very real hazard. Most open boat sinkings occur as a result of pump failures, followed by battery power failures. For this reason, pumping systems in these boats need to be high capacity with redundancy backed up by substantial battery power.

Owners will often argue that because a boat is kept in dry storage or on a lift, the boat doesn't need more than one pump. They argue that they only do day sailing on Sunday afternoons, that the boat is never left afloat overnight and so on. This argument breaks down when the owner changes his mind about that and the boat is launched and left in the water for a few days or weeks. This happens a lot and the surveyor leaves himself open to the charge of "You didn't tell me!" if he lets it pass.

Recommendations for bilge pumping for open boats should be predicated on a boat-by-boat basis since there are too many differences in boats to be able to devise a universal standard. Pay particular attention to stern drive and outboard boats where the center of gravity is in the stern and all accumulated water will run aft (See chapter on COCKPITS for further discussion). These boats absolutely should have a back up pump.

To do an effective job in gauging the pumping capacity it is necessary to determine the ampere hour rating of the batteries and current draw of the pumps. Unfortunately, batteries don't always have the rating displayed. You can learn to rate batteries with reasonable accuracy by their size. The larger the battery, the larger the ampere hour rating will be.

The quality of the battery also makes a difference. So many of these small boat batteries are of such poor quality that their reasonable expected life span is barely a year. These are the kind that sell for $40 or $50, have thin plastic casings and are usually loaded a lot of fancy printing on the outside to make up for the lack of quality. The seaworthiness of the vessel depends on the reliability of the bilge pumps. These batteries are not sufficiently reliable to run the pumps (particularly without a charging system) and should not be used in boats. It doesn't make sense to risk the whole boat for want of a couple of good batteries.[3]

Open boats, particularly outboards and stern drive of particularly high value, and which are kept afloat, should be equipped with a marine charging system. It's simply not reasonable to expect that the batteries alone will keep the boat afloat. In places like Florida and the Gulf Coast, where torrential rainfalls are common and averaging as much as 80" per year. Battery systems cannot be relied upon to discharge these enormous amounts of rainfall, particularly when owners do not attend their boats regularly.

Freezing Climates

Climates that experience hard freezes pose special problems for plumbing systems. Surveys performed in spring or early summer deserve special attention for potential ice damage to plumbing systems. There's not much to this except looking extra closely to any part of a plumbing system that could trap water, freeze and break. With such a wide variety of plumbing systems on boats these days, there's a lot of opportunity for oversight when doing a lay up.

Pay special attention to pumps, valves and strainers. Carefully examine all plastic valves, piping and fittings for cracks. Watch out for plastic deck drain fittings that inadvertently get plugged up, fill with water and freeze. Remember that lots of people are utterly unaware of the need for winterizing and thousands of boats are just hauled out and forgotten. The smaller the boat, the more likely this possibility. In southern states, boats are left afloat, often without any winterizing at all. Even here in Florida I find many boats from the north that have travelled south with ice damage. Most of it consists of cracked pumps, strainers and fittings, but occasionally I find damage to water tanks, mufflers and pipes.

---

[1]   As an interesting experiment, stop a boat in a seaway and watch the bilge pumps. If the outlets are low and have no risers in the discharge line, you may see water flowing out the base of the pump.

[2]   ElectraSan units have both steel and aluminum parts, which accounts for why they degrade so rapidly.

[3]   For a thorough discussion of battery quality and ratings, see Nigel Calder's *Boat Owners Mechanical and Electrical Manual*, Second Edition.

Chapter 16

Sea Trials

Possibly the most difficult part of the sea trial is paying attention to the work at hand rather than watching the beautiful scenery go by. The objective of the sea trial is to prove the operation and performance of the vessel, its machinery, controls and equipment. This is the point where the sum of the separate parts of the survey come together and the assessment of the performance of the vessel and its overall operation is made.

It was pointed out in the Hull Survey chapter that it is not enough to merely examine a boat in a static condition, but that a most thorough survey involves making examinations while the vessel is underway. The significance of this is that faulty conditions may show up while the vessel and its systems are under stress, that do not show up while just sitting tied to the dock. For this reason, the more strenuous the test to which it is subjected, the more likely it is to reveal otherwise hidden faults. Unfortunately, we don't get to pick the weather conditions for our sea trials, so the client should be made aware of this. Nearly half the year in my home region, the seas are dead calm or nearly so. This doesn't result in very good sea trials, but there is nothing I can do about except to make sure that the client understands that problems may come to light when the boat is bashing into three foot head seas that did not come to light during the sea trial.

The nature of the sea trial is determined by the nature of the vessel and whatever navigation it was intended to perform. How it is to be performed should always be conducted on that basis. A houseboat intended for cruising on inland rivers and lakes is viewed in a different light than an oceangoing yacht. The sea trial of a mega yacht is a vastly different event than for most smaller boats. The objective is always to determine if the vessel is seaworthy for the environment in which it will most likely be used. This is not to say that a client won't purchase a houseboat on the Lake of the Ozarks and transport it to Miami and attempt to operate it there. That's why it was earlier recommended that the surveyor should always "qualify the client" and find out his plans for the vessel. If he plans to use a vessel that is clearly unseaworthy for a particular navigation area, it is only prudent that the surveyor advise him accordingly.

Different geographic regions will engender more or less these kinds of considerations. It's not at all unusual in Florida, for example, to find people who bring a vessel intended for inland navigation (houseboats) to the Atlantic and Gulf coasts and then sell it. When a surveyor finds out that a client intends to purchase such a vessel and sail it to the Bahamas, right away he should know that he needs to protect himself against a potential disaster. If he wants to do something so foolish as to cross the Gulfstream in a houseboat, that's fine, but the surveyor should stay out of the line of fire when the lawsuits start flying. This is what is meant by conducting a sea trial in context of the vessel's intended use, or within the obvious design limitations.

Special Considerations

Surveyors have differing ideas about the scope of what is to be evaluated by the sea trial. Should it be limited to just evaluating the condition of the vessel, or do we go into areas of performance like one might find with a *Car and Driver Magazine* test drive? Most of the answer to that question depends on what level of service the surveyor intends to offer his client, how he intends to position himself in his local market.

Performance criteria that could, but not necessarily should, be evaluated consist as follows:

- Speed

- Sea Keeping

- Maneuverability

- Stability

How we might approach these questions should depend on a buyer's experience level. It will become obvious that to client who is purchasing his fifth or sixth boat, such commentary might not be welcome; he may have come to his own conclusion about that. On the other hand, to one who is inexperienced and is purchasing his first boat, the surveyor's views would usually be quite welcome. Once again, this illustrates how important qualifying the client at the time of initial survey scheduling can be. One needs to know in advance what the client expects.

One aspect that is not open to debate are vessels which, in my view, are patently unseaworthy for the conditions of intended operation, or vessels which have dangerous handling or performance characteristics. Certainly it is debatable, but the surveyor may have an obligation in the eyes of the law, or at least the eyes of a liberal judge or jury, to report certain undesirable vessel characteristics. These might include:

- Vessel does not reach the advertised speed of the broker's listing. Note here that plaintiffs have won such complaints against both builders and brokers.

- Vessel is unstable or rolls excessively.

- Steering response is poor.

- Vessel is underpowered and very fuel inefficient.

- Vessel doesn't trim out properly, rides bow-high with greatly reduced visibility.

- Dangerous passenger safety issues are observed while at sea.

Some surveyors believe that such criteria shouldn't be a part of their survey, feeling that these are subjective decisions that should be left to the client. That's fine so long as the client understands this. But in many cases the client is inexperienced and is incapable of making sound judgements. Is the surveyor going to leave his client to learn the hard way? Some of the items in the above list should be obvious no brainers, for which the surveyor is opening himself up to liability risks if he does not report what amount to conditions. My attitude is that I want to serve the client to the best of my ability, but I also want to avoid having him come back to me complaining that I didn't advise him about a serious problem. This philosophy has always served me well and I recommended it. Keep in mind that if and when the buyer took his initial "test run," he was probably being wowed by the salesman and distracted from taking a serious look at the things he should be looking at. The sea trial is the time to bring his head out of the sales pitch and back into reality.

Doing it Right

The sea trial is the time to really put a vessel through its paces and find out whether it meets the client's expectations. It's not so much a matter of what the surveyor thinks about vessel performance, but a matter of what the client thinks after the surveyor has pointed out to him. I want to keep my personal opinion out of it as much as possible, doing my best to just sticking to the facts. It's up to the client to then decide whether the vessel meets his expectations. My job is to just make him aware of these things.

The presumption here is, of course, that all other elements of the survey have been completed and the vessel is deemed seaworthy enough to actually make a trial run in open water. If there's any doubt about the reliability of the machinery or safety of the vessel, the surveyor should recommend against a trial run pending repair of any faulty condition.

Where and how the trial run is performed is of utmost importance. Owners and brokers will often attempt to limit where and how long the sea trial takes place. Assuming that all is well, a seagoing vessel ought to be trialed in the sea. Sea trials conducted within the confines of a small river, canal or other restricted body of water are not really sea trials. As its name implies, a sea trial is intended to test the performance and handling characteristics at sea. A brief run up "the ditch" doesn't accomplish this. Of course, there are occasions when we are completely limited to such an ordeal, and when we are we should make clear all such limitations in our reports.

Taking Control

I've heard surveyors argue that they should never personally take control of a vessel for fear of liability from accidents. That's a fair argument if one has to do trial runs in restricted waterways. But a surveyor cannot do a good job in assessing handling and performance unless he takes control himself. I've done it for over thirty years, and because I'm very cautious, have never had a problem. But one does have to be acutely aware of the hazards and develop a procedure to avoid them.

It is up to the surveyor to be sure that everything down below is stowed away and ready for whatever kind of sea trial you're going to be conducting. If lamps or televisions fall off of countertops, expect to be asked to pay for them. Bear in mind that the seller probably doesn't know what the surveyor is going to do, so it's up to the surveyor to ensure that everything is ready.

It makes good sense not to operate a vessel in any location where there's potential for collision or running aground. Use good judgement: If an area is littered with lobster or crab traps, it may be prudent not to get behind the wheel. By far, the greatest risk is when the surveyor travel is involved and he is unfamiliar with the waterways. Unless we can get to the open ocean, I do not operate the vessel, but rather instruct the operator on what I'd like him to do, while I observe. This is not as good as doing it yourself, but it sure beats running someone else's boat aground!

Out at sea, once clear of land, other vessels and underwater obstructions, it's a different matter. Here we can be reasonably assured that we can take control of the vessel without mishap. That presumes that the surveyor is a highly skilled and cautious operator; if he's not, he ought not to be doing surveys in the first place. However, it's still fairly easy to make some bad mistakes, so I'll outline a few things to be aware of.

It's quite common for the red and black gear shift and throttle levers to be reversed. Or both may have gold knobs. Pulling an engine out of gear at high speed could be a very costly mistake. On more than one occasion I've grabbed the wrong ones. You expect throttles on the right, shifters on the left, but it's not always that way. There's a good way to avoid this and other mistakes. Before taking control, always ask the operator to bring the vessel to a stop. In other words, don't take control while the boat is going fast. Get comfortable with its operation at low speeds first so that by the time you're ready for a full speed run, you're fully familiar with it.

It's best to get away from congested areas, areas with buoys, fish nets, floating debris or anything else. Your attention is going to be diverted from where you're going to what's happening with the boat. Uncluttered spaces are your best insurance.

Another reason we want to do the haul out first has to do with how well the propellers are attached to the shafts. If the shaft is going to pull out of the coupling, or the props come off, this will most likely happen during the back down test. To avoid this, check the shaft/coupling interface when docking and undocking, prior to the sea trial. Shafts loose in the coupling will almost invariably show up when docking as it slides in and out. Check the props when hauled. Are the nuts tight and cotter pins in place? In this way, one can be reasonably certain that there won't be an accident. Only once have I had a shaft back out, and that's because I failed to check.

Vessel Speed

Speed is often a major consideration for clients, even for slower vessels, so much so that law suits contending false speed advertising are fairly common. It's prudent to question the client as to his expectations in order to find out if he is particularly demanding. Sport fishermen are particularly sensitive to speed so that conducting a speed run is usually the order of the day.

To conduct a speed trial, it is first necessary to take into consideration wind and currents as these factors can badly skew the results of speed trials. If the wind is directly abeam then there will be little affect. The same applies to currents; one needs to know the direction and constancy of currents. As an example, in my home region, swirling currents of the Gulf Stream can cause speed runs of low speed vessels to be extremely unreliable. It's necessary to determine how the currents are running before we can place any confidence in a timed run. For fast vessels, the effects of currents are less significant, but a twenty knot wind whistling through a tower can easily whack 5 knots off the speed, in which case you'll need to try running perpendicular to the wind.

Speed runs can be made either by a timed mile run or by GPS. Almost all boats have a GPS, but it's not a good idea to rely on that alone. I carry my own portable GPS, which has been checked against hundreds of others so that it's accuracy has been well tested. Having tested hundreds of GPS units against radar gun readings, margins of error run up to about 3 knots, but more often run 1.5 - 2.0 knots off. This assumes the unit is getting signals from at least three satellites. On many occasions the speed readout will continually fluctuate over a range that can be quite substantial. In that case, the result is not going to be reliable.

The timed run should be conducted to and fro and then averaged out, to account for wind and current. To get good results the vessel has to be held to as straight a course as possible since any wandering will also skew the results. If the autopilot is reliable, it's a good idea to use it. For fast boats (over 20 knots) a full measured mile should be used. For slower boats, using a ½ mile course will help minimize errors. If the course is determined from a nautical chart, be sure to use knots, not miles. A knot is 1.17 miles.

Handling Characteristics

How the vessel handles should be a major consideration when dealing with inexperienced buyers of small to mid sized vessels who may not know what they're getting into. The point here is to protect yourself by protecting the client. It is especially important to test the handling characteristics of fast boats that might very well have dangerous tendencies. Typical examples are small cruisers with very high centers of gravity that have a tendency to lay over on their chines and not come back up until speed is reduced. Boats like this are downright dangerous and there are quite a few of them out there. Does the surveyor have an obligation to assess and advise the client of such conditions? What do you think a jury would say?

Handling characteristics should be assessed incrementally at various speeds, putting a vessel through a series of turns to see how it will respond. Some boats, due to their design, will behave badly only at a particular speed, much the same way a car can develop a vibration that only occurs at one speed. Try doing this at increments of 500 RPM.

Check how the vessel trims out while getting up on the step. Some boats are so poorly balanced that the bow will stand up in the air for so long that the operator cannot see over the bow for too long a period, and not be able to see where he's going. Others might have a speed range spanning over 1000 RPM in which the vessel refuses to get up on the step. This can effectively render the vessel to be a two speed boat - slow and fast. Most often this involves outboard boats. This later is an example of extremely poor performance for which the client, particularly a novice, deserves to be warned. It's a turkey and nobody wants to own a boat like this. It's an example of a vessel which does not meet a reasonable level of performance and should be considered as a serious design defect. Technically it is not seaworthy because it may cause the operator to travel at speeds with which he is not comfortable.

Chine Riding is a very common problem with outboard and particularly stern drive boats. When the boat gets up to a certain speed, it may want to lay over and ride on one side of the bottom, a situation that can lead to a loss of control. This may or may not be related to propeller torque, but can be the result of both torque and bad hull design. In many cases what happens is that at high speed, a vee hull rises so far out of the water that it is riding nearly on the apex of the vee. Thus, it has a natural tendency to flop over to one side or the other. If it does, this is a design, balance and trim problem. If the boat always flops over to just one side, in the opposite direction of prop rotation, then it is primarily a torque problem, commonly found with single engine boats. When it happens with twin stern drives, it's a hull design and trim problem.

Tunnel or propeller pocket drive boats are prone to having poor steering ability at lower speeds. Very often, these boats have undersized rudders. When docking/undocking, or in a particularly difficult seaway, such as entering an inlet, we will encounter quite a few vessels that are completely uncontrollable. The surveyor will have to decide for himself at what point he feels it necessary that he should warn the client. At the very least, he should be verbally warned. Whether a vessel has propeller pockets, plus the size of the rudders, should serve as an indicator of how well the vessel can be controlled. One would think that a function so vital as steering would not be shortchanged by builders but, unfortunately, it happens all the time. The client has a right to expect to be told whether or not the vessel has adequate steering. Many times poor steering can be corrected by simply increasing the rudder size.

Watch out for larger yachts that have had cockpit extensions. Often accomplished without consulting a naval architect, many yards that perform extensions have no idea what they're doing to the hydrodynamics of the yacht. Over the years, I've seen many extensions that were not only structural disasters, but performance disasters. Only recently I observed such a yacht on which the rudders were *15 feet* away from the propellers. This resulted in a yacht that nearly uncontrollable when docking. It is the prop wash against the propellers that gives a motor yacht steerage at very slow speeds. When the rudders are not near the props, it's not going to steer at low speed by the rudders, and possibly not even by the props.

Two recent examples of dangerous steering conditions will illustrate. One was a fast Hatteras sport fisherman whose owner installed a Boston Whaler and heavy davit on the fore deck. This boat was so bow heavy that at high speed it veered all over the place. Trim tabs do nothing for a bow-heavy boat. The owner, who was operating the boat, complained that I unfairly criticized the handling to the client. Ten minutes later he lost control of the boat and clipped a waterway marker.

The other was a replica of a cruising houseboat a la Trumphy/Mathis design. It had a very deep forefoot and extremely large rudder. The deep forefoot caused the nose of the hull to want to wander, combined with a steering system that had inadequate response time (4 full turns). It required too many turns of the wheel to attempt to correct the wandering with the result that the vessel over-steered so severely that no one could reasonably control it. It went up straight waterways tracking a series of S's, not matter how hard the helmsman tried to avoid this. The client was advised of the condition and eventually the problem was solved by changing the steering system to one that only had two full turns-lock-to lock. This simple but costly solution restored the steering system to one that could easily control the vessel, despite the self-steering tendency of the forefoot. In reality, the basic problem was that the hull was poorly designed but with a little ingenuity we were able to overcome this. The seller was unhappy, but the client was satisfied, and a potential disaster and lost sale was averted.

Main Engines

This section assumes that diesel engines will be surveyed by a diesel specialist. The surveyor's role on a sea trial should be to work together with the engine specialist, covering all areas that he does not. Naturally, if the surveyor is not familiar with that individual, he needs to confer with him and find out what he covers and does not.

As mentioned in the Drive Train chapter, the hull surveyor covers all engine peripheral systems - such as controls, wiring, exhaust and mounts - even if it duplicates the engine surveyor's efforts. We also cover the water supply up to the engine. It should be the goal of the hull surveyor's report to cover as much of the vessel as possible since the hull survey is the primary report.

Engine performance is covered as it relates to overall vessel performance. If an engine doesn't run properly, and that affects the sea trial, then the condition needs to be described in the report. Don't rely on the engine surveyor to do that; this condition affects your work. That essentially means covering any anomalies of performance as referred to earlier. But, since I'm loyal to my client, I want to be assured that the engine surveyor is also doing his job properly. This is doubly important if the surveyor has recommended him on behalf of the client. On more than one occasion the engine surveyor did not do a good job, in which case I'm going to let client and engine man know, long before the shouting starts.

Engine Performance

If one knows what the engine manufacturer's maximum operating range is, it's easy to determine whether the engines are revving up to full speed. If you haven't invested in a photo-electric tachometer, you can still use the boat's gauges. Even if the vessel's tachometers aren't quite right, both engines should go up to wide open throttle and synchronize. This doesn't mean using the Glendenning but using your ear to gauge synchronization. If they don't, bring the fast engine throttle back to match the slow engine to determine how much its off. For gas boats, with their higher engine speeds, max throttle should go up to at least the minimum recommended. For all Crusader V-8 gas engines the recommended operating range is 4000 - 4400 RPM. Mercruiser V-8's will be about the same; in-line and V-6's will be something different.

Diesels should be turning right up to their rated maximum load. For low speed diesels (up to 2500 RPM) they should go within 50 RPM. For higher speed four cycle engines (2800 - 3400 RPM), they should go to within 100 RPM. Plus or minus 200 RPM is not acceptable and indicates a problem that needs solving. On the full no-load test, both engines should go right up to the max. This will determine whether the fueling system is set up right. Diesels should never be allowed to under or over speed.

Under/overwheeling is a common problem as owners experiment with prop sizes and often end up with props that are not quite right. We often get lots of questions about props that we can't answer. Hence the loss in boat speed or increase in engine speed. More often than not it is a loss in boat speed because the more props are reconditioned, the smaller the props get. Diameter is reduced and the blades get thinner and diameter shrinks. Metal is ground away so that the prop changes size and shape. Some prop shops are rather cavalier about what they call "reconditioning." In many cases, it's pure luck if the blade alignment comes back within 1/4" (+/- 1/8"). People often chuckle when I pick up a stick or old paint stirrer in a yard and hold it against a rudder to check blade alignment, but that's really all that's needed to determine if all the blades are in line. 1/8" is about as close as you'll get out of most shops, but when the variation reaches 1/4" performance will be effected. Again, this is another good reason why we want to do the sea trial after the hauled survey. You'll find that most blades are out of alignment in the forward direction. If we know the size and condition of the props, we may be able to explain variations in speed.

It's very common to find older props that have lost as much as an inch off their original diameter due to reconditioning or having been cut down. This can account for a significant loss of speed. The best way to check is to refer to the owner's manual (if there is one) and measure the props against the original specifications. You probably can't measure the pitch, but you can the diameter. Very often significant changes in performance can be traced to changes in propellers, whether in pitch, diameter or number of blades. If performance is not satisfactory, at least the client will have a starting point if the props don't match specifications. It can also be checked whether the original props were cupped and whether the existing props are cupped when unexplained differences arise.

Blade tip bending is common due to hitting objects in the water. Props are very tolerant of minor tip bending, since the maximum thrust occurs at the middle of the blade. Minor damage can be manually straightened.

Engine Instruments

The diesel engine surveyor will connect his own diagnostic gauges to the engine and take readings independent of the vessel's gauges. Most yachts have electric gauges that can be unreliable. I want to include in my report any major variances so I will obtain a copy of the engine man's findings and report any discrepancies. I include a chart of the engine instrument readings because it serves as a useful reference guide for the client. It's nice to have a record of the readings at the time he bought the boat that he can refer back to.

Back Down Test

Accelerating an engine hard astern and then hard forward is a test used to determine the condition of the engine mounting system. This operation is repeated several times for each engine while the surveyor observes the mounts. There should be little or no play to the engine mounts. The base of the mount should have no movement whatever; the engine bracket-to-stud point should not move more than 1/8". If metal engine beds are involved, the securing bolts should also be checked. See **Drive Train** chapter for more details on this subject. **Caution:** *Never conduct a back down test until the props and shaft coupling have been checked. The danger here is loosing a prop if the shaft nut is loose, which they sometimes are.*

Shaft Runout

Shaft runout is the degree to which a shaft runs off center and is measured at the stuffing box. It is not necessary to use a dial indicator since even very small amounts of runout are visible to the eye. This can be caused by a wide range of factors which has nothing to do with the straightness of the shaft. For our purposes excessive runout is defined as any degree of runout that will create any visible shaking or movement of the transmission coupling. Bear in mind that misalignment of struts can cause an otherwise straight shaft to run out of true; a lot of boats suffer this condition and remain that way indefinitely without ever being corrected. It will, if severe enough, shorten cutlass bearing and even transmission life. In moderate degrees, the effects of runout are usually negligible.

Combined with flexible mounts and rubber cutlass bearings, shafting systems are essentially free-floating and self-aligning. You may have noticed that as much as 1/8" of runout at 800 RPM, although not tolerable, can completely disappear at 1400 RPM; this is the self-centering effect of the system. Just because you see a shaft wobbling at low speed, don't make the mistake of condemning it. It may be a completely harmless condition. Unbalanced engines also cause vibration, but oscillation caused by the alignment or shafting is different. Engine vibration usually does not show up at the transmission, whereas shaft wobble results in visible transmission movement. To detect it, simply touch the top of the gearbox near the coupling; the oscillation effect will be in synchronization with the wobble that you see in the shaft. You'll feel it pushing against your fingers. If you don't see or feel the wobble on the gearbox, and if it only occurs at very low speed, then the amount of runout is not likely to cause harm. But if the oscillation is felt in the fingertips, the wobble must be corrected. Vibration induced by misalignment can wreck the transmission or break a shaft. This becomes increasingly true the larger the boat and shaft.

System Vibration

Some boats are put together in such a way that things will vibrate even if the drive system is in perfect condition. The trick is to know when it's just a matter of loose things making noise, or whether it's caused by excessive vibration. Deck hatch covers are the main offenders. The surveyor needs to learn to make this distinction so that he's not fooled by a noisy boat. There is a very simple method by which to gauge whether vibration at cruise speeds or higher is excessive or damaging. If you can see it or feel it, it's excessive. All boats vibrate to some degree but the limit is reached at about the point where it will either interfere with your vision or creates an unpleasant sensation in your body when standing at or near the struts. If it can be felt up on the flying bridge or forward in the quarters, then it's definitely too much. A good procedure is, if possible, to stand on top of the strut mounts, or as close as possible. I use the technique of lightly setting my teeth together. If I feel a "buzz" in my teeth, the vibration is too much. If I can feel it in my face, it's definitely too much.

Helm Response

A reasonably well-designed boat should track fairly straight at both idle and cruise speed. If you've ever owned a boat that didn't track straight, you know how aggravating and tiring it can be after long periods of fighting the wheel. Tracking should first be checked at idle speeds where things like misaligned trim tabs will affect steering. Boats that wander or snake from side to side are probably suffering from excessive play or misalignment of the rudders. Outboards and stern drives are very prone to this and may be caused by either slack steering or vacillating engine RPM at low speed. If bringing the vessel up to a higher speed doesn't eliminate wandering, the problem is endemic to the steering system.

In order for the vessel to track straight, trim tabs have to be parallel. Start first by retracting the tabs completely. Does it still wander or veer to one side? If so, try to visually check tab extension by looking over the stern. If the tabs are fully retracted, the problem lies elsewhere. If the vessel wanders from side to side, the problem is usually either excessive play in the rudder tie rod, or the rudders are castered, meaning that both, not just one of them is out of alignment.

Veering is usually caused by rudder misalignment. It can also be caused by an asymmetrical hull, a hull bottom that is dirty more on one side than the other, too many protuberances on one side (speedos, transducers, intakes, etc.) or a bent prop that is not functioning as efficiently as the other. If none of these things appears to be the cause, an asymmetrical hull may be suspected. This can usually be corrected by adjusting the rudder castor until the problem disappears.

Oversteering is a problem of displacement hulls and planing hulls at displacement speeds, or of planing hulls that are badly over trimmed down by the bow. For fast cruisers, this condition can only be corrected by shifting weights aft. For displacement hulls, it usually means a steering system, as described earlier, that is improperly mated to the boat and requires too much turning of the wheel to get a response. This is known as excessive turn ratio.

Autopilots

We should never make the mistake of engaging the autopilot in a restricted waterway. If the surveyor is going to test the pilot, it should be done on open water with no traffic nearby. Autopilots can refuse to disengage even when the power switch is cut off. I've had instances where the vessel had to be stopped and the circuit breaker thrown to turn it off. Never trust these gizmos. If it's a two station set up, make sure you know how it operates; if you don't know, ask the owner or captain. When in doubt, get someone else to do it and relieve yourself of the risk.

Because of the way gyros operate, an autopilot has to be tested on opposing, 180° courses. It's not uncommon to find that it works in one direction but not the other. If this happens, it's due to a malfunctioning sensor in the gyro. Most autopilots have a power steering function. Spend some time controlling the boat with it since this is one of the better means of proving out the pilot.

Chapter 17

Appraisal

Surveyors provide appraised values on pre-purchase survey reports because they are needed by banks and insurance companies who loan money and insure the boats soon after they are purchased. About 95% of my clients purchasing boats call me to perform a survey, not an appraisal, which are two entirely different things.

But, given the fact that insurance companies and banks have come to rely on survey reports, we have become stuck with this long standing practice. In essence we are suppling a free service to these businesses that ought to be commissioning their own appraisals, just like they do in their very own real estate business. Never underestimate the ability of these outfits to squeeze a dime from someone else. Leave the appraisal out of your report and you're guaranteed to get two phone calls, one from a bank and the other an insurance company, asking you did not provide them with this free service.

Lately there have been a number of surveyors who have been certified by the American Society of Appraisers and who have raised a lot of questions about marine appraisals. Some have suggested that all surveyors should employ complicated rules and formulae for appraising boats. Some have advanced the notion that all surveyors should have an ASA certification. My view is that we should first understand that there is a world of difference between a survey and an appraisal. When a client calls asking for an appraisal, that is an entirely different function.

The vast majority of surveyors consider appraising the value in the course of a pre-purchase survey to be a secondary function. They do it only because banks and insurance companies request it, yea demand it. The fee we charge is for surveying, not for appraising. I don't see how anyone could perform a proper appraisal in less than a half-day's time, and yet I don't know any surveyor who spends more than an hour or so doing it on a buyer's survey. Very few of my clients ever even ask me about price (they've studied the market so they know what's available at what price better than I), so I consider my appraised value more in terms of providing a reasonable valuation for lenders and insurers and not as the formal practice of appraising the vessel's worth. Given my druthers, I'd just as soon not place a value in my reports. If the client also wants an accurate appraisal, then I would charge an additional fee for the time it will take me to do the research. This almost never happens.

Even so, the surveyor should not just make an educated guess, but must make a reasonable effort to substantiate his appraisal. Fortunately, for most vessels, coming up with a reasonably accurate appraisal is not very difficult.

I suppose that if they had their choice in the matter, surveyors would rather not perform appraisals as a routine function of their surveys. In my own work, I see such a wide range of different types and sizes of vessels that I know that I'm far from the most qualified of people to provide a truly accurate appraisal. One day I survey a replica Mississippi River paddle wheeler, the next a big fisherman. Typical of most surveyors in a given area, we see more of one kind of vessel than another. That can make us experts in one or several classes of vessels, but not many others. In fact, by the time a buyer is finished with his own market search, he is usually far more familiar with the pricing of that particular type of boat than I am. Indeed, I find it quite rare that a client is overpaying. And whenever I think he is, I'm usually told that there's nothing else available on the market. If he want's that particular model, he has to pay the price.

In one respect, that gives the surveyor an advantage. Limited numbers of a particular vessel can make it easier to appraise since the surveyor does not have to wade through large numbers of sales, sort out the extremes, and arrive at an average.

Appraising the Fair Market Value of a boat or yacht is substantially different than most other forms of property for several reasons. The wide variety of vessels and relatively limited production numbers of boats and yachts, more often than not, doesn't provide a sufficiently large market for the surveyor to easily research sales data. Then there's the matter of transportability and geographical influences that render some vessels in a particular area more valuable than others.

The market value of anything is often defined as whatever a willing buyer and seller can agree on. That simply is not the case because it is not reasonable to infer that *whatever* price is paid is the reasonable market price. People can and do overpay for purchases, and that fact alone does not make it worth the price that was paid. That's particularly true when the subject sale is not supported by similar sales. If it is unlikely that that sale can be repeated, then the price that was paid is not a fair market price.

Fair Market Value

In the appraisal business, there are a number of different valuations that can be used. The one that surveyors most often use is the simple Fair Market value. As its name implies, *fair* market means normal market. By definition it excludes extreme or inordinate market factors. Fair market is not an absolute value and is predicated on several factors.

First, it is an estimation by the appraiser of a reasonably anticipated liquid value. It does not take into consideration extreme fluctuations in markets caused by economic conditions such as the Black Friday stock market crash in 1987, or the Arab Oil Embargo of 1973-74, both of which briefly disrupted market conditions. Therefore, fair market is not necessarily the current market, a value which is thrown out during such disruptions because it is believed to be temporary. *During periods of stable markets, FMV and CMV should be the same.*

FMC is not an average class value, nor does it take into consideration extremes such as distress sales. When a bank repossesses a boat and puts it up for sale, it becomes a distress sale and its value will immediately drop, even though it may be in as good a condition as any other vessel. Under these conditions, FMV and CMV will be quite different.

Current Market Value

Current market, of course, is the value at the time the appraisal is being made, taking into account economic conditions. If a client anticipating a purchase were to ask for an appraisal, current market is the appropriate value. The client is interested in the value at the moment, not a value that is adjusted for temporary variances. During the Arab Oil Embargo the prices of gasoline powered boats dropped precipitously because of the uncertainty of gas supplies. Although the market was disrupted for a period of several years, it soon rebounded to ever higher levels. Later, oil shortages and higher oil prices translated into higher plastic resin prices and new boat costs shot up. This immediately caused used boat prices to shoot up also.

Then, in the early 1980's, inflation got out of control, raising new boat prices to unprecedented heights. The demand for used boats reached such a level that many of the most popular used yachts simply weren't available at any price. Extremely high prices were routinely offered and rejected. This was followed by a rise in interest rates that brought the market crashing back down again. Then, following the 1987 Black Friday stock market crash, market prices rose very briefly because a lot of people pulled their money out of the stock market and were seeking a place to put it. Many decided it was a good time to buy a boat and so yacht prices briefly shot up, only to drop back to previous levels.

These are some of the anomalies that can cause serious swings in market prices that the current market value appraiser has to contend with. The point is that the survey needs to apply the appropriate value to the circumstance. *Current market value is the liquid value of the vessel as of the time of appraisal, regardless of what conditions were affecting it.* Obvious, a current market appraisal is valid only for a short period of time. Most end users of appraisals are not likely to understand this so it's always best to find out what the client is looking for. In normal times it won't make any difference, but in distressed times it will.

The surveyor needs to decide which value he's going to use. In attempting to appraise current market value, his difficulty will be how to arrive at a number. Neither appraisal guides nor current asking prices are likely to reflect current conditions. Asking prices usually do not begin to reflect an economic downturn until well into a recession, so these are usually of little help. Thus, the value most surveyors use is Fair Market Value.

Insurance companies are generally content with the Fair Market Value. They're not particularly interested in brief swings of market pricing. The underwriter's objective is to determine what the vessel is worth under normal market conditions. That's generally the case for a lending institutions as well. However, I would suggest that since a pre-purchase survey is performed for the purchasing client, the surveyor should stick to using Fair Market Value.

Oddballs and Custom Yachts

Without doubt, custom built and particularly unusual boats are the most difficult to appraise. Especially those that are most radical in their design or construction. For the vast majority of boat owners, resale value is an extremely important consideration. Not many people are willing to pay a half million or a million dollars for something that is likely to loose half its value shortly after taking delivery. Yet that is precisely what happens with a lot of custom built boats. Name recognition and reputation play a very important role in determining resale value, and when one, the other or both are missing from the equation, resale values plummet. John Rybovich was a builder of custom boats, few of which were alike. But the quality and superb design of his yachts created a reputation that no one has yet to equal. Who isn't familiar with the Rybovich name? It's world famous. Because of that, resale of his used boats commanded top dollar, even when those wooden boats were 20-30 years old.

Few custom builders are that fortunate. But then few custom builders are as dedicated to quality as Mr. Rybovich was. Quality and reputation are the key factors in determining the value of limited production or custom yachts. One of the most difficult things a surveyor has to contend with is the client who owns a relatively obscure custom built vessel. Though he may have paid an extraordinary amount of money for it, chances are that its value will decline precipitously.

Design also plays an important role in resale value. Except perhaps for the art world, most markets don't take kindly to designs that widely vary from the normally acceptable. This is particularly true with yachts. Unusually trendy or far out designs have never done well in the resale market, regardless of reputation or quality. They are perceived as being risky - as indeed they are - precisely because they're out of the mainstream and not widely accepted. Rich people don't get rich by throwing their money away; astute buyers stay away from the extremes. That's why production builders also stay away from design extremes, preferring to head in a new design direction only after the market shows signs of acceptance.

A good example of this is some of the trendy designs that came out of Europe beginning in the early 1980's. Typically referred to as the "Mediterranean" style, many of these designs were not only radical, but also very impractical. Yachts shaped like Buck Roger's space ship, the ones that look like floating missile, enticed some of the uninitiated, but experienced yachtsmen took one look at them and immediately recognized their impracticality. What's important from the appraisal standpoint is that so many of these creations lost half their value or more within the first two years. Within five years they were worth only a third or a quarter of original cost. Many had a hard time finding buyers at any price. With a purchase like this, one could hardly do worse in the stock market.

Comparables

The primary method of appraising unusual or custom boats is to assemble a list of comparables. A suitable comparable is any vessel with basically the same characteristics, including style, size, power, quality, equipment and general level of market acceptance. The Internet has truly revolutionized the appraisal process because now huge numbers of boats for sale are almost immediately available to research. This gives the surveyor a much larger base to work from. Whereas I used to have to buy magazines and specialty rags frequently to gain access to ads, now I can just go to the many listing services and pull up dozens of listings for just about any production boat. Or, rather easily find numerous comparables for one-of-a-kind boats.

If you're wondering how one can use asking prices as research for appraisals, the answer is as follows. Brokers generally try to hold asking prices to within 15% of what they think the vessel will bring on the market. Any more than this the broker knows he's wasting his advertising dollars and is not likely to place a photo ad of a client's vessel who is asking way too much. The experienced surveyor, of course, should at least have a general idea of what the subject vessel is worth and is usually capable of recognizing prices that are out of line. He then throws these out. The remainder ones he simply adjusts by 15% or so and that should bring the price fairly close to where it ought to be.

The next adjustment factor involves engines and equipment. In each case of a comparable, the listing needs to be evaluated as to the extent of equipage and the effect and desirability of engine power. One listing may show "low hours," another "recent overhauls," while yet another says nothing about the engines. Obviously, one would need to value weight each of these differently, along with anything else that can be gleaned from the listing.

With only a half-dozen comparables to look at, it becomes fairly easy to "bracket" the price. If still in doubt, the surveyor can always call on several brokers who deal in that class and get their opinions.

Appraisal Guides

The great problem with appraisal guides is that people use them as God's honest truth, picking the price straight out of the columns of numbers without ever bothering to read that part in the front of the book that tells them how to use it. Books will not give you either FMV or CMV but terms like "retail" "wholesale," "trade-in." Some of these books give you a "wholesale" value, as if there really were a wholesale market for yachts. Have you ever seen a wholesale boat market? I haven't.

We're also left to wonder what the heck they mean by retail? That term has to do with pricing relationships between manufacturers, wholesalers and dealers. I haven't seen too many used boats, short of little outboards, being sold by dealers. Therefore, there is no such thing as wholesale and retail markets for used boats, since most sales are between owner and buyer.

So right off the bat we are presented with good reason to be suspicious of books. Some of these are also publishers of automotive books, so it looks like they simply and unthinkingly carried over their practices with cars to boats.

For one thing, we might ask ourselves where did the publishers of these guides get these numbers? Do they go out and survey the market for the sales of tens thousands of different models of boats? Not likely; they'd need the resources of General Motors to do that. The fact is, most of these guides arrive at these numbers by means of a computer model involving declining balance depreciation methods. It's a fairly simple task to survey the market for the most popular types of vessels, determine as a percentage how much value each type or manufacturer's models tend to loose over a certain span of years, and then to apply those percentages across the board.

In order to prove them out, I've done just exactly that. You can save yourself the cost of the book if you can learn to apply their methods. All you've got to do is to determine what the original cost was and then work backward. Take some of the most popular models of any popular boat and see how much they lost each year. You'll come up with an annual depreciation rate similar to 18, 10, 7, 5,5,5, 3. The average mid sized fiberglass motor boat or yacht loses about 50% of its original cost in five years.[1] Slightly larger boats will stretch out to seven years. Higher quality boats will depreciate less, lower quality more. The first year's depreciation will be less for higher quality and greater demand vessels, lower for low quality or less popular vessels. Then you adjust for condition, equipment and whatever other market factors influence your region.

The problem with books is that they tend to set the market rather than being a reflection of it. This is particularly true for boats under $150,000, but once the value exceeds this, the depreciation method becomes less reliable. Small boat buyers are very prone to relying on books, which is very unfortunate because in that case the book is setting the prices.

My experience is that buyers of vessels over $200,000.00, being a bit more savvy, rarely ever consider books. With larger and more expensive boats, it is the market that sets the price, and like the stock market, it is not always reasonable or logical. The important point about the larger boat market is that there are always fewer of any given model than for smaller boats. This, plus the fact that it tends toward a national or even international market which is small and every one, especially brokers, know about every boat currently for sale, as well as recent sales. Especially with the Internet, within an hour's time anyone can know about every boat currently on the market.

If you really want to know what the market value is, books may be okay for Plain Jane, average run-of-the-mill high production model boats, but they're less likely to be accurate in proportion to overall quality and value, regardless of size. When market conditions change significantly is when books go completely off the mark simply because depreciation methods cannot take into account changing market factors. This is why books are so often off the mark.

Determining Original Cost

It is usually a lot easier to determine the market value than the original price of the vessel. Factory list prices are often greatly inflated and usually need to be adjusted downward toward reality. It's usually not as bad as with vehicles, but the same game is still played. No one ever pays list unless he's got a trade-in. Frankly, there's really no way of knowing how much dealers discount list prices because discounts will vary from a lot to nothing, depending on demand and market conditions. Dealer discounts are a closely guarded secret. Moreover, there's an awful lot of hanky-panky going on over sale prices. Invoice prices are not always to be believed. Some dealers engage in the practice of creative paperwork so as to relieve the customer of making a down payment. Typically, builders set prices at double cost, yet there's no hard and fast rule on this because it varies widely with the value of the boat.

Dealer markups run the gamut, from 10% to 50%. Or whatever they can get. When it comes to larger boats, because carrying costs are so high, it's rare to see substantial variations between dealers. There is always the exception to the rule, and one recent instance I'm familiar with involved two 45 footers where, in nearly back-to-back sales, the same dealer got $300,000 more for one than the other. The boats were identical.

Big ticket items like Bertram, Hatteras and Viking take a long time to build and don't spend much time in inventory so that discounts are minimal. As a general rule, the lower the production volume, the less the discount, or even more likely no discount at all. The higher production builders jam their dealers with floor plan, thus forcing them to deal to clear inventory. Here's where discounts are the norm and likely to be substantial.

One way to cut through all the confusion is to assume that all of the factory and customer add-ons will equal the amount of any dealer discounts. This lets us take the advertised list and use it as-is with no adjustment at all, and still feel pretty safe that we've got about the right price. In other words, if you use list, don't add on extra equipment.

It seems that in recent years we're beginning to be relieved of these problems as builders increasing decline to publish list prices. I've encountered situations in which the only way I thought I could get the list price was by asking a dealer. But when the dealer declined to give me an answer, I was in a real quandary. What to do? I resolved the problem by simply telling the truth: Dealer does not publish list price, which is therefore not available.

Extra Equipment

The surveyor has to determine for himself what amount of extra equipment constitutes the "average" for each class of vessel. Once you get a feel for what is "average," this saves a lot of time in the appraisal process. I do this for every type of boat that I deal with so that I don't have to fool around with toting up extra equipment prices, which can be very time-consuming.

Factory add-ons, as we know, can be quite expensive and can greatly influence prices. A good example of this are the molded fiberglass seating modules found on express style cruisers. I was recently amazed to discover that a pair of them for a particular boat cost $6,000.00. Aside from the obvious such as generators and air conditioning, other big ticket items can include fiberglass bridge seating modules, boat davits, tenders, radar arches, bow pulpits, bar modules, outriggers, fighting chairs and bait and tackle centers for sport fishermen, some of which can be wildly expensive. And, of course, the biggest ticket item of all are towers on sport fishermen. As an example, take a look at the cost of major

Tower	$32,000.00
Tackle Center	10,000.00
Fighting Chair	6,500.00
Outriggers	6,000.00
Pulpit & Windlass	7,500.00
Tender Davit	8,000.00
Tender	15,000.00
Wet Bar	3,500.00
Triple Controls	4,500.00
Electronics Package	35,000.00
Total	$128,000.00

add-ons on a 50' sport fisherman.

There's $128,000.00 without even considering the smaller items. With a base price of one million, add-ons can easily add up to 15% of the base price. If you want a really accurate price, it's always a good idea to tote up the estimated cost of add-ons when figuring original cost. If the equipage is not out of the ordinary, one doesn't have to do it because the original base is figured at advertised list.

Figuring add-ons in the determination of Fair Market Value generally works more in the negative than the positive. More often a boat lacks the basic average rather than has more than the average. We should note, however, that the lack of equipment does more to detract from value than an abundance of equipment adds to value. Most yachts over 40 feet seem to have a remarkable similarity in their state of equipage. Buyers don't so much notice it when it's there, but they do notice when it's not. On a fairly late model boat, I figure in excess equipment at half the installed value or less; beyond five years of age, even less. But if it lacks major items of equipment - say it should have radar, and the client wants it - then the client will be thinking in terms of how much it will cost to install it. Then he will key his negotiations accordingly. For that reason, I figure in equipment deficiencies at roughly their list price. Why the purchase price and not the installed price? Because he will never get that much of a reduction and omitting the installation cost accounts for part, but usually not all of this. At least I'm going to be close.

Learning Equipment

Costs The novice surveyor might be wondering how in the world does one ever manage to learn all these equipment prices? Surely it requires an incredible amount of research to find out. Yes, it does, but fortunately one does it over time. Since I used to routinely handle insurance claims, I know pricing backwards and forwards. Baring that, the next best way is to start collecting equipment catalogues. Get on the mailing lists of equipment retailers such as West Marine, E&B and Boat US, go around to boat shows and collect brochures, but don't bother with the ones that don't have pricing. They're useless. Above all things, catalogues of major ticket items is needed. Get catalogues from people like MarQuipt, Galley Maid, Ideal, Furuno, Murray Brothers and Pompanette. Collect builder's brochures, being sure to ask for price lists. I've got Hatteras, Bertram and Viking brochures for almost every year going back 20 years and can tell you what they charged for a bait freezer or bow pulpit in 1976. I have a whole file cabinet full of this stuff and when I need it, it's there. Even though stuff is 5 years old, it's easy enough to adjust the price forward a bit. Wholesaler parts and equipment catalogues are extremely difficult to obtain but when you get one, it's as good as gold. There's nothing more useful than a copy of your regional marine distributor's catalogue. I usually have to beg and plead just to get their worn out copy from last, but I get it and couldn't function without it.

Repair Costs

The instructions for use in some appraisal guides state that to determine market value, the actual cost of repairs should be deducted from the price indicated. While that may work for late model vessels, it surely doesn't work for older vessels. The problem with making direct repair cost deductions is that, first of all, deals are rarely negotiated this way. Secondly, it must be remembered that used boat prices generally reflect the depreciated condition of the vessel. Very few boats are perfectly maintained so that some degree of disrepair is inevitable and much of that is reflected in the price. Thirdly, how does one arrive at a fair cost of repair? Are we talking about the prices of a mobile repair service or upscale yacht yard? Whatever it is, both sides are likely to disagree.

As a rule of thumb, deduction of the full cost to repair defects will work for late model vessels, meaning four years or less. That's because buyers of late model boats don't expect there to be any serious problems and they will usually drive a hard bargain in that respect. For older vessels, most negotiated adjustments work out at about 50% of actual repair costs and that's what I will use for boats five years and older. By the time the age reaches 15-20 years, average negotiated adjustments will drop to as low as 25%. This is because the sale price declines with age, and were one to make full price deductions for all deficiencies, one could easily end up with a calculated value of zero.

Geographical Considerations

In the past, regional variations in used boat prices was quite substantial. Today, as shipping costs have declined and people are more prone to travel, values throughout the eastern U.S. have pretty much leveled off. However, there are always certain models that become very popular in a particular area, but not others, so substantial variations with some boats will always exist. There remains substantial. A good example of this are sport fishermen in the Great Lakes

Boats that are ill-suited for a particular region are likely to command lower prices than in regions where they are particularly well-suited or popular. The smaller or less costly the vessel, the more true this will be. By the time vessels reach a price of $100,000 or more, regional influences begin to decline somewhat. This is because buyers or smaller boats generally limit their search to their home region. It doesn't make much sense to spend a lot of extra money both searching for, and transporting a purchase long distances. The larger the vessel, the fewer there are of them, and the farther buyers will go to find them; the cost of the search and transport becomes less significant.

An example would be a boat with European design for the cold climates of northern Europe in Florida where totally closed-in boats are ill-suited for the climate. Or very deep draft boats in regions with very shallow waters. Examples such as this can be very hard to sell when geographically mislocated.

One way to handle such price adjustments is to figure the cost to sell and transport the vessel out of the region to one that is more favorable. For example, I get an unusually large number of clients from the Pacific Northwest and you have to wonder why would they come all the way to Florida to buy a boat. The answer is simple: they come here to purchase cold climate or deep draft vessels that are located in, but very hard to sell in Florida. In order to sell them, they have to be deeply discounted. Further, the California region has long had a shortage of used boats, which accounts for why prices there are higher. Thus, it becomes worth their efforts as long as the price is right. If the cost to find the boat, plus the cost to transport it home are equal to, or less than, the market value in the client's home region, then he's got a deal.

This leads to the question of what region is the market value derived? Say a client from Seattle is buying a yacht in Hilton Head, South Carolina. Does the surveyor appraise the yacht for what it would be worth in Seattle? No, the point of origin for the appraisal is the market in which it is surveyed. It is not appropriate for a surveyor to attempt to appraise a vessel for market with which he is not familiar. *The appraised value should be for the market region in which the vessel is currently being sold.*

Remember pass-on surveys and what was said in previous chapters about how surveys are used by others besides the client in making business decisions? As long as the surveyor is supplying an appraisal with his survey, his responsibility for the accuracy of that appraisal may go beyond the responsibility to the client. An appraisal of Fair Market Value is derived from the condition of the vessel at the time it is appraised, in the region it is located. It is unethical, and probably fraudulent to use any other criteria.

Contingency Values

Here's an example of a contingency value: *This vessel will be worth $225,000.00 after all the problems are fixed.* That's a direct quote from an actual survey report, and the sort of thing that has been showing up in survey reports with increasing frequency. What's wrong with that is that the surveyor is obviously and intentionally avoiding the issue of what the vessel is worth *now*. It is fraudulent to suggest what a value might be at some future time, predicated on the assumption that defects will be repaired. That is not an appraisal, but a prediction, the sort of thing that must be scrupulously avoided. Worst of all, it's so very transparent what the surveyor is trying to do. The ultimate effect of that is to not only call into question the surveyor's ethics, but to cast doubt on the validity of the entire report.

Explanations

There are many occasions when the surveyor is going to have great difficulty in arriving at a fair market value. Sometimes it is simply not possible to place the value very closely. There is nothing wrong with providing explanations for situations involving a great deal of uncertainty. If one can't place the value accurately, it's far better to say so than to assign a number that suggests that it is accurate. Further, it's a good idea to spell out any unusual factors that may influence market value, or unusual factors within the market itself. A good example would be for a boat selling at a greatly reduced price in a remote location. In once instance I had to provide a lengthy explanation for why a yacht that I had surveyed in Guam was selling for less than half the price it should have fetched. The reason, of course, was the extremely high shipping cost to get it out of Guam. There was no one on the island that wanted to buy it so it had to go back to the continent.

Here was a case where an explanation was necessary. The yacht had a low value in one place but would have a much higher value in other places. Without providing a thorough explanation, a bank or insurance company would likely have difficulty with your numbers. Obviously, the appraisal has to be as is, where is, yet the yacht is likely to be moved soon. I stress the word "likely," because if the yacht is not moved, its value will not change. Were the surveyor to make the assumption that it will be moved, say to California, and appraise it at California prices, he could find himself misrepresenting the value should the vessel not be moved. An explanation giving both values neatly solves the problem.

[1] The original price must include extra equipment add-ons calculated at 10-15% of the base purchase price, and depending on whether there are particularly expensive builder add-ons.

Chapter 18

Reporting

Writing reports is the Achilles"s heel of most surveyors, and few are able to do it well. Make no mistake about it, writing good reports is just plain difficult, a skill that very few people in any profession learn to do well. While some people seem to believe that good writers are born with this particular talent, every good writer will tell you that that is not true. Good writers learn to write well through years of painstaking effort and the study of what constitutes good writing.

Taking the time to write a good report never seems quite so important until one comes across an example of a bad report. Understandably, writers tend to be less critical of their own work than that of others; it's less easy to critique yourself. The writing of survey reports is every bit as important as the physical work of surveying the vessel because the report is the memorialized record of the surveyor's work. It's the document of fact that will be used by the client, as well as others, to make important financial decisions. Not only is it important that the information contained therein be factual and accurate, but it should also be borne in mind that the surveyor's presentation constitutes a direct reflection on his professionalism. In the course of concluding a sale on a vessel a number of people will see and read that report and the surveyor's work will be judged accordingly. To understand the full import of a poorly written report, merely observe your own reaction to one. People rarely notice well-written reports, but a poorly written one always attracts immediate attention. For this reason alone, taking the time to learn to write a good report is well worth the effort.

However, there is an even better reason to learn the art of good reporting: to protect yourself and your client. One of the most important parts of the surveyor's work is to make sure that the client understands the results of the survey. The failure to effectively communicate all necessary information to the client is a failure in performing the service being rendered. From my own experience, I will hazard a guess here that more surveyors get in trouble based on ineffective reporting rather than through any failure in the physical performance of the survey.

Fundamentals

The basic elements of a good report are related to conveying all necessary information in a clear, orderly and concise manner. The purpose of the report is to convey the results of the survey, and as long as the surveyor stays within these boundaries, he'll have a much easier time of it. A good survey report is one which paints as accurate a picture of the vessel as possible, within the limits of the service provided. That means not straying into nonrelevant areas such as methods of making repairs or giving advice. If you're uncertain about what a report should contain, it is suggested that you should spend some time thinking about, and perhaps mapping out, exactly what information you want to convey to the client.

It should be emphasized that what the surveyor doesn't say can be just as important as what he does say. Acts of omission are as important as acts of commission. In preparing his report, the surveyor needs to give as much attention to what he cannot see, survey or test. The surveyor needs to be aware that if he does not put it in writing, for all practical purposes he did not inform the client. Many surveyors have made the mistake of only giving a verbal advice to a client about a condition, without including it in the report, only to have the client come back and say, "You never told me." When a surveyor does this, he is trapped because he cannot prove that he ever told his client.

Tone

A survey report is not a personal document but a professional report that is likely to be seen and read by more than one person. Because of this, survey reports should not be written in the first person or in a personal tone. Nor should they be addressed to a particular person, as in the form of a letter. The style should always be in the third person and the use of personal pronouns *I*, *you*, *we* be avoided as much as possible. The overall tone of the report should be as neutral as possible, and not engage in personal criticism or endorsement in any way.

Learning to Write

If you were to collect a couple dozen survey reports and compare them, it would quickly become apparent why there are so many badly written reports. The reason is simply that surveyors copy each other, particularly beginners. Thus, the bad form and habits are passed on and on. If a surveyor is not already trained in business, scholarly or technical writing, it is not wise to collect other surveyor's reports and imitate them as a means of learning. Many surveyors poses very poor writing skills and there's no point in mimicking their mistakes. It is far better to either get a good book on technical writing or collect some good examples of good reports, scholarly essays such as research or investigation reports written by professional writers (Many examples of professional reporting can be found on the Internet). A good book on basic style is a valuable addition to any surveyor's library.[1] For most people, learning the art of impersonal dissertation is difficult because we're conditioned to speaking in the first person. Obtaining a few good examples and constantly referring to them is the easiest way to learn the art of impersonal narrative.

Writing Style

Having sat on the membership committee of the National Association of Marine Surveyors for many years, I have had the opportunity to read hundreds of survey reports, most of which demonstrated two shortcomings: poor writing skills and the failure to describe conditions or situations coherently and completely. Technical writing is usually acknowledged as the most difficult of all writing skills. Those who learn to do it well do so by long years of thoughtful practice. The novice surveyor should take heart that nobody is born knowing how to write well.

From my own painful experiences, I know only too well how embarrassing or costly poorly written reports can be. It only takes one poorly worded sentence to give the impression that a very expensive problem is no big deal, and to inadvertently lead the client astray. Learning to express yourself in writing benefits not only the client but yourself; when a client has a few hundred thousand dollars at stake, a poorly written report could cost both of you. Several good examples of bad writing are given toward the end of this chapter.

What style you choose, be it technical and formal, or casual and colloquial, is a matter of preference. From the client's standpoint, a report that is rigidly technical and overly formal may not read well or be well understood. Personally, I prefer a more casual approach, avoiding excessive or archaic nautical terminology whenever possible. The objective is to make sure that the client understands what is being said. That is not to suggest that a report should be written like a landlubber, with phrases such as " . . . on the left side near the back of the boat." And if your style is too nautical or technical, chances are the client won't understand. Furthermore, if you write more like you speak, the chances are that you will express yourself well. Probably the best way to achieve this is to think your sentences through as though you had the client in front of you and were explaining to him in your everyday language, albeit cleaned up a bit.

There is a difference between casual and personal styles. Personal style uses the personal pronouns *I, you, we* and is generally not considered professional and therefore should be avoided. Instead, impersonal style should be used; an example is the next sentence which uses *It is meant* instead of *I mean*. By casual it is meant that it lacks the rigidity of formal writing. A casual style is one in which the writer writes similar to the way he speaks, although this should not be carried so far that it begins to affect the appearance of professionalism. The casualness extends only so far as to make technical writing readable, not friendly and personal.

Adequate Time

As with the performance of the survey, if the surveyor allows himself to be rushed in the preparation of his report, he's likely to make mistakes and omit important information. Both clients and brokers usually push the surveyor hard to produce his report quickly. If you succumb to this pressure, beware that it could cost you dearly.

Unfortunately, there will be many occasions when the surveyor cannot avoid rushing his report. Whenever you do so, it is imperative that you proof read it in order to avoid glaring errors.

Format

A well written report follows a logical format starting with an introduction, and moving into a general discription or specifications. This can be done by the use of a form, but using a form to constitute the entire body of the report is poor practice because a form conveys information as though it were a bill of materials and tells precious little about what is really there. The use of a form should not be used as a means of avoiding taking the time to write a comprehensive narrative, otherwise it will become obvious that that was the point. Undoubtedly, the best reports are written by those who take the time to write a mainly narrative report, for which there are no other means of taking a shortcut except by omitting information.

Remember that the purpose of the report is to convey information that is relevant to the client's needs, not to fill up so many pages of paper or to create what looks like a sales brochure.

Introductions

Every report should start off with an introduction that includes who, what, where, when and why. The intro may also contain descriptions of the circumstances under which the survey was conducted. Were we to review a hundred survey reports, we would probably find that close to half of them don't even bother to state the purpose for which the survey was conducted or who commissioned it. The lack of such pertinent information immediately casts doubt on the purpose of the survey and its legitimacy.

The introduction is also a good place to bring to the attention of the reader any important limitations that affect the outcome of the survey, such as bad weather. Many surveyors like to bury these things in the disclaimer at the end of the report, but that's hardly a good idea. If limiting conditions that are not your fault limit the thoroughness of the survey, there's no good reason not to inform the client at the outset of the report where the point is gotten across in no uncertain terms.

Specifications

Once again, if we take a sample of one hundred reports, we are very likely to find an excessive, even extreme, overemphasis on listing specifications and superfluous detail. If the surveyor's purpose is to serve the client, he is hardly accomplishing that by providing a ream of paper containing information in which the client has no interest. When considering what information to include in the specifications, we need to ask ourselves what information is really necessary.

For example, if the yacht already has an owner's manual containing detailed specifications, is it necessary to duplicate that information? Most end users of survey reports would actually be quite grateful if surveyors would desist from loading reports up with useless information. Ultimately, a good report is one that has struck the right balance of what is necessary. Although some reports will contain this information, it is not the purpose of the survey to describe the sum total of everything that went into the construction and equipage of the vessel. There are currently several computer programs for survey reports being sold that will generate a 50 page report for a 30 foot boat. Perhaps one in a hundred persons want this sort of thing but most regard it as an annoyance.

The objective of these things seems to be to try to impress with the volume of paper produced rather than the substance of the report.

My view is that it is not necessary to provide any more than the most basic information that is commonly found in the most professional surveyors' reports. If you use a form, remember that its primary purpose is to guide the surveyor through the survey, to avoid overlooking critical areas, as well as to record important data. Keep in mind that the purpose of a pre purchase survey is to assess condition; the theme of the report should reflect that purpose.

Critical Components and Systems

The primary exception to the above statements are those systems and components that are highly relevant to the safety, condition and economic considerations of the vessel. An example of this would be an exhaust system with water jacketed risers that could leak and damage the engines. Would it be important for the client to be aware of this? Of course, and it would be equally important to know that it had good risers that prevent this danger. Or how about gate valves in place of marine sea cocks?

Very often I use a blanket statement to inform the client that all systems utilized good quality marine materials rather than wasting my time by making an exhaustive description. No one needs the itemization and you can avoid typing three pages of detail by simply stating that all systems are of good quality "except" . . . and then go on to itemize only those that are substandard or exceptional. However, if you use this abbreviated method, beware that you must make the statement that everything is, or is not, up to par. One way or another, the surveyor does have the obligation to inform the client about substandard conditions. If nothing is said, it leaves the impression that various systems were not inspected, particularly if he doesn't use a form.

Inventories

As with specifications, detailed lists of equipment and inventories are often carried to extremes. Yachts up for sale may have all the owner's personal materials taken off, or the yacht may still be in use and just loaded with the owner's personal stuff. Arguments often ensue between buyer and seller because the seller intends to remove a valuable piece of equipment while the broker unfortunately included the item on the listing. A common example is an expensive ship's clock and barometer that was given the owner as a gift. This is one reason to make a thorough inventory of important equipment.

On the other hand, a 50 foot yacht could generate a multi page list so that the surveyor has to draw the line at some point. Obviously, all major items of equipment will be included in the inventory, including the basic equipment necessary for the operation of the vessel. Things such as power cords, anchors, rodes, fenders and weather covers can add up to substantial amounts of money. If such items are needed, but lacking, the client should be made aware of this.

One way to develop a criteria for cutting long lists short when there is an excess of material to deal with is to set a minimum dollar value. For example, a larger yacht may have three or four car stereo/cassette tape units worth $150.00 each. Such inexpensive items are hardly worth itemizing on a million dollar yacht and can actually look silly in the report. I usually set a cut off point of three to four hundred dollars for nonessential items. Remember that the taking of inventories is not the main purpose of the survey.

Good Descriptions

One of the more egregious shortcomings of survey reports is the failure to provide adequate descriptions of defects. This can range from poorly described conditions to failure to provide the location, size or scope of the items being discussed. At all times the writer must remember that the reader, including the client, may have no familiarity of the point being discussed, so unless the writer describes the point fully, the reader may be left in the dark.

Excessive verbiage is just as problematic as excessive brevity. Indeed, too much description can be just as confusing as too little. It is best to seek the right economy of words to make our point fully understood. With too much or too little, the element of professional writing is lost.

The first point of good description is to describe the point completely, especially faults and defects. It is not enough, for example, to state *"There is a scratch on the starboard side of the hull."* The reader will wonder where it is located, how long and how deep it is. Lacking any further details, the reader doesn't know if the scratch is the size of a hair or a deep gouge extending the length of the hull. If a defect or damage is the result of a specific cause such as *"The starboard rub rail is falling off becase the deck to hull join is coming loose,"* we should make it a point to describe that cause fully. To just say, *The starboard rub rail has come loose* is not enough. To fail to describe the cause may also be a failure in reporting and is more serious than just bad writing. Notice how with that simple statement, both the cause and effect are given without a lengthy explanation. In this case, the cause is even more important than the effect. However, if the cause is not known, then that should also be stated. It is very easy to make omissions when we are in a hurry, so it's important to pay close attention to these details.

The second point of good description is to describe the location of the thing being discussed. The surveyor should always be aware that the client may have no idea of the location of the point in question. Describing such things as wiring faults can be particularly difficult, but the easiest way to deal with complexity is to locate the point relative to a prominent feature. Example: *The wire in the bundle of wires immediately beneath the port engine fuel filter.* In this way, the point is succinctly described in one short sentence that anyone could easily find. *A two foot-long gouge that is up to 1/8" deep and 1/2" wide is located 20" down from the second port hole aft on the starboard hull side,* is yet another example of how to locate a point with an economy of words.

Note in the above example, the subject comes first: *"The gouge is located . . ."* not *"located 20" down from the second port hole aft on the starboard side . . ."* Introduce the subject first so that the reader doesn't have to wade through the entire paragraph to find the subject of discussion.

I've heard lawyers say over and over again at marine seminars, "err on the side of verbosity." That's good advice up to a point. That point is exceeded when more is said than needed, especially when you start giving advice or engage in mere speculation. So how do you know when you've said enough? Well, by imagining explaining the situation to someone who hasn't seen it, or isn't knowledgeable about the thing being discussed. Obviously, that means that you need to know something about your client's yachting experience. One should take more time writing a report for a first time boat buyer than with an old salt. Again, think in terms of actually explaining it in person.

A good example of a tricky situation is when the cause of a condition could not be discovered, as when the surveyor suspects something is wrong but cannot actually prove it. Instead of speculating, we can launch into a discussion of potential causes and effects, a strategy that avoids speculation by providing the client with a summary of the surveyor's knowledge or experience on the point. But when erring on the side of verbosity, we need to be careful that we can substantiate what we say. It's not speculation to advise of *potential* cause and effect so long as it is well-founded. Short of that, it may be wise to advise the client that full analysis of the condition is outside the scope of the survey.

Terminology

Many surveyors seem to be unaware of how poorly the imprecise use of terms reflects on their competence and professionalism. Indeed, the misuse of terms and poor expression of ideas is rampant among the works of surveyors.

Erroneous or inaccurately worded expressions have a way of coming into common usage because novice surveyors try to learn how to write reports by imitating what they see in other reports, thereby copying and promoting the use of bad language. The following is a short list of some of the inappropriate and common clichés to avoid:

- **Good Marine Practice** Literally hundreds of surveyors use this term to describe how repairs should be made, yet there is no such standard for repairs. The term is meaningless.

- **Repair and Prove in Order** This is yet another nearly meaningless phrase that might as well not be said. It's a statement of the obvious and appears trite to anyone who reads it.

- **Poor, Bad, Improper** These general adjectives are nonspecific and should only be used when followed by a description of what constitutes poor, bad or improper. The obvious question is "according to whom?" Reading between the lines of many reports that use such vague terminology, it is apparent that surveyors are not comfortable with their own authority. If a fault is not attributable to a standard, they resort to vagueness, apparently not realizing how transparent their lack of imprecision is. If something is not right, describe why it's not right. Avoid looking ignorant by falling back on shopworn clichés.

- **Certified, Approved** These are the two most misused words in the surveyor's lexicon, misused because he fails to indicate by whom the certification or approval is, or should be given. In fact, there is no organization that certifies marine hardware or equipment. The closest there is the U.L. designation "listed."

- **Appears** Here's another abused and misused word. It's a word that contains a strong context of uncertainty, a word that should be used sparingly lest the reader find the whole report an exercise in uncertainty. There are times when it is appropriate and times when it is not. Be careful to use it judiciously.

- **Adequate** Another general adjective that is often used in place of taking the time to research specific facts, as in "The anchor should be fitted with a rode of adequate length." Adequate for what, or according to whom?

- **Prove in Order** Used in conjunction with repair recommendations, this is another vague cliché that lacks specificity.

- **Proper, Properly**   These are nonspecific adjectives. It's no help to the reader to say something is improper without telling what improper means because he probably doesn't know. According to whom and why?

Descriptive Adjectives

The use of inappropriate or just plain incorrect adjectives is also rampant amongst surveyors and goes a long way toward giving the whole profession a bad impression. Hurried reporting is partly to blame for a lot of this, but the problem is that surveyors, like everyone else, become creatures of habit, thus habitually using the same bad language over and over. An interesting feature about bad writing is that the writer rarely notices it in his own work, yet it becomes painfully obvious to everyone else. Here's a few examples taken from reports of surveyors who should know better:

- The vessel has "ample fire extinguishing equipment." Ample?

- "All cell fluid levels were found to be adequate."

- "The propellers appear to be sound at this time."

- "The vessel is found to be basically sound." The report then listed forty items of major defects.

- "A hull potential and bonding system continuity inspection of all accessible through hull fittings, where accessible, was conducted if the vessel was inspected at rest in salt water."

- ". . . the plastic vent housings were cracked and compromised."

- "Several bare wires were twisted under the helm, accessed through the starboard hatch, inboard, and then down through the centrally located hole."

- "Have a qualified marine technician determine function, restore, proving operational and safe."

- "Repair in proper marine fashion."

- "About the bases of all exterior teak trim pieces, a slopped area of 2 to 3" of teak sealer was noted on the fiberglass surrounding same."

Each of the above quotes is an example of truly horrible language that unfortunately is very common. Language like this speaks for itself, but the reason it occurs is because the surveyor is either trying to imitate someone else, or he is trying to be fancy. All he has really done is to succeed in making a fool of himself by proving that he can't write a good report. We shouldn't forget that the report is the only evidence of our work that most clients will ever see, and the first impression is usually a lasting impression.

If you're a novice surveyor, make sure that you are not copying someone else's mistakes. If you're a seasoned surveyor, remember that we all need to take a few hours from time to time to review our work and sort out those mistakes that inevitably become habitual. Pull a few reports and take the time to perform a full edit on them. That way you'll remember not to make the same mistakes in the future.

Statements of Omission

That which can't be seen, tested or known is as important as those aspects of a vessel that can be physically surveyed. The most frequent examples of this are those portions of the internal hull which are not visibly accessible and therefore cannot be surveyed. Every surveyor should make it rote practice to describe in the report all such areas that cannot be seen. Many surveyors include a disclaimer that says that there are areas within the hull that cannot be seen without taking the boat apart, yet does not describe them. A better practice is to actually take the time to describe those areas in the body of the report, rather than in a disclaimer. Just making the statement that there are inaccessible areas is not telling the client much.

The typical disclaimer not only does not describe what areas and how large they are, but they do not give any indication as to the significance of this fact. Consider, for example, that many boats built these days have inner liners that conceal 70-80% of the internal hull. To merely say that "some areas are inaccessible" is not merely inaccurate, but disingenuous. The surveyor should at least describe what percentage is inaccessible, where those areas are located, and what significance this might have on the overall survey. I'll often make a simple listing like this:

- Hull sides in forward quarters have non-removable liners which prohibited inspection.

- Areas beneath and outboard of fuel tanks could not be inspected.

- Hull bottom below master stateroom was not accessible and was not inspected.

- Area beneath galley sole was not accessible and was not inspected.

- There are mufflers located outboard of the fuel tanks and which could not be accessed for inspection. The exhaust system in this area cannot be inspected or serviced without cutting a section of the deck out.

Very often we are unable to test certain equipment. Watermakers, for example, shouldn't be tested in muddy or polluted waters because operation will immediately clog the membranes and you may be held responsible for that. Sometimes we simply don't know how to operate certain equipment and there is no one available who does. We shouldn't be embarrassed to admit our ignorance. When it comes to electronics, there's a lot we don't know. Failure to state in writing that certain equipment was not tested leaves us wide open to negligence claims.

Boats built with new technology and materials can really put a surveyor in a tough spot. If you know anything about research and development in marine construction, you know that there isn't much. An awful lot of materials testing gets done at the boat buyer's expense and you don't want to get caught in the middle of a dispute between owner and builder. The fact is that no surveyor, no matter how skilled, can look at a hull and tell you what the materials are and how it is built. If you stop and think about it, there's very little that you can determine about the construction short of what you can see on the outer surface.

It's only a matter of common sense that the surveyor should include in his statement of limitations that he does not know what the construction materials are — i.e., laminating schedule, reinforcements, resins and cores — and that therefore he, the surveyor, is not certifying the materials and methods of construction, nor the structural integrity of the vessel. Don't assume that this is understood by the client. If the thing falls apart, the client may say, "You never told me." And if it's not in your report, well . . . you didn't tell him. Therefore, it's a good idea to draw up a standard clause for insertion in all of your reports. I include in my statement of limitations that the survey is not an *engineering analysis*. Some surveyors have taken issue with me about that, but how can you perform an engineering analysis without an analysis of how it was built? You can't. Remember that you are performing a *survey*, not an *analysis*. Such a disclaimer is both accurate and appropriate.

Survey Forms

Most seasoned surveyors will tell you that the primary purpose of using a survey form is the recording information and to serve as a guideline for the survey, and that not many people bother to wade through these compendiums of arcane data. For the novice surveyor, I would recommend that he use a form simply because it does serve as a guide that will help ensure that all areas are covered. Otherwise, there is no absolute necessity to use a form.

M.L. "Buster" Chadwick, who was one of the pioneers of yacht surveying, forty years ago devised a survey form that is two legal pages long, printed on both sides in type that one needs a magnifying glass to read. That form has been copied over and over and is still in use today, despite being completely outdated. It was created in the days of wooden boats when it was necessary to know the scantlings of a hull in order to determine whether it was lightly or heavily constructed. Back in those days, insurance underwriters paid attention to such things. Today such arcane data is neither necessary nor wanted, and so the novice surveyor, should he run across one of these forms, should not feel compelled to imitate it just because it is impressive looking.

In my view, the best reports are those which are almost wholly narrative. Yet it must be recognized that narrative reports are very time consuming to write and are much more suitable for larger yachts than small ones, at least economically speaking. The problem with forms is that they are much too constricting and usually do not allow the surveyor to provide information beyond a few words. For standard production boats that are well known, forms may be fine. But for custom or large yachts, forms are usually ill-suited. Fortunately, we no longer have to rely on preprinted forms. With the advent of sophisticated word processing programs, we are given the ability to produce custom forms of our own design, or to alter a form to fit the need of the moment.

Well designed forms are not created at one sitting, they evolve. After decades of trying to create a one-size-fits-all form, I found it couldn't be done so now I have three forms, one each for power and sail, and one for small boats only that is only one page long. A good form is one that divides information up into categories and places essential information in a format that is easy to locate and read. A good way to guide the creation of a form is to include only the following:

- The information that causes you to inspect all critical categories such as Fuel Systems, Exhaust Systems, Safety Equipment, Electrical, Machinery and the like. If the form is laid out in the a manner similar to the way you proceed through the survey, it will be much easier to use, though less easy to read. Take your choice.

- Record vital data such as serial numbers, hull number, registration, etc.

- Record basic equipment endemic to the value and safety of the vessel.

Since most people and businesses keep standard A4 letter size files, you'll be doing everyone a favor if you avoid legal size forms, as some surveyors do, that won't fit in standard files, forcing people to fold them up to fit, and to use special paper for copying.

Dealing with Cause and Effect

One of the more difficult aspects of report writing is making decisions when faced with cause and effect problems. Earlier, the example of a loose rub rail was cited. That, of course, was an easy example to deal with. More difficult problems frequently occur that involve only a limited amount of evidence of a potential problem. An example might be weak evidence of a prior major hull blister repair job, or the suspicion that there is water ingress into a hull or deck core that is not immediately demonstrable.

It is not enough to simply describe the extent of the evidence. Any time there is evidence, no matter how weak it is, of a potentially costly problem, it is absolutely necessary for the surveyor not only to describe the visible condition, but also the *potential* effects: *this* may result in *that*. The failure to do this is the downfall of many surveyors, for in not describing the full import of the situation, they have failed their responsibility to fully advise their client, and in such a way that is likely to leave them legally liable for the omission. Therefore, any time there is even minor evidence of a potentially costly problem, both the cause and the effect need to be fully described.

What do I mean by that? Well, let's say there are some serious stress cracks on the bottom of the hull. The issue that needs to be dealt with is whether there is risk of hull failure. Perhaps you don't know, but obviously it's not enough to merely state the condition without addressing the significance of it. Even if you don't know, you'll still need to address the potential risk; it's not appropriate to assume that the client can make this judgement for himself. It's not enough to think, "Well, I told the client that the crack was there!" without explaining the ramifications. There's a good reason why product manufacturers put all those silly warnings on their products. Your report is your product, so cover yourself.

The surveyor doesn't have to launch into long, windy explanations about this, nor go out on a limb with speculation. In most cases he would probably be well advised to state the minimum necessary to get the point across that the problem may be larger than it appears. He need only state that the evidence *may* be the result of, or *may cause* additional damage, problems or expense. Moreover, if a condition warrants further analysis, either by the surveyor or other experts, he should not expect the client to draw his own conclusions, but should advise the client accordingly.

Fact -vs- Opinion

The essence of the well-written reports are statements of fact. Have you ever seen a report that uses the phrase "appears to be" twenty times? Looks pretty ridiculous does it not? By the time we're done reading such a report, we're left with the distinct impression that the surveyor isn't too sure about anything. That's not the kind of report we want to write, and if we find ourselves doing too much of this, chances are that we're not taking enough time to be certain that we know what we're talking about.

The main body of the survey report should contain a narrative about that which the surveyor is certain. It should be a discourse on the observed facts which are incontrovertible in nature. Of course, there are often instances when the nature of a problem or condition is not clear. But it is necessary for the professional surveyor to guard against the inclusion of too many uncertainties lest he look uncertain himself.

One way to avoid this is to always view what is being said in terms of how one would feel attempting to justify his statements in court, on the witness stand, in front of jury. One doesn't have to be in this profession very long before finding himself in exactly that position. And perhaps until we've actually been there, it's hard to conceive of how often we make statements that we can't defend. Ill-considered statements may be okay in one's personal life, but they're not okay in the professional world where people are investing their money based on your professional advice.

The inclusion of opinions is something that should generally be avoided. By opinion it is meant unsolicited advice. There are, of course, times when the inclusion of an opinion is necessary, but it is best to be judicious about this. The giving of advice is best left out of the report unless it is made clear that such advice is merely that, and not a "recommendation." Beware that "recommendations" tend to take on the status of the absolute, and are usually judged as something that must be done. Certainly, it is a valuable service for the surveyor to provide good advice to his client but, it would be much better if such advice were included in an addendum or a heading captioned "suggestions." In that way it will be clear that it is advice that is being offered.

Achieving Balance: The Positive -vs- the Negative

It is the surveyor's role to be critical and negative and to err on the side of caution. Yet to write a report that only stresses the negative is lacking in balance, unless, of course, the vessel is a total wreck. Balance and accuracy are goals that the surveyor should strive to achieve. Yet, from the hundreds of reports that I've read, it's obvious that many surveyors are reluctant to inject a report with an accurate description of the vessel's condition, particularly when it is not so good. Instead, they seem to prefer to only provide a list of deficiencies rather than making general statements of condition. They're loathe to be critical to the extent of stating that a vessel is poorly maintained, and instead leave it to the reader to read between the lines and come to his own conclusions about the general condition.

There is an inherent danger in writing reports this way, and it mainly comes from the direction of third parties to whom the report may be given and asserted as an accurate assessment of the condition of the vessel. Let us not forget the risks involved with the pass-on survey where a third party makes a financial decision based on that report. The surveyor could easily become legally liable for misrepresentation.

Avoid Clichés

Another thing that many survey reports can be criticized for is the excessive use of clichés like "bristol condition," "mint condition," or "excellent." Superlatives, like art, are a subjective judgment. The use of superlatives only has real meaning after one has taken the time to specifically define the meaning of the term being used. For example:

> "The main engine and other machinery in the engine room of this yacht are completely free of fuel, lube oil or coolant leaks and there is no rust or corrosion on any part thereof. The engines are nicely painted and well-detailed. Brass and chrome plated parts are hand polished. Throughout, the engine room is nearly spotless as the crew hand wipes all machinery and other components in the engine room on a weekly basis. All paint finish on all components is bright and gleaming. All systems, including wire runs, hoses and other plumbing are very neat and orderly and have been laid out with painstaking care and installed with a view toward accessibility and ease of maintenance. Altogether, the engine room is maintained like a showpiece and it is readily apparent that the owner and crew take great pride in keeping this engine room in showroom condition."

This is an actual description that I used to describe the engine room of one of the finest yachts I have ever seen. Notice that the use of superlatives in the above paragraph is fully justified by a detailed description of the condition. The reader is not left with any doubt about what the surveyor's standards might be. Rather, it paints a picture in words that supports the use of superlatives. Instead of "excellent," I used the word "showroom" that pulls up the mental image of a shiny, bright new car, something that nearly everyone is familiar with. Now consider these two statements:

> "The exterior of this yacht is maintained in excellent condition."

> "The gelcoated exterior surfaces of the hull, decks and super-structure are frequently washed, waxed and hand polished and are found to be gleaming bright. No damages, defects or deficient conditions were observed. All hardware is clean, bright and well secured. There is little evidence of general wear and tear on this 15 year old yacht. The overall condition of this vessel is excellent."

The first statement of condition makes an assertion without bothering to back it up with any facts. But notice how the later statement leaves little room for doubt about how the surveyor arrives at his conclusion. Although a superlative is used, now the word "excellent" has real meaning.

Of course it's much easier to deal with positives than negatives, so let's take a look at how we might deal with a vessel that's a real mess. Because we are dealing with the property of others we have to be careful about how we phrase our description. We have to be honest and accurate while avoiding insult or being offensive. Resorting more to detailed description and less on condition summaries will help get us off the hook.

> "The main engines were observed to have a number of coolant leaks, both fresh and sea water, that have resulted in considerable exterior corrosion of the machinery. In addition, there are numerous oil leaks on the exterior surfaces that result in substantial oil loss and a generally poor appearance. It is evident that the engine room has not been subjected to regular cleaning as most surfaces are dirty and have considerable corrosion on the various systems caused by salt spray entering through the hull side ventilators. There is excessive debris in the bilges which are also quite oily and need cleaning."

It doesn't take much imagination to decipher that the engine room of this yacht is a real mess, and yet the surveyor avoids the use of any pejorative adjectives, and instead relies upon a factual and neutral description. There's really no need for the surveyor to inject his opinion; he can let the statements of fact speak for themselves.

Disclaimers

For decades lawyers have been advising surveyors to include in their reports some of the most outrageous disclaimers imaginable, as if somehow these denials of responsibility will protect them from negligence. I'm still awaiting the day when a fellow surveyor tells me that his disclaimer saved him from a judgment, but I'm not holding my breath. Examine a number of survey reports and probably a majority of them will include disclaimers that say, in essence, that the surveyor is not be held liable for his mistakes, errors or omissions, even when he puts them in writing. The disclaimer usually is a form of hold harmless agreement that says by acceptance of the report, the client agrees not to sue the surveyor. This is foolish because one cannot contract out of law, creating an agreement that nullifies statutory or even case law, even if the client should agree to it. The fact is that surveyors are totally liable for the advice that they provide their clients and no statement to the contrary will absolve them from that responsibility. Have you ever seen a doctor or lawyer attach a disclaimer to his work product, in essence saying that he is not responsible for his mistakes or advice that he gives you?

Perhaps lawyers like to see their clients include such nonsense in their reports on the outside hope that some sleeping client, judge, or jury might inadvertently buy that argument. But the real problem with attaching this kind of disclaimer is that it tends to insult the client. What the disclaimer is saying to the client is that the surveyor (1) doesn't take responsibility for his work, and (2) that he doesn't have confidence in his work product. Early in my career, an attorney wrote up a disclaimer for me and advised that I use it. By the time I was called to the carpet for it by several clients, I was so embarrassed that for the last twenty years I have not used any sort of disclaimer that denies my responsibility. It insults the client and, even worse, insults my own integrity. Instead of seeking to avoid responsibility, I now devote these efforts to making sure that I'm doing a good job. Instead of trying to protect myself with legalese, I now protect myself with well-written reports that fully describe:

- Any and all areas that cannot be accessed and surveyed.

- Equipment with which we are unfamiliar and cannot test properly.

- Should we fail to inspect or test something, own up to it and admit it in writing.

- Describe any condition or circumstance such as weather, actions of other persons, or failure of equipment or machinery that inhibits us from performing our service as efficiently as possible, including time constraints.

Finally, both we and our clients should be aware that surveys are usually performed under conditions which are less than ideal. Rather than making disclaimers, I prefer to use what I call a *Statement of Limitations* in which I describe any and all factors which have limited my performance. Because the vessel and the condition under which we perform the survey are usually not under our control, and our ability to perform our function is often limited by these factors, it is critically important to advise the client of these factors. A truly effective disclaimer is one which describes these conditions and makes it clear to the client that these conditions affect the quality of the service being provided. Rather than insulting the client, he is presented with limiting conditions which can justify less than perfect performance and which anyone but the most hard-boiled can understand and appreciate.

Report Summaries

A well-written report doesn't need a concluding summary because it speaks for itself. The problem with rendering a summary is that a summary is essentially an opinion. The question to answer, then, is whether the surveyor is hired to render opinions or presentations of facts. Most surveyors choose to stick to the facts and let the client arrive at his own opinions. Therefore, no surveyor need to feel compelled to render a written summary.

Some surveyors are found who include all manner of information in their reports directed toward banks and insurance companies. What they are attempting to do is to provide a multiple-purpose survey to satisfy the needs of banks and insurance companies. The problem with this is that it is the buyer who is the client, not these other parties. What these surveyors are ultimately doing is providing a free service while assuming additional liability. Too cheap to pay for their own information, banks and insurance companies are perfectly willing to forego the cost of obtaining their own advice and put the responsibility on the pre-purchase surveyor's back, all at no charge! The wise surveyor is one who recognizes who his client is and doesn't extend gratuitous advice to those who aren't paying for it.

Many pre-purchase surveys are found to include the statement, "Vessel is deemed a good marine insurance risk." Since surveyors are not underwriters, one has to wonder how it is that so many surveyors are able to come to this conclusion. In fact, many underwriters resent these statements because the assessment of risk is the function of the underwriter, not the surveyor. More than one surveyor has been made to look very foolish on the witness stand when queried about what standards he uses for assessing and categorizing levels of risk.

The function of the surveyor is to survey and report on condition. It is entirely appropriate for him to assess whether a hull is sound or to determine that a vessel is not seaworthy. It is also appropriate to determine navigation limits if so requested, because seaworthiness is always dependent upon where a vessel will be operated. But he should leave the underwriting decisions to the underwriters.

Beware that summaries always run the risk of offending when they are negative, and often appear as an effort "sell" a vessel when very positive. If the client has seen the vessel, then there's little need to summarize. And since a summary is a subjective judgment, it's probably better to avoid making it. For the "average" boat in "average" condition, there's really little reason to do so. Yet there are always cases of exceptional vessels, be they good or bad, where a summary serves the purpose of alerting the client to special considerations. An unseaworthy vessel is one obvious case. A vessel that is extraordinarily well maintained, fitted out or equipped is another. Summaries may also be necessary to justify an unusually high or low appraisal.

One of the most offensive practices in survey reporting is when the surveyor lists numerous and serious defects on a vessel, and then turns around and summarizes the vessel by saying that it's "sound" or in "otherwise good condition." A surveyor who does this is not fooling anyone and, in fact, is discrediting himself.

There is no mystery as to what prompts surveyors to do this sort of thing. They know that the client who is purchasing a boat that is in poor condition will have trouble getting financing and insurance. They then try to mitigate the import of their findings by downplaying them, apparently trying to make it easier for the client to get insurance and financing. What they don't seem to realize is that they are setting themselves up for potentially very serious liability claims, either from the client or third parties. Consider the following summary taken from an actual survey report:

> "When the above items marked with an asterisk are complied with, this vessel would be considered sound and in satisfactory condition for its intended service at this time with no warranty either specified or implied."

What's wrong with this statement? Well, there are at least four major faults with it. First is the contradiction that no warranty is implied, against the statement that it will be "in satisfactory condition for it's intended service." The second contradiction is made when the writer uses the phrase, "at this time." In point of fact, the report listed nearly 40 minor and major faults, including cracks in the bottom. The vessel was clearly not in satisfactory condition "at this time." So which is it? The listing of defects are statements of fact that the surveyor then attempts to override with a summary opinion that is not believable by virtue of the stated facts.

Next, the surveyor gives no indication of what the "intended service" is, yet he's quite willing to go out on the limb and say that the vessel "would be considered sound and in satisfactory condition for its intended service." That's giving a warranty. And the surveyor makes the mistake of giving a warranty, and but then tries to take it away by saying it's not a warranty. It doesn't take much imagination to see the pickle this surveyor would find himself in should this vessel encounter a serious accident. Statements like this would delight any plaintiff attorney. And if that were not enough, the vessel involved here was a 70 MPH race boat!

Obviously, the surveyor who wrote this absurdity was not aware of what he was doing or saying. He came to a fork in the road and travelled in both directions because he was trying to serve two masters. He was willing to point out the defects, yet at the same time he was willing to contradict himself to help the owner get insurance. Further, he also tried to get fancy with a bit of legalese. Making the statement that a vessel is suitable for its intended service is the same thing as giving it a warranty. Suitability for intended service is a phrase straight out of product liability law and any surveyor willing to make *that* statement is courting self-immolation. Here's another one:

> "The above vessel at this inspection is deemed to be a good fire and marine risk in its present status, if the following recommendations are complied with."

Once again, the surveyor hands us a glaring contradiction. The vessel cannot be a good "risk" in its "present status" when there are existing deficiencies. Then we are left to wonder what is a "good fire and marine risk"? The definition of risk is "exposure to hazard," and hazard means "source of danger," so what that statement really means is, "this vessel is a good exposure to danger." But how can an exposure to danger be good? To an arsonist, perhaps, but not likely anyone else. Does he mean that the boat is likely to catch fire? Because that's what the statement means. Obviously, the writer here is not aware of the meaning of the words he's using, with the result that he has made a complete fool of himself.

With these two examples alone we couldn't get a better demonstration the importance of the need for the precise use of language, along with knowing what you're doing before you do it. Certainly there are many circumstances where a vessel will have a long list of relatively *minor* defects that tends to make the vessel look bad just from the sheer number of items. In that case, it is appropriate for the surveyor to point this out in the summary, so long as that is true. But when the surveyor lists serious defects, and then contradicts himself by saying that they're not serious, or that the vessel is sound or seaworthy, he is exposing himself in more ways than one.

Whatever the case, the inclusion or omission of a summary is something that should be given careful consideration, utilizing it only when there is a clear need to do so, and with a high degree of certainty of the significance of what is being stated. A report that is thorough and clearly and precisely written doesn't need a summary.

Legalese

As the last two citations demonstrate, apparently the temptation to mimic a legalistic tone of writing is too strong for many to resist. Unfortunately for them, words mean things, and to engage in mimicry of legal writing without knowing what one is really saying is foolishness. This is one of the reasons why I advise against attempting to write in a formal style, for unless one is fully trained to do it, the attempt may produce unfortunate results much as it did in the cases cited.

I saved this point for last because by now my reasoning will be clear. There is no good reason whatever why a surveyor should feel compelled to write in an alien dialect such as a legal style. Instead of making the writer appear learned and dignified, his lack of understanding only highlights his ignorance. Surveyors are not lawyers and no one expects them to write like lawyers. No lack of dignity attaches to the surveyor who masters the good use of common language.

Index